THE SOVIET ACADEMY OF SCIENCES AND THE COMMUNIST PARTY, 1927-1932

STUDIES OF THE RUSSIAN INSTITUTE

COLUMBIA UNIVERSITY

The
Soviet Academy
of Sciences
and the
Communist
Party,
1927-1932

BY LOREN R. GRAHAM

PRINCETON, NEW JERSEY

PRINCETON UNIVERSITY PRESS

1967

*The Russian Institute of Columbia University
sponsors the Studies of the Russian Institute
in the belief that their publication contributes
to scholarly research and public understanding. In this way the Institute, while not
necessarily endorsing their conclusions, is
pleased to make available the results of some
of the research conducted under its auspices.
A list of the Studies of the Russian Institute
appears at the back of the book.*

Printed in the United States of America
by Princeton University Press

to the Albjergs:

VICTOR LINCOLN

MARGUERITE HALL

PATRICIA PARKS

Of all the scientific institutions in various countries of the world, the one which is by far the most important, relative to the scientific life of its nation, is the Academy of Sciences of the USSR. No other academy, society, university, or research foundation dominates the field of science in its country to the degree the Academy of Sciences in the Soviet Union does Russian science.

Founded early in the 18th century, its predecessor, the Imperial Academy of Sciences, was already a venerable institution by the time of the Russian Revolution. Only since that political overturn, however, has the Academy come fully to occupy its unique position among scientific institutions. The crucial period for an understanding of how this transformation occurred was the first five-year plan, usually considered to have lasted from 1928 to 1932, but which began to take effect in 1927. The traumas of industrialization and collectivization in this period are by now well known to students of Soviet history. Less well understood is the cultural revolution of the same period, of which the renovation of the Academy of Sciences is part.

At the present time there is no serious historical study of the Soviet Academy of Sciences in any language, to say nothing of an examination of the Academy in the years of the first five-year plan, although a group of Soviet scholars is currently working on a volume which will complete a general history of the Academy by adding the period since the Revolution.[1] The few articles and sections of broader histories published outside the Soviet Union which do refer to the Academy

[1] The first two volumes, covering the Academy from 1724 to 1917, have been published: K. V. Ostrovitianov *et al.*, eds., *Istoriia akademii nauk SSSR*, I, Moscow–Leningrad, 1958; II, Moscow–Leningrad, 1964.

usually mention briefly that during this period there was a
political purge of certain scholars. There was, indeed, a purge
of the Academy, one of the most regrettable pages of its
history, and this study presents many details of that terror
previously unpublished. On the more intellectually interesting
side, however, the Academy was occupied in these years by an
intense controversy over the goals, organization, and functions
of scientific research institutions in the Soviet state. This discussion has attracted almost no attention from Western
scholars.

The Soviet government's policy toward the Academy was
not entirely one of coercion for the sake of political control;
the government was an active supporter of science although
its leaders disagreed about the methods and means of support.
These men believed that science would develop more freely
in Russia than anywhere else in the world. Following several
alternative interpretations of the Marxist doctrine of the base
and the superstructure, which described cultural expressions
as derivative functions of the economic base of society, the
Soviet ideologists spoke of the creation of a "socialist science"
which would quickly demonstrate its superiority over "capitalist science." They promised to promote science even more
vigorously than heavy industry. The Soviet Union, notwith-
standing its persecution of dissident scientists, was the most
enthusiastic supporter of science and technology of all contemporary governments.

A word about definitions is necessary. Throughout this study
the word "science" has been used as the word *nauka* is employed in Russian, or *Wissenschaft* in German. This usage is
required in order to discuss the *Akademiia nauk* in Russian
terms. Therefore the word "science" in these pages includes
the social sciences or humanities as well as the natural sciences
and mathematics. Nevertheless, the greatest emphasis has been
placed on the Soviet attitudes toward the natural sciences.
The reasons for this stress are twofold. First, the discussions of
the planning and organization of science in the Soviet Union

in the period of this study to a large degree concerned the natural sciences. Second, Soviet attitudes toward the social sciences are much better known in the West than the corresponding evaluations of the natural sciences.

I am extremely grateful to the people who have assisted me during the writing of this study. Of special importance were Henry L. Roberts, who attended the birth and early growth of the project with both criticism and encouragement, and Alexander Dallin, who at later periods provided invaluable assistance. The Ford and Danforth Foundations, Indiana University, and the American Philosophical Society awarded grants to me during my research. Much of the source material was obtained during an academic year in the Soviet Union under the auspices of the Inter-University Committee on Travel Grants. Robert F. Byrnes and Stephen Viederman of the Inter-University Committee helped arrange for my study in Moscow, and have frequently been involved in assisting my research. In the Soviet Union I was fortunate in receiving the cooperation and advice of a number of Soviet scholars. My advisor (*rukovoditel'*) in the history faculty at Moscow University, V. I. Bessonova, helped arrange certain details of my study program even though she disagreed with me frequently on important points of interpretation. S. F. Naida, head of the department of history of the USSR in the period of socialism, Moscow University, also facilitated my work. The vice-president of the Soviet Academy of Sciences, K. V. Ostrovitianov, arranged to have several of my questions concerning the history of the Academy answered, as did N. A. Figurovskii, director of the Institute of the History of Natural Sciences and Technology.

In the United States, Victor L. Albjerg, professor emeritus of history, Purdue University, has offered me professional and personal advice of immeasurable value. Woodford McClellan, associate professor of history, University of Virginia, carefully read the entire manuscript and gave me many suggestions for improvement. Fritz Epstein, professor of history, Indiana University, was similarly generous with his time. George Vernadsky,[2] professor emeritus of history, Yale University, graciously gave me the benefit of his knowledge of the persons and events in the history of the Academy. Dean Frank Gucker, Indiana University, and Prof. Herman Pines, Ipat'ev High Pressure Laboratory, Northwestern University, helped me gain access to the papers of Academician V. N. Ipat'ev. Other scholars who assisted me in this project were George Fischer, Marc Raeff, Alexander Erlich, Ernest Nagle, Stephen Cohen, Peter Brock, George Z. F. Bereday, Christopher Wright, Marguerite Hall Albjerg, and John Hazard. My debt to two scholar-librarians, Eleanor Buist and Lev Magerovsky, is very great. Constance Bezer, who is in charge of publications for the Russian Institute, Columbia University, and Roy A. Grisham, Jr., Princeton University Press, expertly shepherded the manuscript through the final stages. Acknowledgments are due to Leonard Schapiro and Random House, Inc. for permission to quote from his *The Communist Party of the Soviet Union*; to Maurice Dobb and International Publishers for permission to quote from his revised, enlarged edition of *Soviet Economic Development Since 1917*; to Janet D. Zagoria and Frederick A. Praeger, Inc. for permission to quote from Boris I. Nicolaevsky's *Power and the Soviet Elite*; to Princeton University Press for permission to quote from Ortega y Gasset's *The Dehumanization of Art and Other Writings on Art and Culture*. Most important of all, in both a scholarly and personal sense,

[2] The transliteration system used in this book is a slightly simplified Library of Congress system, without ligatures. A particular problem in transliteration appears when Russian family names are known abroad in forms at variance with this standard system (Vernadsky, Oldenbourg). There is no transliteration system which will avoid this kind of problem. Thus V. I. Vernadskii and George Vernadsky are spelled in different ways even though they are father and son. The same problem will come up with S. F. Ol'denburg and Zoe Oldenbourg, who are grandfather and granddaughter. It would be clearly wrong either (a) to impose the French spelling on the Russian branch of the family or (b) to keep the woman's name in the Russian form regardless of the fact that she is widely known in the West by a different spelling. Similar problems arise with Ipat'ev (Ipatieff), Gor'kii (Gorky), Mendeleev (Mendeleyev), and others.

was the assistance of my wife, Patricia Albjerg Graham. The dubious interpretations and errors in fact which may remain are, of course, my responsibility. A portion of Chapter II appeared in *The Russian Review* (April 1964), pp. 135-48, and another portion in *Survey* (July 1967), pp. 61-79.

LOREN R. GRAHAM

Grand Island, Lake Superior
August 1967

CONTENTS

THE SOVIET ACADEMY OF SCIENCES AND
THE COMMUNIST PARTY, 1927-1932

*Sergei Ol'denburg (1863-1934), Permanent Secretary
of the Academy of Sciences, 1904-1929*

Nikolai Bukharin (1888-1938), Communist Party leader, and candidate for membership in the Academy of Sciences who in the election campaign of 1928 received the largest number of nominations

CHAPTER I

THE IMPERIAL INHERITANCE

I have lived to the moment when I can proudly announce, in full consciousness, that Russian science exists—that Russian science about which in our youth we could speak of only as a dream, or if you wish, as a faraway ideal. / V. I. Modestov, 1890[1]

The characteristics of Russian science

Scientists usually do not favor the view that science in various countries displays different characteristics. They frequently state that the traditional fields of science study aspects of nature which do not contain patterns formed by human activity and therefore stand apart from man and his cultural traditions. They notice the ease with which any scientist is able to converse on a technical topic with his counterpart in a foreign nation, which often leads them to conclude that science is an international language, one without local dialects.

Such a disbelief in national characteristics is largely justified if one concentrates on the theoretical core of science. Divisions along national lines are exceedingly rare in modern science. If, however, along with science proper, one wishes to consider a number of activities closely, sometimes inextricably, connected with it, such as the organization and political controls of science, the philosophy of science, and the relative development of or traditional emphases on various scientific fields, then the importance of the natural and social environment

[1] V. I. Modestov, "Russkaia nauka v poslednie dvadtsat' piat' let," *Russkaia Mysl'* (No. 5, 1890), p. 90.

becomes manifest. Furthermore, in those areas where the common word for science includes not only the natural sciences but also all other fields of scholarship, "science" obviously contains components of the cultural heritage of the area.

In Russia a number of factors gave science, considered broadly as a social, political, and intellectual activity, distinctive characteristics. Several of these characteristics, such as the effect on scientific research of the immense virgin territories of the Russian state, with their diversity of natural and ethnic areas, were not different in principle from characteristics of research in other geographic regions, such as North America. Other features of the pattern of scientific research in Russia, such as the place of the Academy of Sciences among governmental institutions, can be explained only by referring to the political and cultural history of that area.

In the last few centuries science has been primarily a Western phenomenon, one of the quintessential elements in the cultural, economic, and political expansion of the West. Thus the question of Russian attitudes toward science contains within it broad implications for the perennial discussion of the relative position of Russia vis-à-vis the West. An analysis of the position of Russia with reference to science would contain little intellectual interest if Russia were completely outside the stream of Western scientific thought—as were many areas of the world before the beginning of this century. However, a careful consideration of Russian history in the last 300 years will almost certainly result in the conclusion that while Russia in the 17th century was indeed unaware of the intellectual developments of that great age for science, by the end of the 19th century she was capable not only of educating some of her more fortunate citizens to the level of advanced Western science, but even of producing a few great figures who could extend the boundaries of science in certain areas beyond the positions achieved in the West. Rather than being separated from Western science, Russia before the Revolution had been close enough to that science to be affected profoundly by it, and even to occasionally help form it, but at the same time not intimately enough associated with it to form a natural and comfortable alliance. The peculiar relationship which was established, containing elements of both eagerness to master science and awkward anxiety about its implications for Russia, left an imprint on the pattern of scientific research.

Perhaps the first characteristic of science in imperial Russia the observer would notice is the uncommonly large role played by the central government. In other European countries the governments nourished in varying degrees the scientific centers that spontaneously sprouted in the environment of increasing material and intellectual achievement, but in Russia the government was forced to import such centers complete.[2] This necessity for the total transplanting of scientific studies was a legacy of the Russian culture of the Muscovite and Kievan states, which was singularly devoid of rationalistic and naturalistic elements. However tantalizing the proximity to old Russia of the classical sources in Byzantium and the Arabic sources in the central Asian regions may be to the historian of science, this proximity was for Russia geographical and not intellectual. There was no moment in Russian history when the reception and coalescence of these two important streams of early scientific thought was a real possibility. The few glimmers of scientific enlightenment which did appear in Russia before 1700, notably by means of Catholic or Jewish influences, generated no large response. Consequently, when Russia emerged as a state in the European system during the reign of Peter the Great it possessed no centers of scientific studies, and the responsibility for the creation of such institutions fell upon the imperial government. The formation of educational

[2] The forced birth of a scientific society by governmental edict was not unique to the history of Russia; the Prussian Academy of Sciences in Berlin (*Societas Regia Scientiarum*) and the *Accademia del Cimento* of Florence were created largely through the efforts of the ruling Hohenzollern and Medici families. Here the comparison with Russia ends, however, since in both Italy and Germany there were enough educated men with scientific interests to staff the new organizations, while the Russian government was forced to import foreign scientists.

and scientific institutions was for Peter a necessary step for the strengthening and modernization of Russia, not essentially different in his mind from the development of a navy or of industries capable of producing modern arms.

Peter the Great sponsored the first nonclerical schools in Russia—the navigation and mathematics schools, the artillery academy, the short-lived but fascinating Glück gymnasium, and in 1725 the Academy of Sciences which included in its charter provision for a gymnasium and a university. This pattern of central control was continued throughout the history of the empire. The scientific researchers and teachers of Russia were wards of the government.[3] With the exception of church schools and a few private schools, which were isolated from the advanced scientific research of the West, all schools in tsarist Russia were taught by civil servants.[4]

Science was associated in the minds of Russians with the revolutionary reforms of Peter the Great. Science was opposed to old Russia, to the religion of the Orthodox church, to the superstitions of the people. It was a threat to those nobles who hoped to maintain their positions on the basis of blood rather than achievements. It was promoted by those people who wanted Russia to become a modern state. Consequently, the conflict between science and the values of the old order was quite sharp, perhaps more marked than anywhere else in Europe. But while this disparity between science and the old culture in Russia was very large the result was not a public struggle between the two, a debate between two different systems, but instead a deepseated estrangement. In contrast to western Europe where the old values, especially those of religion, were defended by spokesmen who were often highly educated themselves and even on occasion conversant in sci-

---

[3] The most interesting private endeavors in Russian science were the scientific societies, founded in large numbers in the 19th century. James Swanson, of the University of South Florida, is currently making a study of the societies and early Soviet attitudes toward them.

[4] Nicholas DeWitt, "Scholarship in the Natural Sciences," in C. E. Black, ed., *The Transformation of Russian Society*, Cambridge, Mass., 1960, p. 399.

ence, and where consequently a genuine debate occurred, in Russia the opponents of science were rarely capable of such a dialogue. Among the Slavophiles of the 1840s and 1850s, it is true, were spokesmen of Old Russia who possessed intellectual sophistication, but their leaders pointedly chose not to oppose science. Their hope was to utilize the techniques of Western science and technology without sacrificing what they considered the superior moral values of traditional Russian culture. It is not among the Slavophiles, often more Western in intellectual outlook than they cared to admit, that one must look for the opposition to science in Russia, but to religious groups, which feared what they considered the undermining of divine authority, to the aristocracy, which resisted the egalitarian nature of advancement in scientific activity, and intermittently to the government which moved to block the importation and propagation of politically subversive doctrines by Russian students who studied the sciences in western Europe. These forces of resistance to the development of science vacillated in intensity and were sometimes in conflict with each other. Even the most conservative rulers of Russia recognized that science could benefit their country and bring glory to their crown; they promoted, albeit often ineffectively, its development as long as science did not threaten the established order.[5] The Church, an almost constant opponent to science, had at least to its credit its disapproval of the Magnitsky era; the aristocracy contained a number of people with interests in science and its ranks were open, at least legally, to scientists from lower classes who achieved distinction. Nevertheless, the opposition to the development of science offered by these three great inertial forces in the last 150 years of Russian history—government, church, and aristocracy—was immense.

A certain preoccupation with theoretical or descriptive research rather than with engineering has often been cited as a

[5] Though he was one of the most conservative rulers of Russia Nicholas I (1825-55) actively promoted the development of scholarship in the sciences. His extreme distrust of Western political theories limited his achievements, however.

characteristic of the history of science in Russia. The great achievements of Russian scientists before the Revolution—those, for example, of Lobachevskii, Mendeleev, Pavlov, But-lerov—were primarily in nonapplied fields. The great works in the geographical sciences, either done by Russians, as in the case of Krasheninnikov, or promoted by the Russian government in the cases of Gmelin and Pallas, may be termed descriptions and compilations rather than applications. Those projects in the applied sciences which displayed promise were often abandoned far short of completion: Zhukovskii's and Chaplygin's work in aerodynamics, Popov's work on radio, Tsiolkovskii's rocketry experiments, Dolivo-Dobrovolskii's research on alternating current.

An effort to explain this preoccupation with theory and massive description must touch on the extremely difficult topics of the motivations of Russian scientists, the nature of the Russian economy, the impact of foreign technology, the geography of the Russian state, and the policy of the Russian government toward education and research in science. The most important reason why Russian scientists did not consider technology as important to their concerns as scientists of most Western countries was the relative underdevelopment of Russian industry. Industry was the logical focus of applied research, for which a clear precedent existed after the creation in Germany of the influential industrial chemical research laboratories in the last half of the 19th century. But not only was Russia's industry underdeveloped, it was largely controlled by foreigners who depended on external research bases. Thus Russia was deprived of both the pull toward technological research which the needs of a great industrial plant would have provided and the push toward new native industries generated by industrial laboratories.

Support for the view that the relative absence of technological research in prerevolutionary Russia stemmed more from the economic situation than from elusive factors like national characteristics, can be seen in the fact that a number of Rus-

sian émigrés trained in the schools of imperial Russia contrib-
uted significantly to technology when transplanted to another
economic environment. In the United States alone the contributions of Sikorsky and Seversky in aeronautics, Ipat'ev in
chemical technology, Zworykin in electronics, and Timoshenko
in applied mechanics illustrate the Russian talent for applied
science. And Soviet achievements in engineering in building
up the economy, waging a successful major war, and the
development of atomic weapons and space vehicles are even
more impressive. Indeed it may be difficult to convince people
with short memories that the Russians were once known as
excellent theoreticians but poor engineers, although a study
of 19th century Russian science and education confirms the
impression. If the Soviet reputation has changed in recent
years the economic and academic transformations of the late
1920s and the 1930s are partially responsible.

The prerevolutionary preference for pure science was also
in part a result of the desire of Russian scientists to prove the
worth of science in Russia. They were often not content with
restricted topics of investigation; they desired topics either
of grander scale than elsewhere or deeper in theory. This
desire to pursue research which would gain prestige for Russia,
easily identifiable in the writings of such men as Lomonosov
and Mendeleev, prompted Russian scientists to stay abreast of
the latest developments in western Europe, even though on
the level of applied science Russia was hopelessly behind.
Thus Russia tried to compete in the area of science which, at
her stage of development, benefited her least—advanced theoretical research.

The trend toward pure science first became discernible in
the second quarter of the 19th century. The early Petrine
Academy, similar to most early scientific societies, devoted
considerable time to solving the problems of applied science,
and even the 1836 charter spoke of the attention the Academy
should give to useful knowledge, but in the 1830s and 1840s
theoretical science became increasingly the center of the

Academy's attention. Count Uvarov, the noted minister of education and ideologue of government policy, who was president of the Academy from 1818 to 1855, hoped that by directing academic studies in Russia toward mathematics and classical and oriental languages he could avoid the subversive doctrines promoted by European economists and political theorists. At the same time, he gave important assistance to the development of Russian traditions of excellence in these fields. The emphasis in the Academy of Sciences of the 19th century on pure learning might have been compensated for by the industrial laboratories and universities if either had devoted much time to the applied sciences. Unfortunately, this was not the case. As already mentioned, industrial laboratories were practically nonexistent. The faculty members of the universities often received their educations in Germany, where the prestige of pure science was also preeminent; in the manner of disciples everywhere, the Russian students often carried their teachers' views to extremes.

The turning away from absorption in pure science which so obviously occurred after the Revolution began in the last decades of the empire and surely would have intensified even had the Revolution not taken place. The expansion of industry in Russia could not be sustained indefinitely by foreign engineering skills. The ranks of technical specialists, both in industry and agriculture, grew rapidly before the Revolution. The Free Economic Society, which existed from 1765 to 1915, encouraged the dissemination of "useful" knowledge. During the 19th century a number of important engineering schools and technical institutes were founded. The largest of these were the Institute of Ways and Communications (founded 1810), the St. Petersburg Technological Institute (1828), the Moscow Higher Technical School (1830), the Petrovskii Agricultural Academy (1856), and the Sosnovka Polytechnical Institute (1902). Even the Academy of Sciences was touched by the growing interests in engineering when a technological advisory committee, the Commission for the Study of Natural

Productive Forces (KEPS), was created in the Academy in 1915.[6] Nevertheless, the Academy remained above most of these changes in the Russian economic and educational environment; in 1927 it was still largely absorbed in the spirit of pure science.

There were of course numerous reasons for Russians to be proud of their achievements in the theoretical sciences. Russia had possessed a great mathematical tradition from the earliest days, starting from the seeds imported by Bernoulli and Euler. The growth of this tradition was particularly dramatic in the first half of the 19th century when such mathematicians as V. I. Buniakovskii, M. V. Ostrogradskii, N. I. Lobachevskii, and, at the end of the period, P. L. Chebyshev, announced the independence of Russia in the mathematical sciences.

Not all the areas of science could be tied to mathematics to the degree that the physical sciences were. In the life and earth sciences the drives toward prestige and generalization prevailed also, but resulted in a different sort of product, that of descriptive studies of enormous scope:

> These are the so-called group-research projects such as are found in astronomy (for example, V. Ia. Struve's star catalogues), geology, meteorology, geobotanics, plant and animal ecology, and so on. All these studies were primarily descriptive in nature. Ever since K. M. Ber's [Bär's] "History of the Animal World" (1828-1837), to the current fifteen-volume set of "Flora of the USSR," the Russians have been keen on meticulous, detailed, and descriptive surveys of nature, from stars to seaweed. These systematic survey projects were conducted by a large number of scientists and at times individual projects span decades.[7]

At first glance there may seem to be little in common between these great collective works in the life and earth sciences and the abstract tradition of physics and mathematics,

[6] See pp. 22-23.
[7] DeWitt, "Scholarship in Natural Sciences," p. 398.

yet there is a genuine parallel. Rather than applying themselves to specific problems facing Russia in, for example, agriculture or minerals production, the Russian scientists produced
massive, spectacular, general studies of the biological or geological environment of Russia. Such works did indeed attract
the attention of the Western world, and they provided the
raw material for conclusions of general import, but they were
almost never applied by the Russians, at least not until recent
decades. In 1927 the Russians presented at an international soil
congress in Washington a detailed soil map of the entire country, the final product of decades of research, an achievement
unmatched by any other large country in the world, and yet
one finds little indication, before or after the Revolution, that
the Russians used this information effectively in recommending
agricultural policies on the basis of local soil conditions.[8] The
geological and topographical survey work of the Russians was
outstanding long before the Revolution, but little effort was
made to integrate and apply this information.

One of the reasons for the widespread use of research teams
for compiling data in Russia was the necessity to explore the
great virgin spaces of the Russian land. The geography of
Russia left a considerable imprint on Russian research. Siberia,
the Arctic, and central Asia became objects of expeditionary
research in the same way that the American West was studied
in the United States. The Great Northern Expedition of 1733-
43, the most spectacular of many geographical explorations in
the 18th century, was a chain of exploring parties involving
hundreds of men. Academician L. de la Croere equipped himself for his part of the expedition with nine wagon loads of
scientific instruments, two landscape painters, an instrument
maker, and a scientific library of several hundred volumes. The
three scholars participating in this expedition published 13
major works based on their findings.[9] One must compare the

[8] S. F. Ol'denburg, "Polozhenie nashei nauki sredi nauki mirovoi," in Abram
F. Ioffe, ed., *Nauka i tekhnika SSSR, 1917-27*, I, Moscow, 1927, 40.
[9] For the geographical explorations in the 18th century, see V. F. Gnucheva,

date of this scientific expedition to that of the highly publicized 1804-1806 expedition of Lewis and Clark in America to note the advanced state of Russian work in this area.

Even after the great exploratory expeditions were abandoned, their effects continued to be absorbed into Russian natural science. The strength of geology, botany, zoology, and ethnography arose from the expeditionary work. Since the explorers charted their courses overland by celestial navigation even astronomy and meteorology were affected. Furthermore, the scope of the Russian land provided particular vantage points for studying eclipses and the transits of Venus, which attracted much attention in the 18th century.[10] The penchant for compiling enormous specimen collections and writing lengthy descriptive works was of course given much impetus during the explorations.

The principle of personal succession was another important feature of Russian science. The Academy of Sciences elected a new member only when one died; his replacement was usually one of his students, a scholar whose approach was often quite similar to his.[11] In the universities the tradition of succession was also strong. Thus the physicist A. G. Stoletov trained his successor P. N. Lebedev. Lebedev in turn handed the tradition on to Academician P. P. Lazarev.[12] The physiologist I. P. Pavlov was a product of the Russian physiological school founded by I. M. Sechenov. The founder of geochemistry, Academician V. I. Vernadskii, was a scientific descendant

Geografieheskii departament akademii nauk XVIII veka, Moscow, 1940; V. I. Grekov, *Ocherki iz istorii russkikh geografieheskikh issledovanii v 1725-1765 gg.*, Moscow, 1960; F. A. Golder, *Bering's voyages: an account of the efforts of the Russians to determine the relation of Asia and America*, 2 vols., New York, 1922-1925; and P. Lauridsen, *Vitus Bering: The Discoverer of the Bering Strait*, Chicago, 1889.

[10] Harry Woolf, *The Transits of Venus: A Study of Eighteenth-Century Science*, Princeton, 1959; see particularly pp. 115-26 for a description of activities in Russia.

[11] Michael Kitaeff, "Akademiia nauk SSSR," Russian Archives, Columbia University, p. 39. The principle of personal succession was also a characteristic of German science. It was not important, however, in industrial research.

[12] The term "academician" denotes a member of the Academy of Sciences, a position achieved only by election.

of V. V. Dokuchaev. The Moscow school of mathematicians was formed around an absorption in abstract theory which passed through a number of generations.

A last characteristic of Russian science, and perhaps one of the most disputable, was a certain chaotic, disorganized quality that extended from the trivia of poor housekeeping to a general lack of research management. Academician Ol'denburg lamented that Russian science lacked that certain "balance" and polish that were present in Western science. The chemist Ipat'ev noted that foreigners were more often struck by the disarray of his laboratory than the results he achieved in it. In Mendeleev's time there was a saying among chemists that the worse the appearance of a laboratory the better the research done there.[13] Furthermore, many grandiose projects were discarded after only a small amount of work. Management and coordination of scientific research may have been more seriously needed in Russia than in any other state with a modern scientific program, a condition explainable, no doubt, by the fact that no other state as backward as Russia attempted to maintain a completely modern scientific program. Such defects in Russia's scientific tradition were to be far more important to the Soviet critics of Russia's existing scientific institutions than its numerous outstanding merits.

The Imperial Academy of Sciences

The progenitor of the Soviet Academy of Sciences, the Imperial Academy of Sciences, was founded in 1725 by order of Peter the Great, who died before its first meeting. The subject of discussion for over 20 years before its actual appearance, the Academy was based on a plan authored by Peter's court physician, L. L. Blumentrost.[14] Blumentrost's plan for the Acad-

---

[13] O. N. Pisarzhevsky, *Dmitry Ivanovich Mendeleyev* (in English; Soviet transliteration), Moscow, 1954, p. 21.

[14] On the early academy, see K. V. Ostrovitianov, *Istoriia akademii nauk SSSR*, I; A. S. Lappo-Danilevskii, *Petr velikii, osnovatel' imperatorskoi akademii nauk v St. Peterburge*, St. Petersburg, 1914; P. Pekarskii, *Istoriia imperatorskoi akademii nauk v Peterburge*, St. Petersburg, 1870; M. I. Sukhomlinov, ed., *Materialy dlia istorii imperatorskoi akademii nauk*, I, St. Petersburg, 1885;

emy, as modified and approved by Peter and the Senate, was clearly the result of a diligent comparative study of foreign academies and an appraisal of Russia's scientific potential. The goal of this project—and one of the characteristics which distinguished it from previous academies—was the cultivation of native Russian science from imported seeds. The entire organization would consist of three tiers, with the top layer entirely foreign and the bottom partly Russian. The uppermost level would be composed of academicians who would investigate the sciences in their highest development and also serve as professors of their special fields. The academicians would bring university students with them from western Europe who, together with Russian students, would form the second level, or university. The university students (adjuncts) would in turn act as teachers in the third level, the gymnasium. Thus, one institution, the Academy of Arts and Sciences, would assume responsibilities which in other states three different institutions undertook. The obvious aim of the scheme was the gradual rise from the bottom to the top of the Russian elements.

Unfortunately, only the top level of the institution enjoyed a permanent existence. The gymnasium at first prospered but in later years lost much of its importance. The university did not come into existence until 1747 and finally expired at an unknown date, sometime after 1765.[15] Long before the disappearance of the gymnasium and the university, however, the goal of cultivating ethnically Russian science was abandoned. The Academy was largely an organization of foreigners, most of them German-speaking. The first Russian academician was not elected until 20 years after the birth of the society and an incredible century and a half passed before the ethnic Russians won control of the Academy.[16]

A. Kunik, *Sbornik materialov dlia istorii imperatorskoi akademii nauk v XVIII veke*, St. Petersburg, 1865; and Alexander Lipski, "The Foundation of the Russian Academy of Sciences," *Isis*, XVII (December 1953), 349-54.

[15] Moscow University, the oldest Russian university today, was established in 1755.

[16] The gradual ascent of Russians to the upper level was painfully slow. A partial explanation of this phenomenon lies in the fact that the gymnasium and

Although no attempt will be made here to describe the history of the Academy during the two centuries of its existence from 1725 to the period of this study, a consideration of several characteristics of the Academy, particularly the political issues involved in its administration, will be helpful in understanding the Academy at the beginning of the 20th century.

The legal foundation of the Academy was the successive charters which were issued in 1747, 1803, and 1836.[17] The significance of the charters, however, was slight, since the Academy was from the beginning treated as a branch of the government and subject to imperial command. The original project drawn up by Blumentrost and approved by Peter the Great granted the Academy the privileges of self-government, including the right to elect its own members and president. However, this provision was violated from the start. The entire 1725 project, carrying Peter's signature, was hidden from the academicians by the court librarian, J. D. Schumacher, who acquired personal control of the Academy, establishing the precedent of rule by court favorites, which became a feature of the Academy's history. The promised right of electing their own presidents was withheld from the academicians until the advent of the Provisional Government in 1917. Instead, the

---

university disappeared. A brief summary of the ethnic composition of the Academy is:

	Total no. of members	Russians	% of total who were Russians	% of foreigners who were Germans
18th century	107	28	26.2	65
19th century (to 1908)	189	121	69.3	64

(A. S. Lappo-Danilevsky, "The Development of science and learning in Russia," in J. D. Duff, ed., *Russian Realities and Problems*, Cambridge, England, 1917, pp. 173-74.) For those interested in an ethnic and genealogical analysis of the members of the Academy in the last half of the 19th century, a most valuable source is T. K. Lepin, Ia. Ia. Lus, and Iu. A. Filipchenko, "Deisvitel'nye chleny akademii nauk za poslednie 80 let (1846-1924)," *Izvestiia buro po evgenike* (No. 3, 1925), pp. 7-49.

[17] *Materialy dlia istorii imperatorskoi akademii nauk*, I, St. Petersburg, 1885; *Nouveau règlement et nouvel état de l'Académie Impériale des Sciences de St. Petersburg*, 1803; Ostrovitianov, *Istoriia akademii nauk SSSR*, pp. 687-710.

presidents were appointed by the crown and they in turn confirmed the membership of new academicians.

The academicians did not submit passively to arbitrary rule. The history of the Academy is replete with revolts and disputes, a number of them in the 18th century involving physical violence. At times the attitude of the crown toward the Academy was not so much oppressive control, however, as oblivion. Perhaps the most remarkable aspect of the Academy was the fact that it never ceased to exist altogether. Several decades after its establishment one observer described it as *"L'académie sans académiciens, la chancellerie sans membres, l'université sans étudiants, les règles sans autorité, et au reste une confusion jusqu'à présent sans remède."*[18]

The 1747 charter acknowledged the disappearance of the hope of academic self-regulation by stipulating that the president could expel any academician "if needed." Furthermore, the academicians were required to submit work plans in advance of their research. According to the new charter, "at the beginning of every year . . . every academician must inform the Assembly in written form what he will work on in the coming year, and as each third of the year passes, that is, when the time comes to receive his salary, he must tell the president by letter what he had done. . . ."[19] The requirement for submission of work plans is not a feature of 20th century Russian science alone.[20]

In the early period of the reign of Catherine the Great several projects for the administrative reform of the Academy aimed at protection of the academicians from bureaucratic persecution were initiated, notably by the first significant

[18] A. A. Vasil'chikov, *Semeistvo Razumovskikh*, I, St. Petersburg, 1880, p. 83.

[19] *Istoriia akademii nauk*, I, 442-43.

[20] Much popular opinion to the contrary, the development of institutionalized scientific research has not been a transition from completely independent research efforts to increasingly planned and coordinated endeavors. One of the very earliest of the organized scientific academies, the *Accademia del Cimento*, so carefully coordinated its work that all publications were submitted as anonymous contributions to scientific knowledge. The entire academy worked on the same topic. See Martha Ornstein, *The Role of the Scientific Societies in the Seventeenth Century*, New York, 1913, pp. 96-100.

Russian scientist, M. V. Lomonosov, and the great Swiss mathematician Leonhard Euler, but no changes were made.[21] Indeed, the reign of Catherine was a period of decline for the Academy that continued into the beginning of the 19th century. The directors of the Academy in these years, such as S. G. Domashnev, E. R. Dashkova, and P. P. Bakunin, were favorites of the crown who cared little for the welfare of the Academy, although Princess Dashkova made some improvements in financial administration.

The beginning of the 19th century marked a new age for the Academy, and the beginnings of an independence of Russian science which not even the mysticism and arbitrariness of the last years of the reign of Alexander I (1801-25) quelled. The new charter granted the Academy in 1803 gave it more freedom than ever before. The Academy was no longer subject to the command of any governmental department which might wish its services; according to the new charter only the Holy Synod and Governing Senate could give the Academy orders, although other bodies might ask it for advice. The Tsar continued to appoint the president of the Academy and to confirm the election of members. In most cases, however, the Tsar permitted the Academy full discretion both in the election of members and in the conduct of its research. Despite the fact that academic freedom did not exist in principle, within the Academy itself the tradition of independence, and the desire to protect that tradition, grew steadily.

The most serious limitation on scholarship in the 19th century occurred during the Magnitskii era, the decade after 1817, when Mikhail Magnitskii, a leader of the Russian Bible Society, attempted to impose his own form of religious mysticism on the educational institutions of Russia. During this bizarre epoch in the history of Russian education professors who expounded the virtues of humanism or rationalism were

21 *Istoriia akademii nauk SSSR*, I, 169, 318; A. Kunik, *Sbornik materialov*, II, 371-72; B. Menshutkin, *Russia's Lomonosov*, Princeton, 1952, pp. 79-80; and M. I. Radovskii, *M. V. Lomonosov i peterburgskaia akademiia nauk*, Leningrad, 1961, pp. 180, 200.

expelled and courses on natural history were converted into theological expositions of divine pattern in nature. This period was less disastrous for the Academy of Sciences, however, than for the universities. After 1818 the new president of the Academy, S. S. Uvarov, a conservative defender of the Russian system but also a person genuinely interested in scholarship, led the academy into a period of true greatness. Ironically, Uvarov accomplished the strengthening of Russian science by introducing more talented foreigners into the Academy, particularly Baltic Germans educated at Dorpat University.

The 1803 charter of the Academy, with its grant of greater autonomy and more emphasis on theoretical research, left an imprint discernible over a century later. Between 1803 and 1927 the rules and organizational procedures of the Academy hardly changed. In 1836 a new charter was issued, but it did not differ in any essential way from that of 1803; the new regulation freeing the members from pedagogical responsibilities was largely a recognition of the existing situation. In 1841, when the Russian Academy, the center of studies in Slavic literature, was reunited with the Academy of Sciences, the latter organization took on the formal structure which it retained until 1927.[22] The three main divisions studied were the physical and mathematical sciences, Russian language and literature, and the historical and philological sciences.

As the emphasis on pure science grew, several of the academicians decided to make a further attempt to reform the Academy. In the late 1850s and early 1860s, when all in Russia were discussing reforms, a group headed by K. S. Veselovskii, permanent secretary of the Academy from 1857 to 1890, worked out several versions of a new charter for the Academy which were widely discussed in the press. Veselovskii wished to free the Academy completely from concerns with applied science and expand the total research effort markedly. Its president,

[22] Count Uvarov had proposed another project which would have established three separate academies on the French pattern, but he failed to obtain the approval of Nicholas I. M. I. Sukhomlinov, *Istoriia rossiiskoi akademii*, 8 vols., St. Petersburg, 1874-87, viii, 361.

D. N. Bludov, a favorite of Alexander II, disapproved an early
version because the expansion of research the reformers envisioned would have meant large budgetary increases at a
moment when the national treasury was hard pressed as a
result of the land reforms.[23] The reformers also met opposition
from the scientists outside the Academy, especially from certain
of the university professors who did not wish to see the Academy enhance its standing. Science in the universities had
expanded greatly in the 19th century. In 1863 a university
reform had given these institutions autonomy, increased the
number of departments, and raised faculty salaries. A number
of university professors maintained that the Academy had
"outlived its century"; henceforth, the abode of advanced research, they said, would be in the universities. This shift of
importance from the old academies to the universities was
already clearly discernible in western Europe. The conflict
between the Academy and the universities in Russia was accentuated by the relative political conservatism of the academicians compared to the university professors. This political
disparity was particularly true as long as the Academy was
controlled by the Baltic Germans.

The Academy in the last half of the 19th century was divided
into political and nationalistic factions which collided whenever a vacant chair needed to be filled. One of the best known
of the incidents occurred when the famous chemist D. I.
Mendeleev, the author of the periodic table of elements, was
nominated to fill the chair of the late academician–chemist
N. N. Zinin. The Baltic German faction favored a member
either of their nationality or at least closer to them in political
sentiment. Mendeleev had often criticized the tsarist government for its educational policies and was closely associated
with the university professors who frequently criticized the
Academy for its conservative political views. In the secret vote
Mendeleev was blackballed by 10 opponents, mostly Germans

23 B. Modzalevskii, "Akademiia nauk, imperatorskaia sanktpeterburgskaia,"
in *Novyi Entsiklopedicheskii Slovar'*, F. A. Brockhaus and I. A. Efron, eds., I,
St. Petersburg, 1911, col. 653.

it seems, but perhaps helped by one or two ultraconservative Russians. In the years following the Mendeleev incident Russian scientists gradually gained control of the Academy. Mendeleev himself undoubtedly could have become a member later but refused to permit his name to be introduced, still smarting from the affront of 1880.[24]

The political orientation of the Academy changed during its last decades under tsarism. With the Russification of the Academy and the increasingly liberal sentiments of scholars in Russia, the Academy no longer could be described as a citadel of conservative views, although the Academy was to the end of the regime more aloof to political grievances than the universities. While the Mendeleev incident was in part a reflection of the Academy's political conservatism, the incidents involving the Academy which raised eyebrows in St. Petersburg after the turn of the century issued from the Academy's increasing willingness to offend its patron, the tsarist government. In 1902 the belles-lettres section of the Academy (*Razriad iziashchnoi slovesnosti*) elected Maxim Gorky to honorary membership, provoking Tsar Nicholas II, whose minister of internal affairs suspected Gorky of subversive activities, to angrily countermand the offer. In response to this crude violation of academic privilege, academicians Anton Chekhov and Vladimir Korolenko resigned from the Academy.[25]

A somewhat similar but more tumultuous episode occurred in the revolutionary year 1905, when 16 (later 17) members

[24] On the Mendeleev affair, see N. A. Figurovskii, *Dmitrii Ivanovich Mendeleev, 1834-1907*, Moscow, 1961, pp. 188-96; G. A. Kniazev, "Iz proshlogo akademii nauk: D. I. Mendeleev i imperatorskaia akademiia," *Vestnik Akademii Nauk* (No. 3, 1931), p. 34; and A. M. Butlerov, *Sochineniia*, III, Moscow, 1958, 128. A Soviet view of Mendeleev's philosophical and political beliefs is given in P. P. Ionidi, *Mirovozzrenie D. I. Mendeleeva*, Moscow, 1959. Permanent secretary Veselovskii maintained that the chemist Butlerov engineered the whole affair; that is, he nominated Mendeleev for the Academy knowing perfectly well he could not be elected. Butlerov allegedly hoped to discredit the Academy. (Ionidi, *Mirovozzrenie*, pp. 32-33.) Still another explanation given for Mendeleev's failure to be elected is Count Dmitrii Tolstoi's dislike for the chemist. See Beverly S. Almgren's review of *Dmitrii Ivanovich Mendeleev, 1834-1907*, by N. A. Figurovskii, in *Isis*, LIV (September 1963), 432.

[25] An interesting postscript to the Gorky episode was that after the February Revolution the Academy corrected the wrong not by holding another election but by merely sending Gorky an invitation to the next meeting. Korolenko also

of the Academy signed the "Memorandum of 342 Scholars," which criticized the conditions of education in Russia. Published in the St. Petersburg papers, the note called for a national assembly and censured the government for forcing professors and academicians to work under onerous material and intellectual conditions. The immediate reaction of the president of the Academy, Grand Duke Konstantin Konstantinovich (1858-1915), was to discipline all the offending academicians. When the permanent secretary, S. F. Ol'denburg, informed the president that the members of the Academy were on the point of submitting their resignations, the truculent Romanov at first replied, "Well, what of it? It will be a *guerre à outrance,* maybe the Academy will cease to exist, the struggle will be ended by *faute de combattants.*" After second thoughts, however, Konstantin recognized that the destruction of the Academy of Sciences was not as inconsequential as he originally maintained. He calmed the General Assembly of the Academy with an informal speech in which he said that although he still disagreed with their memorandum, he continued to respect them as academicians.[26] The one resignation actually submitted, that of the botanist I. P. Borodin, was considered withdrawn and the Academy returned to its work.

World War I forced the Academy to turn at least part of its attention to applied science. In 1915 it created the Commission for the Study of Natural Productive Forces (KEPS), an organization which in a modified form would have a long history in the Soviet period. The primary duty of the new body was to serve as a technological advisory committee for war needs, but its activities in the area of industrial research and minerals exploration were important to the economy as a whole.[27] KEPS

---

reclaimed his membership after 1917. G. A. Kniazev, "Maksim Gor'kii i tsarskoe pravitel'stvo," *Vestnik Akademii Nauk* (No. 2, 1932), cols. 33-34.

[26] This speech was not included in the minutes of the meeting, but a copy of it was found in the archives of the Academy after the Revolution. G. A. Kniazev, "Iz proshlogo akademii nauk; poritsanie akademikam za uchastie v 'zapiske 342 uchenykh,'" *Vestnik Akademii Nauk* (No. 4, 1931), cols. 13, 22.

[27] KEPS was suggested by Academicians A. P. Karpinskii, B. B. Golitsyn,

should be recognized as a significant prerevolutionary predecessor of the new forms of research bodies in the applied
sciences which the Soviet government urged after 1927.

Although several commissions undertook tasks directly connected with military needs, the activities of the Academy were
affected by World War I to a lesser degree than might be
expected. The volume of research publications actually rose
during the war to a peak in 1917, even though sales abroad had
shrunk to one-tenth the prewar volume. Public interest in
scholarly books, especially in natural science and technology,
was accentuated by the war effort. The war illustrated in
Russia, as in many nations, that science is an important source
of strength to governments in providing the basic knowledge
for military technology. A result was a tendency in major nations to separate "science" from "education," and to devote the
attention to science that governments had already given trans-
portation, industry, and education. The Academy's report for
1916 optimistically noted, "For us victory will mark the renaissance of Russia, a renaissance in which science will play an
honored place. . . ."[28] Academician Ol'denburg, who fully
employed the power of the permanent secretary's office to
shape the Academy's activities during this time of expansion,
became more and more aware that the Academy of Sciences in
Russia was becoming a type of institution unknown in other
countries; it was graduating from its status as a small scientific
society into a directorate of the cultural and scientific life of
the nation. The attraction this concept held for Ol'denburg
goes far toward explaining his actions after the Bolshevik
Revolution.

Despite two centuries of governmental interference and con-

V. I. Vernadskii, N. S. Kurnakov, and N. N. Andrusov. (Letter to the author
from N. A. Figurovskii, Director, Institute of the History of Natural Sciences
and Technology, Academy of Sciences, Moscow, June 1961.) For a survey of
the activity of KEPS from 1915 to 1921 see B. A. Lindener, *Raboty rossiiskoi
akademii nauk v oblasti issledovaniia prirodnykh bogatstv Rossii; obzor deiatel'-
nosti KEPS za 1915-1921 gg.*, Petrograd, 1922.

[28] *Otchet o deiatel'nosti Rossiiskoi akademii nauk za 1916*, Petrograd, 1917,
p. 16.

trol, the Imperial Academy of Sciences, as it existed in the first decades of the 20th century, was an institution of remarkable talent and achievement. In a country extremely backward educationally and only beginning its great development economically, the leading scientists were abreast of those in western Europe. A highly educated and cultured man of western Europe would probably have felt more at home in the Academy of Sciences in St. Petersburg than anywhere else in Imperial Russia. There he would find his language spoken; mutual friends and books would abound. If he had gone to either the imperial court or to the universities he would have found similarly Westernized Russians, but these institutions differed in atmosphere from Western counterparts. The imperial court of Russia was marked with an obscurantism rare even in the conservative courts of pre-1914 western Europe, while the universities of Russia were arenas for the peculiar radicals fostered by the antiquated political system of tsarist Russia. But in the Academy of Sciences the Western scholar would find knowledge being pursued in conditions similar to those in learned organizations in his own country. Even there, one must admit, a distinct difference would be apparent: in Russia centralization of governmental power and the relative lack of development of other centers of research had produced an academy that still attempted to dominate scholarship as the 18th century academies had done in Europe. To the communist reformers of Russia after 1917 this unique legacy became an opportunity which, once seized and then transformed, resulted in a framework of scholarly research totally new in history.

Revolution

From 1917 to 1927 the Academy of Sciences retained the essential features it inherited from the prerevolutionary epoch. The major exception was the election of a new president. Immediately after the Provisional Government came to power the Academy chose Academician A. P. Karpinskii as the first freely elected president in the history of the Academy. Despite his advanced age Karpinskii continued to fill the presidential chair through the most traumatic years the Academy ever experienced—1927-1932—until his death in 1936 at 89. In May 1917 the Academy also changed its official name from "The Imperial Academy of Sciences" to the "Russian Academy of Sciences."

Aleksandr Petrovich Karpinskii (1847-1936) was a specialist in geology, particularly paleogeography and tectonics, who was well known abroad, serving on a number of international geological committees. In many ways Karpinskii was a logical choice for president of the Academy of Sciences after the Revolution. He was popular among scientists as an eminent scholar of unquestioned integrity, with no record of political activities. At the same time, he symbolized the new orientation of the Academy in giving attention to both basic scientific research and practical applications. He directed the exploration of valuable mineral deposits in the Urals region and had been instrumental in founding KEPS, which served as an organizational model during the later attempts to give science a more planned direction. In administration Karpinskii was not a strong leader, usually yielding to advice from other quarters, particularly the permanent secretary of the Academy.

The majority of the members of the Academy warmly greeted the overturn of the tsarist government but the advent of the Bolsheviks was much more unsettling.[29] The first revolution cleared the obstructions to the development of knowledge in Russia under the guidance of the Westernized academic community; the second revolution threatened a rejection of that community by the Bolsheviks acting in the name of the proletarian and peasant masses. The academicians were overwhelm-

---

[29] S. Voronov, "Iz proshlogo i nastoiashchego akademii nauk," *Novyi Mir* (May 1930), pp. 138-39, maintained that the Academy met the February Revolution with considerable opposition, but there is no evidence to support this view. Voronov wrote this article during the Soviet reform of the Academy as an attempt to discredit the old Academy; he centered his attention on the few monarchist members. Lunacharskii was much more unbiased when he observed that the Academy welcomed the February Revolution despite the presence of a few supporters of the monarchy. A. V. Lunacharskii, "K 200–letiiu vsesoiuznoi akademii nauk," *Novyi Mir* (No. 10, 1925), pp. 99-112.

ingly opposed to the Soviet state, and two full members of the Academy, P. B. Struve, the political economist, and M. I. Rostovtsev, the historian and archaeologist, emigrated to the West.[30] Other scientists felt unsure of the Soviet regime and hesitated in their loyalties. A. F. Ioffe took flight to the White-controlled areas of the Ukraine, but later reconsidered and returned to Soviet Russia, where he became a partisan of the communist regime. The suicide of famed Academician A. M. Liapunov in 1919 was partly a result of the death of his beloved wife, partly the crisis of Russia. V. I. Vernadskii, a liberal democrat, as were many other members of the academic profession, became ill in the fall of 1917 with tuberculosis and went south to Poltava to stay with relatives.[31] The area was at that time in Soviet hands. When the Germans came in March 1918 he went to Kiev, where he played an important role in scientific affairs for a number of months.[32] Vernadskii decided to stay in the Soviet state, where he became a spokesman for the liberal segment of the old academic community. He is credited with the remark, "I must fight, but I can do so only in my own country, not from the other side of the frontier. Let happen what will."[33]

Thus some scientists who loathed bolshevism were willing to try to live with it. Radicalism had not infrequently been associated with scientific thought in 19th century Russia, and scientists usually preferred the political left. One such scientist, probably more radical than most, expressed his feelings frankly:

> Yes, we agree that ninety-five per cent of the Communists are dark and pernicious people. We agree that Bolshevism, in its present form, is an anti-cultural phenomenon, destroying Russia. But what could replace it? . . .

[30] Struve, the theorist of "legal" Marxism in the 1890s, and later a leading Kadet, was active in exile in conservative émigré organizations. Rostovtsev became a member of the faculty first at the University of Wisconsin and then at Yale University.

[31] Interview with George Vernadsky, East Haven, Conn., July 21, 1964.

[32] Vernadskii served as the first president of the newly organized Ukrainian Academy of Sciences. See p. 170.

[33] Michael Kitaeff, "Akademiia nauk SSSR," p. 45.

In a revolution extremist doctrines are victorious. We do not believe in the victory of Girondists. And of all the extremist doctrines we prefer the leftist, the red. . . .[34]

On November 15, 1917 A. V. Lunacharskii, Commissar of Education, published an appeal to the old intelligentsia to help the Revolution: "The people are calling to you to work with them. . . . There is no return to the past."[35] The Soviet government vowed its support and encouragement to those members of the old intelligentsia who were willing to cooperate with it.

The Academy's attitude toward the Soviet appeal was visibly hostile. The Physics–Mathematics Section met in November 1917 and actually discussed whether or not the members should recognize the Bolshevik government.[36] The youngest member of the Academy, the chemist V. N. Ipat'ev, who was far from being a Bolshevik, dissuaded the department from passing anti-Soviet resolutions, maintaining that "control of the state belonged to the group capable of setting up a strong government."[37]

The entire report of the Academy for the revolutionary year of 1917 was filled with a deep tone of pessimism about the future, and hostility toward the new government. Permanent Secretary Ol'denburg, author of the report, was at this moment at the deepest point in his discouragement; within a year he had forestalled his bitterness and begun again to promote the fortunes of the Academy.[38]

During the Civil War the Academy shared in the general crisis of Russia. The reports of the academicians contained descriptions of the great difficulties facing anyone who con-

[34] Boris Sokolov, *Nauka v sovetskoi rossii*, Berlin, 1921, p. 20.
[35] *Sobranie uzakonenii i rasporiazhenii rabochego i krestianskogo pravitel'stva* (No. 5, 1917), art. 1.
[36] V. N. Ipatieff (American spelling), *The Life of a Chemist*, Stanford, 1946, p. 260.
[37] *Ibid.*
[38] The morose Ol'denburg commented in the report: "We are struck with the wisdom of those people of the East who say, 'When contemporary circumstances lead you to despair, seek aid from those who lie in their tombs.'" *Otchet o deiatel'nosti Rossiiskoi akademii nauk za 1917*, Petrograd, 1918, p. 6.

tinued to attempt research: bitter cold, lack of sufficient working space, inadequate lighting, even starvation. As early as the
spring of 1919 the difficult conditions caused the deaths of
internationally prominent researchers. The tragedy was evident
in announcements of only a few words: "On May 20, Academician E. S. Fedorov, the founder of modern crystallography,
died as a result of prolonged malnutrition which had drained
his strength."[39] Others similarly lost included A. S. Lappo-
Danilevskii, A. A. Shakhmatov, B. A. Turaev, and S. S. Venge-
rov. Among less prominent workers in the Academy, death was
even more widespread; one source lists the total loss of academic personnel in 1920 as 42, and there may have been more.
With the end of civil strife in 1922, however, and the invigora-
tion of the economy resulting from the relaxed New Economic
Policy, conditions in the Academy rapidly improved, although
shortages of certain materials persisted.[40]

Within the Academy itself during the years of the Civil War
and the New Economic Policy there was a constant dispute
between those academicians who desired to keep the Academy
true to its old traditions and therefore as insulated from Soviet
society as possible, and those who, while not communists,
disliked seeing the Academy become less important in the total
fields of Soviet science and governmental affairs. According to
S. Belomortsev, a former worker in the Academy, Academicians

[39] Quoted in Konstantin F. Shteppa, *Russian Historians and the Soviet State*,
New Brunswick, N.J., 1962, p. 4, from *Izvestiia petrogradskogo nauchnogo
instituta P. F. Lezgafta*, I (1920), xxxii. The BSE gives the date of Fedorov's
death as May 21.

[40] According to Soviet historians the guiding policy for the Academy in the
postrevolutionary period was established by Lenin's "Draft Plan of Scientific–
Technological Works" ("Nabrosok plana nauchno-tekhnicheskikh rabot), written in April 1918. (V. I. Lenin, *Polnoe sobranie sochinenii*, 5th edn., xxxvi,
228-31.) Soviet histories of the Academy include the text of the Draft Plan.
There is very little evidence, however, that Lenin's plan affected the activity
of the Academy in any way. The archives of the Academy on the first years of
the Soviet government contain no mention of the Draft Plan. Lenin's call for
the Academy to "draw up, as rapidly as possible, a plan for the reorganization
of industry and the economic development of Russia" was ignored. See G. A.
Kniazev and A. V. Kol'tsov, *Kratkii ocherk istorii akademii nauk SSSR*, Moscow–Leningrad, 1964, pp. 78-81. Early communication between the Academy
and Soviet officials is also discussed in V. A. Ul'ianovskaia, *Formirovanie
nauchnoi intelligentsii v SSSR, 1917-1937 gg.*, Moscow, 1966, especially pp.
44-95.

S. F. Platonov, F. Iu. Levinson-Lessing and I. P. Pavlov accused the permanent secretary, Ol'denburg, who was in charge of relations between the Academy and the government, of excessive servility toward Party and government officials. Ol'denburg's critics hinted that he feared he would be condemned for his past associations, since he had been a member of the Provisional Government, and was the father of the émigré monarchist S. S. Ol'denburg.[41]

Sergei Fedorovich Ol'denburg (1863-1934), who has been mentioned several times as the leading personality in the affairs of the Academy in the first quarter of this century, was educated in Russia, Poland, and England, and a specialist in Oriental studies. As a young scholar he attracted attention with his knowledge of classical studies, Indian dialects, and Buddhist folklore. In 1895 he was elected to the chair of Indian Languages and Literature at the University of St. Petersburg, a post he held for over 30 years. In 1901 he became a member of the Academy and three years later its permanent secretary. During his life he published over 300 items, many on the organization of science.

Ol'denburg was simultaneously a prominent member of the aristocracy and a scholar of international reputation; he represented many of the finest elements of the 19th century Imperial Academy of Sciences. His membership in a princely family of German origin did not prevent him from associating with democratic political organizations during the last years of the empire. He was a leader of the Constitutional Democratic Party, which favored a Western-style democracy. After the Revolution he made a heroic effort to adjust to a political environment that was obviously distasteful to him, but not through the rather common path of "inner emigration"—a withdrawal from politics. He continued to expose himself to the

[41] Sergei Belomortsev, "Bol'shevizatsiia akademii nauk," *Posev*, xLvi (November 18, 1951), 11. S. S. Ol'denburg wrote the two-volume *Tsarstvovanie imperatora Nikolaia II*, Belgrade, 1939-49. In earlier years Ol'denburg was an Octobrist and evidently believed in limited democracy, but with emigration his views became increasingly conservative. His daughter, Zoe Oldenbourg, is the well-known French writer.

Soviet milieu; perhaps no other aristocrat of Russia made such an attempt to accommodate himself to changed conditions. In part, his family's tradition of directing others determined his actions. But throughout he maintained his cultural standards and promoted scholarship in Russia.

A more objective analysis of Academician Ol'denburg's position than that of his contemporary critics within the Academy indicates that he wanted to avoid both a communist seizure of the Academy and the diminution of its role in Soviet scholarship; all his efforts were directed toward a modus vivendi between an independent Academy and the Soviet government, based on mutual benefit.[42] Ol'denburg felt maligned on all sides, since the communists frequently criticized him for playing a deceptive diplomatic game aimed at keeping Marxists out of the Academy,[43] while the academicians often chided him for subservience to the Soviet authorities. Ol'denburg realized that his position was precarious; in July 1927 an article in *Leningradskaia Pravda* darkly hinted that there were many "former people" in the Academy; other critics said that one or two academicians who represented the Academy to Soviet society were "covered with a thick Soviet veil, but how they looked in their natural appearance . . . was not clear."[44]

By 1927 the Academy was the most important unreformed

[42] V. T. Ermakov stated that several of the academicians seriously proposed that the Academy be given the status of an "autonomous republic" in the Soviet governmental system. This proposal is not quite as absurd as it might seem; something of a precedent existed in the fact that university professors and academicians were assigned certain seats in the State Council which the Russian government reorganized as a part of the new legislature in the wake of the 1905 Revolution. Ermakov, "Bor'ba kommunisticheskoi partii za perestroiku raboty nauchnykh uchrezhdenii v gody pervoi piatiletki," unpublished dissertation for the degree of *kandidat*, Department of the History of the Communist Party of the USSR, Moscow State University, 1956, pp. 121-22, citing TsGAOR, f. 3316, op. 23, d. 592, l. 1.

[43] The anonymous author, "Materialist," demanded in early 1923, "In the sixth year of the proletarian revolution we may ask, What has changed in this reactionary nest? Is the Academy of Sciences of the R.S.F.S.R. any different from the Academy of Sciences of the Russian Empire? . . . How many materialists and atheists are sitting in the Academy?" "Ob akademii nauk RSFSR," *Pod znamenem marksizma* (No. 1, 1923), p. 191.

[44] Voronov, "Iz proshlogo," pp. 143, 147.

tsarist institution.[45] Not a single academician was a Party member. In the early 1920s the Communist Party did not have the talent to replace the Academy and could not afford to eliminate it.[46] New staffs for other institutions could be found rather easily, but distinguished and able scientists such as the members of the Academy were very limited in number. By 1927, however, the beginnings of a new generation of Marxist scholars, gathered around a separate institution known as the Communist Academy, provided an alternative to the Academy of Sciences, although still of inferior calibre, particularly in the natural sciences.[47] The replacement or reform of the Academy was almost certainly only a matter of time; this institution without a single Party cell and with an uncensored press, even for works in history and the social sciences, was an anomaly in Soviet society. Furthermore, the Party was developing its own views on the role of science and technology in a socialist society that could be implemented only with the assistance of the Academy of Sciences or its equivalent. Nevertheless, it would be a great mistake to portray the future of the Academy, seen from the late twenties, as predetermined. Granted the desire of the Communist Party to bring it under control, the wish was not the same as the actuality, and there were many possible variants of control. Furthermore, the Marxist interpretation of the place of science contained several alternatives, each of which could affect the Academy differently. The future path of the Academy in 1927 was not, then, apparent, but it was clearly to be controversial and significant.

[45] An organizational chart of the Academy in December 1926 appears in Appendix B.

[46] The helplessness of the Party before the Academy during the early twenties is illustrated in Lunacharskii's query:

Just what could we demand of the Academy? That it suddenly, all in a big crowd, transform itself into a Communist gathering, that it suddenly cross itself in a Marxist fashion, put its hand on *Capital*, swearing that it is a genuine Bolshevik? . . . Everyone knows that a genuine conversion of this sort could not be.

Lunacharskii, "K 200–letiiu," p. 109.

[47] The threat of the Communist Academy to the Academy of Sciences is discussed on pp. 74, 119, 178, 180, 193.

CHAPTER II

SOVIET STRATEGIES FOR
SCIENTIFIC DEVELOPMENT

*It is not only a new economic system which
has been born. A new culture has been born.
A new science has been born. A new style of
life has been born.* / N. I. Bukharin[1]

*The State Planning Commission is the most
original product of the Bolshevik Revolution.*
/ J. G. Crowther[2]

Within every society there exists an "environment for science"
which, to a greater or lesser degree, promotes the development
of science by providing fertile soil for individual creativity. A
number of variables can be adjusted in the hope of facilitating
this creativity, albeit adjustment is not easily effected. Examples
of such attempts to provide an optimum environment for the
flourishing of science may be found in the educational system,
in the coordination of research programs, in the granting of
material support (laboratories, equipment, research funds),
and in various kinds of personal incentives. Manipulation of
such variables is not a new development, nor one unique to
science under totalitarian governments, though the control of
such factors as the philosophy of science can be attempted only
by a society with very tight controls over intellectual life.

The Communist reformers of Russian science were openly
seeking the optimum environment. No previous government in

[1] "Theory and Practice from the Standpoint of Dialectical Materialism,"
Science at the Cross Roads, London, 1931, p. 23.
[2] *Soviet Science*, London–New York, 1936, p. 15.

history was so openly and energetically in favor of science. The revolutionary leaders of the Soviet government saw the natural sciences as the answer to both the spiritual and physical problems of Russia; science was to them not only the refutation of Russia's age-old religious mysticism but the key to the great wealth of the Russian land. Science would modernize both Russia as a state of nature and Russia as a state of mind. Toward this goal, the leaders of Soviet Russia wished to develop a reform of the country's scientific institutions and a strategy for future scientific development that would ensure the superiority of science in Russia over science in other countries. This reform movement misfired, as did so much of the experimentation in the Soviet Union in the 1920s, but those writers who have characterized the Bolsheviks as the "wreckers of science" without probing any further into the events of the time have missed much of the drama of the situation, even if they have correctly described the more violent episodes.[3] Rather than destroy science, the Soviet leaders hoped to transform it, to create a new "socialist science." It might be too much to maintain that the Soviet planners of the twenties were seeking a "science of science" in the sense that this phrase has recently been used, but there is no question but that they asked some of the most important questions about science and they were groping toward a few answers when their activities were curtailed by Stalin.[4]

In order to translate their aspirations into achievements, however, Soviet political leaders, ideologists, and scientists needed to reach certain agreements about the function of science, its relative importance in the development of a new

[3] For example, see A. I. Zavrotskii, *Krasnye vandaly: obzor sostoianiia nauki v Sovetskoi Rossii*, Shanghai, 1934.

[4] For a discussion of recent efforts to promote science by examining it as a separate activity, see Stevan Dedijer, "The Science of Science: A Programme and a Plea," *Minerva* (Summer 1966), pp. 489-504. Dedijer condemns those countries which even yet know the "number of their donkeys, but not the number of their research workers." As an example to others he points out that the United States began to make surveys of the number of research workers "as far back" as 1938. He is evidently unaware that the Soviet Union published a number of such studies in the 1920s. See pp. 45-46.

economy and culture, and the means of promoting it. And here difficulties so numerous arose that the entire enterprise was endangered even before the orthodoxy of the thirties terminated both the public differences of opinion and the vital remnants of research into the nature of science. These difficulties were ones of the interpretation of Marxism. There existed such a diversity of opinions on the place of science according to Marxism that entirely different, if not opposing, policy recommendations could be given Marxist justifications. It is necessary, therefore, to consider briefly the connection between science and certain issues of Marxist ideology, such as the theory of the base and superstructure and the doctrine of the unity of theory and practice. Both of these concepts are relevant to the more specific issue of the planning of science, to be considered in the last half of this chapter.

Base and superstructure

Soviet textbooks of Marxism–Leninism define the fundamental elements of society as (1) the productive forces, (2) the productive relations of people, which, together with the productive forces, form the "economic base" of society, and (3) the ideological superstructure. This definition of the principles of historical materialism has remained orthodox for many years and is a fairly accurate schematic representation of Marx's and Engels' own writings.[5] But any attempt to probe further into the meanings of the words used and the exact relationships involved runs into serious problems of interpretation on which large differences of opinion have existed among Marxists, including many who considered themselves quite orthodox. What,

[5] For the constancy of this scheme, compare the discussion of "Base and Superstructure" given in a 1926 Soviet encyclopedia to a 1963 philosophical dictionary: *Bol'shaia sovetskaia entsiklopediia*, IV (1926), 354; *Filosofskii slovar'*, Moscow, 1963, pp. 39-40. Marx's best description of these concepts is K. Marx and F. Engels, *A Contribution to the Critique of Political Economy*, in *Werke*, XIII, Berlin, 1961, 8-9. The mere fact that the scheme itself has remained constant does not, of course, deny the different interpretations of the base-superstructure concept. Marx himself gave varying emphasis to intellectual activity as a part of the production process.

exactly, is a "productive force"? Is it a machine, a technique, a natural resource, a source of energy? How dependent is the superstructure on the base? Can the superstructure change the base in a fundamental fashion? If we include philosophic forms in the superstructure along with legal, political, religious, and aesthetic ones, do we include the philosophy of science? And how about science itself? Surely science must be connected with the economic base, since it unlocks enormous productive forces. But then can the philosophy of science be totally separated from science itself? And if the Soviet state in the twenties hoped to create a unique "socialist science" did this not already imply that science was in the superstructure, was derivative, and would take on different forms as a result of economic change?

Curiously enough, the theoreticians who promoted the concept of "Proletarian Culture" in the years immediately after the Revolution and who called for a basic transformation of the arts, did not believe that science was similarly a part of the superstructure. The group publishing the journal *Proletarian Culture* (*Proletars' kaia kul' tura*) was led by A. A. Bogdanov (1873-1928), a person very much enamored of science, who warned on several occasions that science must be treated carefully by the revolutionaries.[6] Bogdanov, a medical doctor and both a friend of Lenin's in politics and his protagonist in philosophy, believed the proletariat would cause the creation of a completely new culture in the social sciences and the arts; but he thought that even bourgeois physicists and chemists were

[6] Trotsky did not believe in the possibility of the creation of a proletarian culture, citing shortage of time as a reason; Lenin and Lunacharskii saw both national and supranational elements in culture, and believed that certain aspects of a culture carry definite class characteristics; Bukharin, however, believed that a proletarian culture could be created. The view of Lenin and Lunacharskii received Party sanction. One should be careful not to conclude that those who believed in the creation of a proletarian literature also favored a proletarian science. Bogdanov did not believe in a new science; Bukharin said that he did, as illustrated by the admittedly rhetorical quotation at the beginning of this chapter. See M. Kim, *Kommunisticheskaia partiia-organizator kul' turnoi revoliutsii v SSSR*, Moscow, 1955; Anatoli Lunacharskii, *Stati o sovetskoi literature*, Moscow, 1958, pp. 176-77; Herman Ermolaev, *Soviet Literary Theories, 1917-1934*, Berkeley, 1963; L. Trotsky, *Literature and Revolution*, New York, 1925.

arriving at a "single thermodynamic" method which was universally valid. In these most advanced sciences the proletarian
epoch would not result in a new ideological creation.[7] But
even Bogdanov believed that science would take on some new
characteristics in the new epoch, particularly those of "collective labor," and his respect for contemporary Western science was often lost in the revolutionary clamor for a new
culture.

Bogdanov's Proletarian Culture group was subordinated by
the Party in 1920 as a result of its extragovernmental attempt
to dictate policy in the arts, but Bogdanov's opinion that the
advanced sciences are "homogeneous," or constants, even in
societies with different economic bases was held by a number
of Soviet writers of the twenties.

A long debate occurred in the first decade of the Soviet
state between two different factions in Soviet philosophy, frequently called for convenience the "mechanists" and the "Deborinites." This discussion has recently been studied in great
detail by an able Western scholar, and no attempt will be made
here to delve into the same issues.[8] The controversy was connected indirectly, however, with the discussion of the place of
science in the Marxist base-superstructure scheme. The mechanists, who were dominant in the early twenties, believed, as
a general rule, that dialectical materialism was inherent in
natural science and that all leading scientists were, at least
subconsciously, dialectical materialists. The task of the Marxist
philosopher was to openly formulate the principles already
contained in the body of scientific theory. The "Deborinites,"
named after the leading member of their group, A. M. Deborin,
attributed a more active role to philosophy, and particularly to
the laws of the dialectic, which they believed should be guiding

[7] See Bogdanov's lectures delivered to the *Proletkul' t* group in the spring of
1919: A. A. Malinovskii, *Elementy proletarskoi kul' tury v razvitii rabochego
klassa*, Moscow, 1920, pp. 83-85; also, his *Tektologiia, vseobshchaia organizatsionnaia nauka*, Moscow, 1922.

[8] David Joravsky, *Soviet Marxism and Natural Science, 1917-1932*, New York,
1961. For a discussion of the base-superstructure issue, see also his "Soviet
Views on the History of Science," *Isis*, XLVI (March 1955), 3-13.

principles for the scientist in his work. Thus, the Deborinites, who gradually gained the ascendancy, defended the Marxist philosophy of science as an active element; indeed, a number of them insisted on the "class" nature of science itself; the mechanists, on the other hand, often either discounted philosophy as an autonomous discipline, spoke of it mainly as a summation of general scientific laws, or foresaw a merging of science and philosophy.

Neither the mechanists nor the Deborinites adopted unanimous opinions on the position of science in the base-superstructure scheme. Nevertheless, the two groups did differ in their emphasis. The victory of the Deborinites in the late twenties marked an increasing willingness to put science in the superstructure, a tendency which lasted after the Deborinites were succeeded as leaders of Soviet philosophers by Stalinists. Thus, the belief of such mechanists as I. I. Stepanov that science is nearly homogeneous in different social systems was followed by the beliefs of the Deborinites that science is tinged with class interests.[9] V. P. Egorshin, a young student of Deborin, was one of the most straightforward on the subject, maintaining that "modern natural science is just as much a class phenomenon as philosophy and art. . . . It is bourgeois in its theoretical foundations."[10] Another writer of similar orientation maintained that "science is one of the highest, if not the highest, layer of the superstructure."[11] The ideologists who won the approval of Stalin after 1931 believed the relationship between the base and the superstructure was more involved than either the mechanists or Deborinites had granted, but they still included science in the superstructure. O. Iu. Shmidt, a future member of the Academy, commented in a 1932 article on "Natural Science" in the major Soviet encyclopedia: "In each

[9] I. I. Stepanov, "Engel's i mekhanisticheskoe ponimanie prirody," *Pod znamenem marksizma* (No. 8-9, 1925), pp. 44-72.

[10] V. P. Egorshin, "Estestvoznanie i klassovaia bor'ba," *Pod znamenem marksizma* (No. 6, 1926), p. 135.

[11] S. Vol'fson, "Nauka i bor'ba klassov," *VARNITSO* (February 1930), p. 23.

epoch the level of natural science is determined in the final analysis by the level of development of the forces of production. However, natural science, as a part of the 'superstructure,' is essentially influenced by other parts of the 'superstructure,' especially philosophy and religion, and at the same time influences in its turn the development of the forces of production."[12]

The question of the exact position of science in the Marxist ideological scheme was not settled in the twenties, and, indeed, remains a controversial topic to the present day.[13] In the late twenties, however, the new view toward science reflected a significant change in attitudes toward scientists. The campaign against bourgeois scientists that began in earnest in 1929 could be more easily rationalized by maintaining that science itself could be either "bourgeois" or "socialist." As the industrialization campaign grew in intensity, the cultural front broadened until it involved those people, such as scientists, who had so far managed to stay free of political engagement.

The unity of theory and practice

The principle of the unity of theory and practice, to which Soviet Marxists gave particular interpretations of considerable significance, was originally a result of Marx's and Engels' opposition to speculative philosophy rather than a viewpoint concerning science and technology. Practice is not only the proper goal of philosophy, thought Marx, but also is its most rigorous test. He criticized past generations of philosophers for considering philosophy a subject of contemplation, rather than a guide to action. One of Marx's most famous statements reveals his view on the relationship between theory and practice:

---

[12] *Bol'shaia sovetskaia entsiklopediia*, xxiv, 1st edn., 1932, 559.

[13] For changing attitudes, see S. G. Strumilin, "Nauka v svete ucheniia I. V. Stalina o bazise i nadstroike," *Izvestiia akademii nauk: otdelenie ekonomiki i prava* (No. 4, 1951), 287-88; Strumilin, "Nauka i razvitie proizvoditel'nykh sil," *Voprosy filosofii* (No. 3, 1954), pp. 46-61; D. M. Troshchin, *Mesto i rol' estestvoznaniia v razvitii obshchestva*, Moscow, 1961, p. 58; I. A. Maizel', *Kommunizm i prevrashchenie nauki v neposredstvennuiu proizvoditel'nuiu silu*, Moscow, 1963. The 1961 Party Program stated that "science will become, in the full sense of the word, a direct productive force," in other words, a part of the economic base. ("Programma kommunisticheskoi partii sovetskogo soiuza," *Pravda* [July 30, 1961]) The future tense is significant.

"The philosophers have only *interpreted* the world in various ways; the point however is to change it."[14]

To Marx and Engels this opposition to idle philosophic speculation implied a similar opinion on science: the true test of value of a scientific theory, they thought, is the applied science which results from it.[15] Man did not begin to understand chemical substances such as alizarin dyes until he produced them himself from coal tar. The Copernican system was not really "proved" until calculations based on it permitted the prediction of previously unknown planets.

Marx and Engels further maintained that the impetus of science in history was the needs of the prevailing modes of production, i.e., practice. Here the connection between the base-superstructure scheme and the unity of theory and practice becomes evident. Astronomy was one of the first sciences developed, they believed, because societies with agricultural economies calculated seasonal changes on the basis of the stars. Marx attempted to illustrate this in *Capital*, by maintaining that the necessity of predicting the periods of the Nile's floods created Egyptian astronomy. Once created, however, he continued, astronomy acquired needs of its own, such as the expansion of mathematics. The last observation, which reveals the more subtle aspect of the Marxist interpretation of science, concerns an essential point. Since science could acquire "needs of its own," the more developed any particular science, the more difficult it became to relate its progress to the modes of production. Indeed, at particular moments, theoretical science could influence the modes of production, rather than the reverse. Equipment constructed to help further scientific investigation could result in productive innovation. Thus the determining influence of practice was, according to Marxism, only in the long run. As Engels commented,

According to the materialist understanding of history, the determining element in the historical process in the final analysis is production, and the reproduction of active life.

[14] Marx and Engels, *Werke*, III, Berlin, 1962, 7.
[15] *Ibid.*, XXI, 276.

Neither Marx nor I ever said any more. If somebody distorts this principle into the belief that the economic element is the only determining element, then he has transformed our statement into an empty, abstract phrase saying nothing.[16]

It becomes clear that the principle of the unity of theory and practice could be interpreted in various ways. The principle contains a reference to a time scale which distinguishes between long-run and short-run phenomena. According to the most liberal interpretation of the doctrine no conceivable topic of scientific research could be considered a violation of it, since no one could definitely affirm that in the future practical application would not issue from the topic. And in the long-run practical needs properly defined would elicit the proper research. Therefore certain Marxist scholars believed science would be much less hobbled by practical interests in the Soviet Union than in the West, where commercial interests allegedly reigned supreme. V. T. Ter-Oganesov commented that it was always the capitalist, not the socialist, who wanted to know if such and such scientific development could be given a profitable application.[17] And the prominent Soviet theoretician, Nikolai Bukharin, who was to be one of the leading speakers on the topic of the planning of science, similarly rejected the view that science in the Soviet Union would be constricted: "All the poverty [of the view] that the 'utility' of science means its degradation, the narrowing of its scope, etc., becomes crystal clear. . . . Great practice requires great theory . . . we are arriving *at a social synthesis of science and practice.*"[18]

Nonetheless, the major emphasis of the Soviet Marxists dealing with science in the late twenties was on receiving practical benefits rapidly. There were two reasons for this emphasis. The first was the obvious one that Soviet leaders were committed to

[16] Marx and Engels, *Sochineniia,* 2nd edn., Moscow, 1965, xxxvii, 394.

[17] V. T. Ter-Oganesov, "Industrializatsiia SSSR i voprosy organizatsii nauki," *Nauchnyi Rabotnik* (September 1926), pp. 5-6.

[18] "Theory and Practice from the Standpoint of Dialectical Materialism," p. 21. See also his "Science and Politics in the Soviet Union," *New Statesman and Nation* (July 11, 1931), pp. 37-38.

state interests. Like members of state bureaucracies everywhere, they believed that resources expended on academic topics should promise clear rewards. The Soviet state, still very young and weak, needed a quick return on every investment in order to resist foreign enemies and begin constructing a new society. Long range research projects would simply have to wait.

The second reason for the drive toward pragmatic research was ideological. True, the doctrine of the unity of theory and practice provided room for research projects without evident practical applications. But according to this doctrine, disinterested theoretical science could provide benefits for production only in the short run; in the long run, practice would determine science. Therefore it seemed to Soviet planners that the benefits of theoretical research projects should at least be visible, even if somewhat hazily. Intellectually such a belief was erroneous even within the framework of Marxism, since the proximity of theoretical science to application is according to Marxism not a proximity relating to visibility, but one of causal sequence. A short causal sequence could be quite invisible if it depended on an unknown theory.

But however unjustified the requirement of the promise of visible benefit from research may have been from a theoretical Marxist point of view, this requirement suited the industrializers very well. It provided a rationalization for making scientific research a service function of industrial expansion. In Russia theoretical science would respond to the call for industrialization, just as simplified Marxism said it should; thus the subordination of theoretical research to engineering was transformed from an alternative of policy to a logical necessity flowing from the stream of history.

Other characteristics of scientific activity in the 1920s, both in western Europe and in Russia, provided support for the revolutionaries' belief that the new scientific program in Russia must be oriented toward practice. In western Europe the division between pure and applied science and the disdain of the pure scientists for their fellows in applied science were un-usually great—more marked, perhaps, than at any earlier moment in European history, and also larger than in subse-quent decades, when a *rapprochement* became apparent. The distance between pure and applied science had grown rapidly since the early 18th century, when the scientific societies and academies made no clear division between the two activities. Instrument-makers and military engineers were among the most important members of the early societies. In the 19th century, however, pure and applied science asserted their identities in the minds of scientists as each found an enormous area for expansion. The industrial revolution established engineering as a profession, not a craft or mere military skill, while the de-velopment of physical, mathematical, and chemical theory provided equal room for the theoretical scientists. By the early 19th century, scientists were beginning to pride themselves on their indifference to practical application. Science, as Schiller said, was a goddess, not a milch cow.

The socialist critics of the early 20th century believed that scientists had extended this reverence of pure science to an extent which, in a world still full of people deprived of basic necessities, bordered on the immoral. Henri Poincaré exposed himself to such criticism when he commented, "I do not say: Science is useful because it teaches us to construct machines; I say machines are useful because, working for us, they will one day leave us more time for scientific work."[19] Poincaré's statement is typical of the pure scientist's frequent attitude toward research, which so irritated the socialist writers.

One of the characteristics of Russian science previously discussed was the heavy emphasis on theory in the exact sciences and the collection of data in the life sciences rather than on technological experimentation. The split between pure and applied science occurred in the Academy of Sciences

[19] *La Valeur de la Science*, Paris, n.d., pp. 182-83. The book was available in Russian (*Tsennost' nauki*, Moscow, 1906), and came under the criticism of the Marxists.

sometime in the first quarter of the 19th century. The relative absence, compared to western Europe, of either industrial research laboratories or advanced engineering schools compounded the problem in Russia. Even had no political revolution occurred in Russia in 1917 a great expansion of technical research and education would have been nearly inevitable. The particular ideological bias of the Bolsheviks toward uniting theory and practice gave the shift toward engineering additional impetus.

The planning of science

The planning of science became a subject of much discussion in the Soviet Union in the 1920s. Planning was—and is—the goal of socialist and communist theorists in all human activities, and particularly in economics. Science, however, presents unique problems as an object of planning. Even among the advocates of a planned economic system one could find many people who would insist that theoretical research cannot be planned in a genuine sense. Surely there is an essential difference between science, which depends on the discovery of unknown facts and the construction of new hypotheses at indefinite times in the future, and industrial production, which depends on the converging of at least theoretically ascertainable quantities of new materiel, properly trained personnel, and equipment. Scientific research seems to contain a constant feedback element; the future path of research is frequently determined by what was most recently learned. And the most ardent opponents of the planning of science maintain that there is something creative, perhaps mystical, and certainly mysterious, in the process of advanced theoretical research which totally defies rational investigation.

All Soviet Marxist writers on the subject of science favored greater coordination of the research program, but their views ranged over a large spectrum, from the denial of any significant difference between physical and mental labor, and, therefore, a firm belief in the planning of science, to an affirmation of the essential intuitiveness of the process of discovery. No serious effort to actually plan Soviet scientific research was made before the industrialization period of the five-year plans. As late as 1925 Trotsky, at a congress of chemists, said that individual chemists conducting their own research without worrying about social utility were really producing that utility. This permissive attitude toward scientists was an integral part of the government's cultural policy in the period 1922-27, and many quotations could be cited to substantiate it, including a cheerful observation by M. I. Kalinin, titular head of the Soviet state, that communism was unwittingly being constructed even by the scientist who consciously opposed it, but nonetheless went on with his work.[20]

These comments by Soviet leaders indicate clearly that a policy of enforced planning controls, grimly administered from above, was not intended in the twenties. Nevertheless, the *idea* of the planning of science was even in this period clearly accepted by most of the government administrators, as well as by many economists and sociologists; the scholarly journals contained many articles discussing the ways in which such planning could be accomplished. In the relatively free period before the first five-year plan the writers on the planning of science seemed to believe their designs would be accepted voluntarily, at least by scientists with a political commitment to the regime. As the transition from the New Economic Policy to forced industrialization occurred, the pressure for greater coordination of research grew constantly, and the increasingly coercive nature of the planning controls became obvious. The subsequent chapters of this study on the reorganization of the Academy give several examples of the use of the slogan "planning of science" for political purposes, although the desire to achieve rationality in research never completely disappeared.

[20] Joravsky explored the government's policy of leniency toward scientists during the first two-thirds of the twenties in his *Soviet Marxism and Natural Science*, pp. 65-67, 97-98.

By the time of the First All-Union Conference on the Planning of Scientific–Research Work in April 1931 much of the intellectual interest in the planning of science had disappeared. Bukharin's speech at that congress represented the last genuine investigation into the planning of science in the Soviet Union for many years. Therefore that conference will be considered topically in this chapter on the theory of the planning of science although chronologically it falls near the end of the period under study.

The first step in planning any activity is the gathering of empirical information. In the years between 1921 and 1934 workers at the Academy of Sciences made statistical and organizational surveys of the scientific personnel and institutions of the USSR which were remarkable in detail and in awareness of the potential of science and scientific institutions as natural resources. Anticipating similar work in other countries by a decade or more,[21] the five volumes of surveys, not to mention less ambitious handbooks and outlines, provide an enormous amount of data for the study of the growth of scientific disciplines and institutions in a country still relatively underdeveloped by Western standards.[22] The editors of one of these volumes, published under the auspices of the State Planning Commission, commented in the foreword: "The significance of these studies is the fact that we have here the first attempt at a statistical study of the scientific organization of the USSR. . . . A statistical study of scientific organization is a necessary advance toward a planned organization of science."[23] The organizational surveys were sponsored by a commission of the Academy of Sciences entitled "Science and Scientific Workers of the USSR" under the principal direction of Academician S. F. Ol'denburg. One volume, published in 1930, covered the

[21] See Dedijer, "The Science of Science," p. 501.

[22] S. F. Ol'denburg, ed., *Nauka i nauchnye rabotniki SSSR*, 4 vols., Leningrad, 1926-34; O. Iu. Shmidt and B. Ia. Smushkevich, *Nauchnye kadry i nauchno-issledovatel'skie uchrezhdeniia SSSR*, Moscow, 1930; see also L. V. Sergeevich, "Zadacha sobiraniia nauki," *Nauchnyi Rabotnik* (September 1926), 31-34.

[23] Shmidt and Smushkevich, *Nauchnye kadry*, p. 3.

activities of 1,227 scientific-research establishments and 151
higher educational institutions (*vuzy*) with 411 different departments. It included not only academies, universities, and
research institutes but also scientific societies, associations of
doctors and other professions, and local organizations.[24] The
emphasis was on the gathering of raw data which could be used
according to the new techniques of the social sciences for
exploration of the sociology and political administration of
science, and even for investigations of the social and genetic
sources of creativity. The fact that this data was never ade-
quately used, as a result of the atrophy of the social sciences
in the Soviet Union after the twenties, does not destroy the
interest or value of the surveys.

Perhaps the most dramatic evidence of how widely the
aspirations of some Soviet investigators missed the reality of the
thirties can be seen in the case of the eugenicist Iu. A. Filipchenko. As a result of his concern for the fate of the Russian
intellectual elite, which he thought was not reproducing itself,
Filipchenko and his coworkers conducted a detailed survey of
the genealogical backgrounds and social and ethnic origins of
all the members of the Academy of Sciences from 1846 to
1924.[25] Filipchenko, a recognized geneticist and director of the
Bureau of Eugenics of the Academy, considered the dissemination of marriage advice to be one of the duties of his bureau,
and hoped to strengthen the genetic position of Russian
scholars.

The possibility of a Soviet sponsorship of eugenics for the
cultivation of talent may seem remote to contemporary ob-

24 *Ibid.*
25 Lepin, Lus, and Filipchenko, "Deisvitel'nye chleny," pp. 7-49. See also
his numerous other articles in *Izvestiia buro po evgenike* and *Izvestiia buro po
genetike i evgenike* in the period 1922-26. Also "Spornye voprosy evgeniki,"
Vestnik Kommunisticheskoi Akademii (No. 20, 1927), pp. 212-54. David H.
Miller of Columbia University gave me the benefit of his research into Filipchenko's activities. Corresponding Academician N. P. Dubinin, one of Lysenko's
major opponents and director of the Institute of General Genetics of the Academy of Sciences, recently praised Filipchenko's work of the 1920s and 1930s.
N. P. Dubinin, "I. V. Michurin i sovremennaia genetika," *Voprosy filosofii* (No.
6, 1966), p. 69.

servers who are familiar with the later Lysenko episode, but the twenties were a period when many things seemed possible. Although Filipchenko backed away from radical eugenic proposals, other writers in this period spoke of how the dissolution of bourgeois family relations would permit couples to choose sperm donors of great intellectual ability who would provide for "1000 or even 10,000 children."[26] This would have been the planning of science (or scientists) to the ultimate degree. Such recommendations were never seriously considered as public policy, but they provide an example of the dimensions of the fervor for a planned society and a planned science.

Much, but not all, of the Soviet discussions of the planning of science were connected with the scientific management of labor movement, which was under the leadership of the "worker-poet" Alexei Gastev, a later victim of the purges, and who was in the twenties head of the Central Labor Institute of the All-Russian Central Council of Trade Unions. A disciple of the American expert on labor efficiency, Frederick Winslow Taylor, Gastev abandoned his former activity as a reader of his *Shock-work Poetry* to proletarian culture groups in order to help improve the productivity of Russian factory workers. Largely as a result of the work of Gastev and his followers, Taylor and Taylorism became household words to Soviet planners. This movement came to be known as "NOT," initials for "scientific management of labor" (*nauchnaia organizatsiia truda*), and its companion movement, which concentrated on improving the productivity of scientific workers was "NONT," "scientific organization of scientific labor" (*nauchnaia organizatsiia nauchnogo truda*). NOT became the obsession of Gastev; he sincerely believed that eventually the trend toward standardization and rationalization of functions through time and motion studies would transform every worker's existence, "even his intimate life, including his esthetic, intellectual, and sexual values."[27]

[26] Quoted in Joravsky, *Soviet Marxism and Natural Science*, p. 306, from A. S. Serebrovskii, "Antropogenetika," *Mediko-biologicheskii zhurnal* (No. 5, 1929), p. 18.

[27] "O tendentsiiakh proletarskoi kul'tury," *Proletarskaia kul'tura* (Nos. 9-10,

Gastev's apotheosis of efficiency and standardization, perhaps a convenient or even necessary doctrine for a backward state facing a modernization drive, was controversial from the very beginning, even among the most ardent advocates of rationalization and planning. A. A. Bogdanov, spokesman for the early proletarian culture movement, felt that Gastev placed too much emphasis on the management engineers, who might therefore emerge as an elite; sophisticated researchers within the NOT movement believed that Gastev, like his model, Taylor, failed to understand the importance of psychological elements in labor management. Taylor was a severe reductionist who used as his principal tool a stopwatch; each task a worker performed was assigned a "normal time," which usually was shorter than the worker was accustomed to. Such an approach did result in certain improvements in labor efficiency, but at a rather primitive level. Taylor was succeeded in the United States by Frank and Lillian Gilbreth, who attempted to go beyond the piecework approach to improving labor efficiency by taking group psychology into consideration. The psychological roots of efficiency and creativity became the primary concerns of the newer scientific management of labor, rather than their superficial evidences in certain physical operations. Gastev himself made some efforts to incorporate the new methods, but never fully succeeded. Here again the demise of empirical social science research in the USSR played a role.[28]

1919), p. 43. Kendall E. Bailes, Columbia University, helped me in investigating the NOT movement.

[28] Both Gastev and his institute disappeared in the purges. In 1955, as a part of the revival of social science research in the Soviet Union, a new Scientific-Research Institute of Labor similar in many ways to Gastev's old institute was established under the new State Committee on Problems of Labor and Wages. In 1962 Gastev was formally rehabilitated by Aksel I. Berg, Chairman of the Scientific Council on Cybernetics of the USSR Academy of Sciences. A Iu. A. Gastev, who is currently working on teaching machines in the Soviet Union, and who sees the old Central Labor Institute as a forerunner of cybernetic methods, is very likely Alexei Gastev's son. In recent years there has been a remarkable resurgence of interest in NOT in the Soviet Union. See A. I. Berg, "Lenin i nauchnaia organizatsiia truda," *Pravda* (October 24, 1962); V. D. Banasiukevich, "V. I. Lenin i nauchnaia organizatsiia truda," *Istoriia SSSR* (No. 2, 1965), pp. 108-13; *Nauchnaia organizatsiia truda dvadtsatykh godov: sbornik doku-*

The two different approaches represented by Taylor and Gilbreth were evident in the Soviet Union among the people who saw the planning of science as an effort to raise the productivity of scientific researchers. Some NONT workers emphasized the petty details of improving research techniques and the use of laboratory equipment; others delved into psychological and sociological studies of the nature of scientific creativity. All the NONT workers agreed, however, that scientific research could be submitted to analysis, its principles could be ascertained, and its conduct could be improved. As one writer commented, "At the end of the first quarter of the twentieth century the problem of the scientific organization of scientific labor [NONT] can be considered just as pressing as the general problem of NOT at the beginning of the last quarter of the last century."[29]

Typical of those authors who believed that great increases in the productivity of scientific research could come from analysis of simple research operations, such as taking notes, was K. Kh. Kekcheev, who in his articles ridiculed the "simply primitive" research practices of Russian scholars, a result, he thought, of the bourgeois emphasis on individuality and idiosyncrasies of scientists. But Russian scientists inherited from the previous regime were even more backward than leading foreign bourgeois scientists, he continued. One of his targets was the Russians' "great love" of notebooks for research data at a moment when foreign researchers were shifting to standardized cards. Kekcheev believed that the productivity of research could be increased in two ways—by improving the work methods of the scientist, and by improving the physical surroundings in which the scientist works. Kekcheev and other workers in the NONT movement published articles in which they called for courses in scientific bibliography for all graduate students in the sciences,

---

mentov i materialov, Kazan, 1965. For an article by Gastev see "O metodologicheskikh voprosakh ratsionalizatsii obucheniia," in A. I. Berg *et al.*, eds., *Kibernetika, myshlenie, zhizn'*, Moscow, 1964, pp. 459-72, especially 466-67.

[29] Mikhail Dynnik, "Problema nauchnoi organizatsii nauchnogo truda," *Nauchnyi Rabotnik* (No. 1, 1925), p. 180.

the coordination of information dissemination and translation services by central governmental bodies, studies of optimum environmental conditions for researchers, time studies of research operations, and novel forms of publication, indexing and distributing offprints.[30] They repeatedly emphasized that their efforts were of greater significance than their critics granted: "There are people—and they are not few in number—who think that the organization of labor is a matter of minor importance and that a talented man can obtain great results with the most primitive organization of labor. This is partially true, but it is also true that with a well organized 'scientific production' such a scientist might be able to give science even more."[31]

All NONT researchers maintained that a socialist government made possible more rapid advance in the organization of scientific research than elsewhere. First of all, researchers in the Soviet Union were supposedly committed to collectivized research and therefore less insistent on their rights to peculiar, inefficient research methods. Second, the centralized economy would permit superior organization of the publishing and indexing of scientific literature. V. V. Arshinov, who called for publication of every important scientific article in two different places—in a journal and in collected topical volumes of related articles—commented, "Thanks to the fact that all our scientific and technological publishing activities depend on governmental funds, a reform is incomparably easier for us to make than for our colleagues abroad. . . . We are not tied down by tradition,

[30] See K. Kh. Kekcheev, "Organizatsiia truda uchenogo," *Nauchnyi Rabotnik* (No. 9, 1926), pp. 21-30; "Biudzhet vremeni studentov," *Nauchnyi Rabotnik* (No. 10, 1926), pp. 38-53; V. V. Arshinov, "O nauchnoi organizatsii nauchnogo izdatel'stva," *Nauchnyi Rabotnik* (Nos. 7-8, 1926), pp. 31-37; V. O. Pal'chinskii, "Organizatsiia nauchnogo izdatel'stva i blizhaishie prakticheskie zadachi," *Nauchnyi Rabotnik* (No. 9, 1927), pp. 9-14; B. P. Veinberg, "Metodika nauchnoi raboty i podgotovka k nei," *Nauchnyi Rabotnik* (No. 12, 1926), pp. 5-20; N. A. Podkopaev, "O planirovanii nauchnoi raboty," *Vestnik Akademii Nauk SSSR* (No. 3, 1931), cols. 1-6; N. G. Levinson, "Tekhnika umstvennoi raboty," Nauchnoe Slovo (No. 3, 1928), pp. 141-63; A. Ziskind, "Organizatsiia nauchno-issledovatel'skoi raboty v promyshlennosti," *Front Nauki i Tekhniki* (June 1931), pp. 49-56; V. V. Dobrynin, "Problema organizatsii tvorcheskogo truda," *Nauchnyi Rabotnik* (Nos. 5-6, 1928), pp. 54-64; and Mikhail Dynnik, "Problema nauchnoi."

[31] Kekcheev, "Organizatsiia truda," p. 22.

routine, or the slow pace of historical development."[32] The next decades would illustrate fully that bureaucratic inertia and difficulty of reform are not peculiar attributes of institutions in capitalist societies.

The NONT workers who emphasized research methods were never able to rise very far above mild discussions of such topics as how best to compose bibliographies—on cards or in loose-leaf notebooks. Here and there, however, in the discussions of the need to aid the scientist to find data there were indications pointing to the coming revolution in information retrieval techniques, a revolution which 30 years later helped bring back the whole NONT discussion with a new cybernetic vocabulary.[33] It is surely not merely an unhistorical reading of the present into the past to find such indications in NONT-worker M. Dynnik's observation in 1925 that,

> Technological apparatuses, proposed by NONT for the accumulation, preservation and use of empirical material, must be constructed in order for a scientific worker to be able at any moment to extract those facts needed for a generalization from the entire mass of preserved information. . . . These "NONT-mechanisms" should by no means mechanize scientific work, but contribute to the free development of creative thought.[34]

The often utopian and naïve efforts of NONT workers to apply quantitative methods to a study of creativity is exemplified by the work of N. P. Suvorov, who tried to compute the

---

[32] Arshinov, "O nauchnoi organizatsii nauchnogo izdatel'stva," p. 34.

[33] G. Popov remarked in *Izvestiia* on May 27, 1966: "What we need in order to get rid of cases of scientific barrenness is the introduction of scientific organization of labor [NOT] not only at industrial enterprises but above all at research and design institutes. Moreover, control here must be no less strict than in industry. It is necessary to mechanize as much as possible the labor of the scientist. . . ."

[34] Dynnik, "Problema nauchnoi," pp. 184-85. Compare Dynnik's call for what amounted to computers with later predictions by Soviet educators that science students would carry "mental work machines" in their pockets to provide factual information and formulas. See Oliver J. Caldwell and Loren R. Graham, "Moscow in May 1963" (Office of Education Bulletin), Washington, D.C., 1964, p. 29.

effectiveness of theoretical scientific research by algebraic formula.[35] Suvorov felt that some method must be devised for
rating the successes and failures of individual scientists. Such
ratings, he believed, would greatly facilitate the planning of
science, since one important planning task was the assignment
of the most talented and promising scientists to the most difficult problems. Suvorov based his method on a study of the
18th century Russian scientist Lomonosov. The rating period of
a scientist, he said, must be based on a "cycle," or the length
of time that a scientist requires to produce a "major" scientific
discovery (would the legions of scientists who never produce
a "major" discovery lose their title to the name "scientist"?).
Suvorov said that the length of this cycle differs for each scientist; Lomonosov supposedly possessed a cycle of six years.
Within each cycle Suvorov rated scientific research in four
categories:

1. "Classical" works of great scientific significance.
2. "Outstanding" works, which would be noted in the
course curriculum on the university level.
3. "Regular" works, which would be noted in a standard
scientific journal.
4. "Compilative" works, not demanding independent analysis.

On the basis of these four types Suvorov set up a rating
formula:

$$T = At + 3B + \frac{C}{X} + \frac{D}{2X}$$

where T = "effective time," t = the number of years of the
report cycle (for Lomonosov, six years), X = the average
number of "regular" works a year. A, B, C, and D equal the
number of works of the first, second, third, and fourth categories, respectively. If a scientist accomplished one major work
(a category "A" work) his effective time already equalled his

[35] N. P. Suvorov, "O metodakh izucheniia effektivnosti nauchnykh rabot,"
Nauchnyi Rabotnik (December 1928), pp. 23-33.

actual time, so any B, C, or D works were bonuses making his effective time greater than actual time. Using this formula on Lomonosov for the period 1751-56 Suvorov computed that Lomonosov did 33 "effective" years of work in this six-year period. Without dwelling on the numerous weaknesses of Suvorov's formula, the first of which is that the categories "A," "B," etc., involve the arbitrary rating which Suvorov was trying to avoid, it is fair to assume that many NONT workers considered Suvorov's system as only half serious or as a tentative, preliminary model. Nevertheless, Suvorov did not believe his formula a joke, and his effort clearly indicates the lengths to which the scientism of planning science sometimes extended.

Intellectually more interesting than studies of research methods or effectiveness ratings of scientists were the investigations of NONT researchers into the psychological characteristics of outstanding scientists. The shift toward such research occurred after 1924, when the inadequacies of the earlier emphasis of the movement on simple physical operations became clear. One of the NONT researchers who attempted to bring psychological research to bear on the problem of creativity was Mikhail Dynnik, who believed that by studying such functions of human intellect as attention, perception, memory, synthesizing ability, judgement, and abstraction the optimum personality for scientific research could be defined.[36] Dynnik believed that the degree of development and the mutual relations between the above functions determine a person's suitability for scientific work, but that in order to locate potentially outstanding scientists one should not look merely for high performance in all categories. He cited research which indicated, for example, that a number of scientists who have great powers of analysis and synthesis have very weak memories. The task of NONT, he said, was to find the best combinations for certain kinds of

[36] Dynnik, "Problema nauchnoi." Dynnik's effort to type scientific workers by their traits and thereby employ them more efficiently was similar to the ideas of a later Soviet author whose work falls outside the time limits of this study. See I. Finkel', *Sovremennyi kapitalizm i nauchnoe issledovanie*, Moscow, 1936, p. 99.

research, and to prescribe exercises, such as mnemonics, to improve the combination of any one person. Although Dynnik did not, therefore, deny the possibility of improving a person's ability to do scientific research, he believed that truly great scientists are born, not made. His whole attempt to locate persons with the optimum correlation of mental abilities for scientific work obviously stressed inherent differences between personalities, and the failure of his research to be continued stemmed in part, no doubt, from the growing aversion of Soviet educators to individual intelligence testing.

The transition to emphasis in the NONT movement on psychological factors was also marked in the case of V. V. Dobrynin, who attempted to define the optimal environmental conditions for scientific research, and included under the slogan "rationalization of labor" such factors as the family and sexual life of the scientist. Dobrynin, in fact, wished to isolate all factors which influence the work of "creative collectives," and he promoted the organization of a society for the promotion of creativity. The functions of this society were very unclear; Dobrynin's definitions of the factors influencing creativity were nearly unlimited in scope. He defined the duties of the society as (1) rational organization of the personality, labor, and life of the creative worker (education, recreation, family relations, study conditions, etc.), (2) rationalization of collective organizations of creative labor (invention bureaus, organization of institutes, libraries, etc.), (3) rationalization of professional activities (thematic planning of research, exchange of information, popularization of science, etc.)

The nebulous nature of Dobrynin's proposals obviously disturbed many of the scientists who were to be the objects of such "rationalizations." In early 1924 Dobrynin gave a report to the Academy of Sciences on the "Organization of Creative Labor" in which he recommended that the Academy establish a special organ for promoting creativity. Nothing seems to have been done about this proposal for several years, but in 1927 Dobrynin was again given an opportunity to present his ideas to the Academy, where they provoked considerable controversy. A special commission of academicians was appointed to consider the possibility of accepting Dobrynin's proposal for the establishment of a laboratory "on the organization of creative labor." At a meeting of the Academy on February 6, 1928 the members "recognized the value" of the project but instead of creating a laboratory within the framework of the Academy itself they declared in favor of an unofficial organization of workers in the Academy. The Academy was obviously trying to avoid primary responsibility for an ill-defined project. It did appoint, however, a group to help organize the new society, consisting of Dobrynin, S. F. Ol'denburg, A. E. Fersman, A. K. Borsuk, V. P. Kashkadamov, and A. B. Andreev.[37] These men were supposed to obtain the cooperation of the Moscow Conservatory, the state committee on inventions, the universities, and other organizations concerned with creativity in the arts and sciences. Nothing more was heard of Dobrynin's group. Whether it was quietly shelved by the Academy or collapsed because of its own deficiencies is unknown.

The concerns of the scientific management of labor movement for the planning of science essentially revolved around problems of individual creativity. NONT did not concentrate on the most logical problems of the planning of science, those of thematic planning and the establishment of national priorities in science. Despite all the writing about the planning of science which one can find in the Soviet journals of the twenties, the only moment when these major problems received full attention was at the First All-Union Conference on the Planning of Scientific-Research Work in Moscow, April 6-11, 1931.[38] Almost a thousand delegates, including 607 scientific workers and 23 full members of the Academy of Sciences, attended the conference. The keynote speech on the methodology of planning science, delivered by Nikolai Bukharin, by

[37] V. V. Dobrynin, "Problema organizatsii," pp. 54-64.
[38] The verbatim stenographic report of this conference was published: *Vsesoiuznaia konferentsiia po planirovaniiu nauchnoissledovatel'skoi raboty, 1-ia,* Moscow–Leningrad, 1931.

that time a member of the Academy, marked a high degree of sophistication in the approach of communist planners to the problem of charting the development of scientific research. Representatives of scientific researchers in agriculture, health, transport, and industry spoke on the problems of the planning of science in their particular areas.

Nikolai Bukharin (1888-1938) was one of the major figures in the Bolshevik Party, a friend of Lenin's and a specialist in economics and sociology. He had at one time associated himself with the left wing of the Party, and had in particular opposed in 1918 the signing of the Brest-Litovsk Treaty with the Central Powers. Bukharin later became a defender of the New Economic Policy, which permitted limited private enterprise and relatively free cultivation of the land. After 1928 Bukharin was considered a member of the so-called Right Opposition, which criticized Stalin's policy of forced industrialization and collectivization. In 1928 and 1929 Bukharin came under increasing criticism from Stalin, culminating in his expulsion in November 1929 from the highest organ of the Party, the Politburo. In subsequent years, until his arrest and execution during the great purges, Bukharin continued to play a secondary but nonetheless significant role in the Party. He was always interested in scholarship, and, particularly, science. He was editor of the *Large Soviet Encyclopedia*; he also took an active role in administering scientific research through several governmental committees; and he was an editor of a series of volumes on the history of science and technology.

Bukharin was a strong advocate of the planning of science, which he felt was particularly needed in Russia. In agreement with Academician Ol'denburg, who called lack of orderliness a primary characteristic of Russian science, Bukharin believed that the planning of science was more necessary in Russia than in advanced Western countries. Bukharin particularly objected to the opinion commonly expressed by his scientist acquaintances that scientific research was based on intuition or subconscious indications. Is it not possible, he asked, to have an "irrationally-arrived-at solution to a rationally-posed problem?" Bukharin believed that one should not divorce the process of rational knowledge from intuitive guesses. True planning would provide for such guesses: "A concrete 'guess' is an unconscious continuation of a conscious process."[39] The more experiments and computations the scientist made the more likely his intuition was to be correct. Therefore, through conscious planning of such experiments the accuracy of intuition would be sharpened.

Bukharin's major contribution to the debate on the planning of science was the definition of the phases of science which, in his view, were amenable to planning. He isolated five different aspects of science which could be planned.

First was the determination of the share of the country's labor and budgetary resources which would be devoted to science. This decision, noted Bukharin, should be made at the highest level of the Party and economic hierarchies. Science would receive a very high priority compared to other aspects of the national economy; the Soviet Union accepted the challenge of catching up with the capitalist countries in science in a maximum of 10 years. Therefore, *"the scientific-research framework must grow even faster than the leading branches of socialist heavy industry."*[40]

A second phase of science which could be planned, Bukharin told the assembled scientists, was the logistical support of scientific-research institutions, an activity not very different, he thought, from the support of other types of Soviet institutions.[41] Nevertheless, Bukharin warned, one must not take false economy measures where scientific institutes are concerned. Academician Ol'denburg had complained that occasionally the

---

[39] *Vsesoiuznaia konferentsiia*, p. 36.

[40] Underlined in Bukharin's text, *ibid.*, pp. 41-42. To assign any phase of economic or cultural development a rate of growth more rapid than heavy industry is, in the Soviet vocabulary, an assignment of highest possible priority.

[41] It turned out to be very different. See below, p. 66, especially the footnote.

buying of foreign scientific literature had ceased because of low funds.[42] Temporary economies could not be tolerated in the science program in the way in which they could in industry, Bukharin concluded.[43]

A third aspect of the scientific effort which was susceptible to planning, according to Bukharin, was the geographical placement of scientific-research institutes. The goal here was the elimination of the old "St. Petersburg center." Institutions should be decentralized geographically even though central management was retained. Centers would be constructed in Siberia, Kazakhstan and in other areas where the scientists would be close to the problems to be studied. These centers should evolve into enormous "combines" (*kombinaty*) consisting of mutually helpful research institutions, educational establishments, and factories. Here Bukharin sketched the model for such provincial centers of science as Novosibirsk later became.

A fourth element of scientific research which should be planned, said Bukharin, was the determination of the supply of personnel, or "cadres." The main issues to be settled by planning organs in this area were: (a) the *number* of scientific workers the country wished to maintain in the field of research, (b) the *distribution* of the researchers among the various scientific fields, (c) the *qualifications* of workers to perform their tasks, and (d) the correct *use* of all workers of all qualifications through a system of personnel assignment.

A fifth and last element of planned science, according to Bukharin, was the *subjects* of scientific research themselves, although he admitted at the outset that subject planning was the most difficult of all the planning assignments. Bukharin did not venture far into this topic, but he did observe that the most important criterion in planning the topics of scientific

[42] *Ibid.*, p. 66. One source said that Ol'denburg's complaints led to his resignation as permanent secretary. The later oppression of the Academy was probably more important. *The London Times*, March 2, 1934, p. 16.
[43] *Vsesoiuznaia konferentsiia*, pp. 48-49.

research should be service to socialist construction. Do not fear to use the word "utilitarian," he urged, since it signified a thoroughly Marxist appreciation of the connection between theory and practice.

Passing on to the administration of the scientific-research plan, Bukharin stressed that the most general principle of the planning of science must be that top planning organs should stipulate only the "main directions" of scientific work; they would do this by assigning important problems to individual institutes.[44] Local officials should have considerable autonomy, he believed, in investigating problems which arise during the course of the work. To refuse to investigate potentially rewarding problems which come to light during research merely because these diversions were not provided for in the work plan, would be, Bukharin warned, a "bureaucratic braking" of research, and not intelligent planning.[45]

To deal with this problem of interesting sidetracks in research the plan must have a certain amount of "suppleness and elasticity." Each institution or laboratory must have a known quantity of free time which can be utilized during the course of the work; this time was to be listed in the plan as a "reserve." Bukharin cautioned, appropriately enough in view of future developments, that this reserve must not play the role of a loophole or springboard for wrecking the plan.[46] The reserve should be quite small compared to the entire allotment of time, and the reserve must *always* be utilized, in ways which the local officials would determine. The reserve of time "encourages initiative not at the expense of the plan but within the limits of the plan."[47] The reserve for the scientists bore resemblances to the private plots of the collective farmers in agriculture; both farmers and scientists were to have minute domains of their own.

Bukharin noted that the plan should make allowance for the

[44] *Ibid.*, p. 55.
[46] *Ibid.*, pp. 57-58.
[45] *Ibid.*, pp. 53-55.
[47] *Ibid.*

idiosyncrasies of individual scientists. Especially prominent
scientists should be given facilities and time for special researches on the basis of their characteristics and inclinations.
This permissive attitude toward individualistic scientists is not
a compromise of the principle of planning, insisted Bukharin,
but marks a thorough application of that principle. On the basis
of planning, these talented scientists could be given full support by assistants and specialists who would perform the petty
details and leave more time for speculation to the head scientists. This division of scientific labor, Bukharin believed, would
greatly increase the productivity of scientific research.[48] The
scientist should not be held as strictly accountable for results
in his work as should workers and directors in factories,
Bukharin noted. The correct research plan would provide for
a large amount of "scientific research risk," realizing that even
a failure is often instructive.

Bukharin obviously provided for more latitude in the research plan than some Western observers of the Soviet Union
in the industrialization period would have imagined. Nevertheless, he still avoided the troublesome problem of just how
detailed a scientific research plan could be. N. A. Podkopaev
addressed himself to that question in an article which appeared at the time of the planning conference.[49] Podkopaev
recognized that the problem was a very difficult one and that
the degree of planning would be different in different disciplines. He believed that certain types of research—particularly,
field work performed by expeditions and most work in the
humanities—could be fully planned to "the smallest details."[50]
The most difficult subjects to plan, he said, would be the
youngest of the natural sciences which are "arenas of strenuous
exploratory work. . . ." Podkopaev believed that there existed
two extremes to be avoided in matters of planning. A too detailed plan would tend to make research "statistical," and would
lead to the "arrogant attributing of the logical demands of the

[48] *Ibid.*, pp. 58-59.
[49] N. A. Podkopaev, "O planirovanii," cols. 1-6.
[50] *Ibid.*, col. 1.

mind to complex, multiform, and changeable nature."[51] On the other hand, there existed the opposite danger—and the one considered more threatening in 1931—of the refusal to compose any sort of plan at all, or the restriction of the plan to a general statement of the problem. Such an attitude, said Podkopaev, conceals an unconscious hope for the "self-flow" (*samotek*) of science, a belief in "naked empiricism" which would return science to its former status in the hands of capitalism, that of a toy of scholars.

The correct approach to planning, said Podkopaev, consisted of the strict observance of the previously planned "general line" of research combined with a flexibility on details. The goal should always be greater planning, if that can be obtained without harmful effects. The greatest obstacle in the path of planning is not the nature of the research, he said, but the "inertia of the mind."

The planning of science, he concluded, must contain a strict accounting of how a scientific worker spends his time, both in the laboratory and at home. From studies of such accounts Podkopaev believed much valuable information about the sources of creativity could be obtained. Scientific creativity must lose its status as a "holy of holies," he said, and become a product to be studied, altered, and promoted much as one does material products. The principles of mental labor may be different from those of physical labor, he observed, but surely such principles do exist.

These, then, were the general principles of planned science enunciated in the Soviet Union up to 1931. They ranged from a stress on empirical data on the organization and personnel of the science establishment, to enthusiastic calls for increased creativity by the promoters of NONT, to the efforts to establish priorities and identify the functions of science planning made by the delegates to the All-Union Conference on the Planning of Scientific-Research Work.

To what extent was the emphasis on the planning of science

[51] *Ibid.*, col. 4.

important and meaningful?[52] In certain areas the achievement of the Soviet Union was considerable and should be recognized to a much greater degree abroad than has been the case. The two areas in which the Soviet Union led the way in thinking about scientific research were (1) recognition of science as a natural resource and the collection of data concerning it, and (2) the posing of legitimate questions about the ways in which a government can aid the development of science. The particular responses the Soviet Union produced to these challenges involved in subsequent years a great deal of coercion and suppression of freedom, but many Western nations have recently found themselves faced with at least similar questions as they attempted to develop national science policies.

The Soviet Union in the twenties was by Western standards a relatively underdeveloped country, but it was not underdeveloped in the sense that many nations in Africa, Asia, and Latin America are today. It possessed a substantial industrial plant, an educational establishment with traditions of excellence in certain areas, and rich natural resources. It was also the beneficiary of an almost unprecedented outburst of revolutionary energy directed toward modernization. In science this energy was particularly clear. If one reads recently published advice on promoting science in the underdeveloped countries he almost immediately learns how irrelevant much of that advice is to Russia in the twenties. A major point of that writing is to urge the underdeveloped countries to make a large emotional and financial commitment to the idea of promoting science. Such a commitment must precede the discussions of priorities in science. One Western author, speaking primarily of science in noncommunist Asian countries, wrote:

> I have seen over and over again scientists from those countries, who worked hard and produced interesting results while staying in a Western country, falter and fail when

[52] Other discussions of the planning of science, involving the reactions of the members of the Academy of Sciences, are on pp. 176-89, 197-200.

returning home to research conditions which were by no means worse than those they had in the West. Partly, it might be the influence of the environment, the sight of too many people sitting around in the streets, doing nothing. Partly it might be a secret conviction that it is just impossible to do research in an underdeveloped country.[53]

The Soviet Union psychologically committed itself to science not only infinitely more than present-day underdeveloped countries, but even more, relatively speaking, than the advanced Western countries in the prewar period. Bukharin's call to promote scientific research more rapidly than heavy industry remained valid throughout the industrialization period and was confirmed many years later by A. N. Kosygin.[54] Thus those analysts of the Soviet Union who have maintained that Soviet leaders have always assigned the highest economic priority to heavy industry should consider whether scientific research should not be at the top of the list. Making economic assessments of scientific research presents special problems, but recently there has been progress in this area.[55]

When one goes beyond the question of commitment to science, however, the Soviet achievement in the twenties and early thirties in planning science is much less clear. One contribution already noted was the effort to collect information concerning science, but the compilation of statistical surveys is only a preparatory step to planning. Many of the articles which, according to their titles, concerned the planning of science were not much more than hortatory proclamations that science "must be planned."[56] Even in the simplest of articles, however, certain priorities of planning were implicit. In general, the closer the author stood to the Party, the more he urged that scientific

[53] Michael J. Moravcsik, "Improvement of Science in Developing Countries," *Minerva* (Spring 1966), p. 389.

[54] "Za tesnuiu sviaz' nauki s zhizniu," *Pravda* (June 15, 1961), p. 2.

[55] See the discussion of an economic definition of research and development in Alexander G. Korol, *Soviet Research and Development*, Cambridge, 1965, pp. xi-xiv.

[56] See, for example, Z. Mindlin, "O planirovanii nauchnoi raboty," *Kommunisticheskaia Revoliutsiia* (No. 3, 1928), pp. 59-64.

research be a service function of industry. The closer he stood to the scientists themselves, the more he talked of the ultimate value of all scientific research.

The most interesting effort to elaborate a national policy on science was Bukharin's presentation to the planning conference. His attempt to isolate the aspects of science that can be planned was of genuine significance and even now would be pertinent reading for science administrators, including those in democratic countries. His attention to the geographical place-ment of scientific research establishments was an early recog-nition of the great economic and cultural impact such institu-tions can have on surrounding areas. His concentration on the peculiar logistic requirements of scientific research institutions was the beginning of many special exemptions granted in the Soviet Union to research organizations. And his allowance for free time in the research plan can be described as either recog-nition of the inevitable or an intelligent appreciation of the unpredictability of scientific discovery.

But in the final analysis not even Bukharin made anything approaching a theoretical breakthrough in the planning of science. If one reviews the proposals on the planning of science which he advanced, it becomes clear that these proposals con-cerned two types of activity, which, whenever possible, should be carefully distinguished. The one type of activity has been fairly well planned by the Soviet Union and a number of Western countries in the decades since 1930, and particularly since World War II; success in planning the second type of activity has been conspicuously absent. J. R. Steelman under-lined the difference: "At the outset it is well to distinguish between planning for research and planning of research. It is well accepted that consistently productive research must be planned for in the sense that competent men must be as-sembled, facilities provided, and equipment installed for their use."[57]

It is the "planning for research" in which governments have

[57] J. R. Steelman, *Science and Public Policy*, III, Washington, D.C., 1947, 28.

been most successful. Four of the five aspects Bukharin insisted could be rationally planned may be classified as "planning for research" rather than "planning of research." These four were: (a) the determination of the share of the country's labor and budgetary resources that would be devoted to science; (b) the support of scientific research institutions; (c) geographical placement of research institutions; (d) the scientific personnel—their number, distribution, qualifications, and use.

When Bukharin discussed the problem of planning the subjects of scientific and engineering research, he actually did no more than present a table of priorities; the problems which promised the most to the Soviet government should receive the greatest attention. But he did not attempt to define the criteria by which the government could decide just which research alternatives would benefit the government most. Questions of time are crucial in making choices; the decision between pursuing cancer research and oceanographic research cannot be made simply by asking which promises the most in terms of state interest. Both, of course, could be immensely important to a state, but unless some sort of conjecture about the length of time and amount of money expended before a return of large benefits can be made, the discussion remains rather pointless. And no criteria for such estimates beyond simply asking the opinions of the leading scientists in the field have been advanced. Thus, in the end, the planning *of* science remains an extremely resistant problem.

The distinction between planning of science and planning for science is a useful concept which introduces light into many discussions of science policy and planning even though the distinction cannot be maintained indefinitely in practice. The planning *of* science is truly impossible; planning *for* science over short periods of time is a viable approach, but after an appreciable length of time the unpredictability of the actual progress of science will upset and transform these plans. The logistic support of scientific research institutions was earlier cited as an example of planning for science. Yet obviously it would be impossible to order far in advance the correct equipment for any research laboratory. The kinds of equipment and amount of materiel needed will depend on the path of actual scientific research, and the further into the future one attempts to look, the wider the spectrum of alternatives of equipment, materiel, even personnel. Thus, there is a very real and essential difference between the planning of science and the planning of industry. The troubles the Soviet Union has encountered in planning industrial production have arisen primarily from trying to plan the whole industrial plant at once, with all its interdependent products. If a person attempted to plan the activities of *one* plant in isolation, having the ability to order in advance all necessary materiel and personnel, he could construct a plan very far into the future with small margins of error. Planning in isolation the work and logistical support of a large physics laboratory, however, would break down much more rapidly. In recent years Soviet planners have recognized these differences more openly than in the beginning period of rapid industrialization.[58]

The distinction between "planning for science" and "planning of science" also becomes blurred in the sense that a negative decision to plan *for* a certain scientific topic frequently makes impossible any thought of the planning *of* the same project, even if the latter could be done. Thus a nation with scarce resources to devote to science will have to decide not to provide for certain kinds of research. Such a decision will inevitably determine the direction of research itself, since it will eliminate the possibilities of certain kinds of investigations. Thus, one might say, the distinction between the planning of science and the planning for science breaks down. Even here, however, the distinction has some value. First of all, it is primarily negative decisions in the planning for science which directly control the

[58] The Nobel Prize-winning chemist, N. N. Semenov, who is also a leading administrator of Soviet science, commented in 1959: "When you come down to it, it is impossible and irrational to plan the supply system of the Academy of Sciences. The output of the Academy's scientific endeavors does not represent material processed by machine but scientific value, which can never be planned in detail." *Izvestiia*, August 9, 1959.

planning of science. A decision to go ahead in planning for a certain topic in no way guarantees that progress will indeed be made.[59] Furthermore, although the effect of a negative decision in the planning for science may be great on the progress of science itself, there is still a theoretical difference which should be kept in mind between the path of scientific theory and the path of the logistical support of investigations of that theory.

Today, several decades after the original debates among the Marxists on the planning of science, the problem remains unsolved, but much has been learned in the interim.[60] The "planning for science" goes forward at such a tempo that the entire scientific environment, East and West, is being transformed, while the "planning of science" seems to have lost much of its original allure.

The planning system for science

A plan must include a director. Much of the essential history of the Soviet Union's attempts to establish planned science is contained in the rise and fall of various planning committees.[61] During the first years of Soviet power, the government had

[59] Contrary to much popular opinion, a major scientific problem (as distinguished from a technological problem) cannot be solved merely by devoting attention to it. The difficulty in finding a cure for cancer despite the enormous attention given it is related to deficiencies in basic scientific knowledge which energy alone has so far failed to overcome. For many years man has planned *for* a cure for cancer, but no one has the plan *of* the cure.

[60] After the early 1930s the locus of the important writing on the planning of science shifted from the Soviet Union to England, where the "scientific humanists," especially J. D. Bernal, presented some of the most interesting concepts. See, for example, Bernal's analogy of the advance of science with that of a military front, and his suggested tactics for planning science. (J. D. Bernal, *The Social Function of Science*, London, 1939, pp. 236ff.) Bernal's work was at least partially inspired by the Soviet commentators on science. He called one of the papers given by Soviet delegates in 1931 at the International Congress of the History of Science and Technology, "for England the starting point of a new evaluation of the history of science." (See *ibid.*, p. 406, and *Science at the Crossroads*, London, 1931.) Bernal was a little negligent of the damage that can be done to science through controls, and the "scientific humanists" were soon opposed by the Society for Freedom in Science, led by Michael Polanyi and J. R. Baker. See Bernard Barber, *Science and the Social Order*, New York, 1962, p. 232; also, James B. Conant, *Science and Common Sense*, New Haven, 1951, pp. 296-99.

[61] The best single source on the legal aspects of the administration of Soviet

little time to worry about the exact nature of the goals it wished to assign to the scientific establishment. The result was a proliferation of planning bodies, each with slightly different goals and none with clearly delineated powers. It was always assumed that some day there would be one central planning organ for all Soviet science, but that goal receded deeper into the future. When the Soviet Union finally in the late 1920s made serious attempts to establish centralized planning the field was cluttered with various other governmental and semigovernmental committees with ambiguous powers.

Under the system of government established by the 1918 Constitution, the competency and powers of the organs directing science were defined by the legislation of the individual republics.[62] The Council of Peoples Commissars (Sovnarkom) of each republic, and especially the Commissariats of Education, assumed important functions in directing scientific institutions. This control of science on the republic level was not so much an expression of the federal nature of the union of Soviet republics as the neglect of the central organs to assume the direction of science. According to the constitution, these central bodies, the All-Russian Congress of Soviets and its Central Executive Committee (VTsIK), could, in addition to their enumerated powers, "decide on any other matter which they deem within their jurisdiction."[63] The central government did not, however, elect to utilize this sovereign power in the direction of science; with a few exceptions, each republic in the early years supervised its own scientific establishment, albeit often quite inadequately and feebly, through its own Council of Peoples Commissars.

Geographically the Russian Soviet Federated Socialist Republic (RSFSR) was by far the dominant Soviet republic; its scientific superiority was supreme. Indeed, most of the Soviet

science is G. I. Fed'kin, *Pravovye voprosy organizatsii nauchnoi raboty v SSSR*, Moscow, 1958. Unfortunately, the historical sections are not detailed. A list of abbreviations found in the planning system discussion is given in Appendix A.

[62] Fed'kin, *Pravovye voprosy*, pp. 290-94.
[63] See Merle Fainsod, *How Russia is Ruled*, Cambridge, Mass., 1963, p. 354.

scientific talent was concentrated in Petrograd (after 1924, Leningrad) with Moscow running for many years a rather poor second. The Commissariat of Education (Narkompros) of the Russian Republic received the most important powers in the direction of science, for it was empowered to supervise the Academy of Sciences, the research laboratories belonging to the universities, and many of the independent research institutes. These institutions investigated both the natural and social sciences, just as the pedagogical institutions under the Commissariat of Education taught both. Their immediate administrative head was a section of the commissariat entitled the Chief Administration of Scientific Institutions (Glavnauka), headed by F. N. Petrov from 1923 to 1928. Each republic possessed such an office in its Commissariat of Education; the closest approach to nationwide coordination of science in the early twenties was the effort the several Scientific Administrations (Glavnauka's) made at their infrequent conferences. These meetings were the scenes of many jurisdictional disputes between the Scientific Administrations, the universities, the Academy of Sciences, and the central governmental agencies. The Academy of Sciences repeatedly accused the Russian Scientific Administration of bureaucratic interference in scientific research.[64]

The direction of applied science was the particular concern in these early years of the Supreme Economic Council (VSNKh), an organ with enormous legal powers after the Bolshevik Revolution, which was originally intended to direct the national economic plans. It had been assigned the task of "working out a unified production plan for the whole of Russia and of the Soviet Republics friendly to Russia."[65] The Supreme Economic Council lost these powers to the State Planning Commission (Gosplan), established in February 1921, but retained importance as the administrative center of na-

[64] Fed'kin, *Pravovye voprosy*, p. 292.
[65] Maurice Dobb, *Soviet Economic Development Since 1917*, New York, 1966, p. 338.

tionalized industry. On August 16, 1918 the Council of Peoples Commissars of the Russian Republic established a special Scientific–Technological Department (NTO) under the Supreme Economic Council which promoted the application of science to industry.[66]

The function of the Scientific–Technological Department was to distribute among all the scientific and technological institutions of the republic special assignments arising from the needs of the economy, and to exercise control over the fulfillment of these assignments. Here was an excellent example of conflicting jurisdictions: the Scientific–Technological Department was obviously destined to clash with the Scientific Administration when it attempted to enforce the fulfillment of research tasks assigned to institutions under the Scientific Administration's supervision.

The first technological task that the Soviet government approached on a planned basis was the electrification of the country; the famous Governmental Commission for the Electrification of Russia (Goelro) was established February 21, 1920. The plan was not viewed simply as a schedule for electrification, but as a method for transforming the entire country on the basis of heavy industrialization.[67] Lenin's well-known slogan, "Communism is Soviet power plus electrification of the whole country," conveys the fervor of the times.[68] The chairman of the Electrification Commission was the engineer G. M. Krzhizhanovskii, a former revolutionary and fellow exile of Lenin's in Siberia and a future vice-president of the Academy of Sciences. Krzhizhanovskii in later years spoke of the birth of the Electrification Commission with great pride:

> Our country was still in the midst of the calamity of war; we were still continuing to roll into the abyss of deepest eco-

[66] See *Sobranie uzakonenii i rasporiazhenii rabochego i krest'ianskogo pravitel'stva RSFSR*, Moscow, 1917-32 (No. 61, 1918), art. 671, for the resolution establishing NTO.

[67] For a Soviet discussion of the Goelro plan, see I. M. Nekrasova, *Leninskii plan elektrifikatsii strany i ego osushchestvlenie v 1921-1931 gg.*, Moscow, 1960.

[68] *Ibid.*, p. 14.

nomic disorder. And then, according to directives of the Party, there was created the first long-range economic plan. We proceeded to collect a handful of people, scientific and technical workers, and under the immediate guidance of Vladimir Ilich Lenin, we tried to pick our way among the economic chaos surrounding us, tried to harness to the conquest of science and technique those active elements among the workers and peasants whose creative power we perceived and recognized in the midst of ruin and war. In this plan we daringly sketched an impression of our future, a design of that building which we can and must convert into reality. Very soon we were assailed with banter: people said it was not a plan of electrification but of "electric-fiction"; they said it was poetry, an imaginative creation, far from reality.[69]

Lenin believed that the plan was anything but "electric-fiction"; when he reviewed the completed electrification program in December 1920 he labeled it a "broad and excellent scientific labor."[70] The plan, based on electric consumption in 1913, called for a tenfold increase in 10 to 15 years; it was fulfilled, Soviet sources announced, in 10 years.[71]

The Eighth All-Russian Congress of Soviets approved the 650-page Electrification Commission plan in December 1920 and simultaneously gave the Council of Labor and Defense (STO) responsibility for coordinating the entire economy.[72] The Council of Labor and Defense gradually assumed during the period of War Communism many of the functions that had originally been assigned to the Supreme Economic Council; the resolution of the Congress confirmed its superior position.

With this new sovereignty the Council of Labor and Defense inevitably became involved with the scientific institutions. On February 22, 1921 the Council of Peoples Commissars of the

[69] Quoted in Dobb, *Soviet Economic Development*, p. 339, from Krzhizhanovskii's report to the Fifth Congress of Soviets of the USSR, *Palnovoe Khoziaistvo* (No. 5, 1929), p. 9.

[70] Nekrasova, *Leninskii plan*, p. 10.

[71] *Ibid.*, p. 12; Dobb, *Soviet Economic Development*, p. 339.

[72] *Ibid.*

Russian Republic created a State General Planning Commission (*Gosudarstvennaia Obshcheplanovaia Kommissia*)
under the Council of Labor and Defense which was responsible
for "working out the measures of a general governmental
character for the development of knowledge and the organization of research necessary for the realization of the governmental economic plan. . . ."[73] The Council of Labor and
Defense concentrated its efforts on the electrification plan and
for several years found little time for the other ambitious
functions which had been assigned to it, such as "promoting
knowledge." Consequently its role in the coordination of scientific research was a very restricted one; here is another example
of the gap between the stated and the actual functions of the
governmental coordinating bodies. The blurring of jurisdictions
was spreading.

Still another organ concerned with scientific research was
the Special Temporary Committee of the Council of Peoples
Commissars of the Russian Republic, which lasted only a little
more than two years. This committee was created on June 22,
1922 for the purpose of "determining all scientific and material
needs of scientific institutions and for enacting all necessary
measures for satisfying these needs."[74] The goal of this committee was not to direct science as such, but to assist scientists
in solving their financial, supply, and personnel problems. In
the early 1920s many such bottlenecks could best be eased by
specific crash programs, since no overall economic or scientific
plan existed. The Special Temporary Committee undertook
such missions. The Special Temporary Committee was particularly important in releasing emergency funds for research
work, in sending scientists abroad, in organizing expeditionary
work, and in conducting the 200th jubilee of the Academy of
Sciences in 1925.

[73] The statute of the State General Planning Commission is contained in
Sobranie uzakonenii (No. 17, 1921), art. 106.
[74] The resolution creating the Special Temporary Committee and the one
eliminating it may be found, respectively, in *Sobranie uzakonenii* (No. 42,
1922), p. 493; and (No. 77, 1924), p. 776.

In the period before the adoption of the 1924 Constitution, Soviet science was no more rational or "planned" than the science program of any other state, and considerably more poverty-stricken than most. The Civil War's effect on science was not easily repaired; the scientists who emigrated took much knowledge and talent with them, the subscriptions to foreign journals were allowed to lapse, and communications with the outside world were disrupted. The government was able to turn its attention to science only sporadically. Granted there were committees responsible for science, but they did not fully understand their relationships to each other, much less to the scientific institutions under them. The statement of Dr. Friedrich Pollock concerning the economics of the Civil War period is equally applicable to science in those years: "There were, it is true, many plans, but there was no Plan."[75]

The grand dream of the rational state—not only planning scientifically, but planning science—was not forgotten. With the formation of the Soviet Union by the adoption of the 1924 Constitution, the debate over a supreme planning organ broke out afresh, with greater intensity than ever before. Now it seemed natural that all-Union committees should take over the functions previously performed on the republic level. The most logical way to accomplish this seemed to be a replacement of the Special Temporary Committee of the Russian Republic by a permanent Science Committee located on the all-Union level directly under the Council of Peoples Commissars of the USSR. Some suggested that the new committee have broader interests than science alone, suggesting that the organ be named the All-Union Committee of Science, Art, and the Preservation of Nature and Historical Monuments.[76] Others said that since the committee would have such eclectic interests and would exercise such an important influence it should not be a mere committee, but should have full rank as a commissariat. Even

[75] *Die planwirtschaftlichen Versuche in der Sowjetunion*, Leipzig, 1929, p. 235.

[76] Fed'kin, *Pravovye voprosy*, p. 296.

the idea that the Academy of Sciences itself might be transformed into such a body was considered.

The Academy's place in the overall organization of Soviet science continued to be uncertain, despite its official title as the "supreme scientific institution of the USSR." The hollowness of this guarantee during the reform period is indicated, moreover, by the fact that the Academy was not the sole possessor of this rank; the Communist Academy was awarded a charter on November 26, 1926 by the Central Executive Committee, naming it the "supreme all-Union scientific institution."[77] Behind this contradiction in titles lies the continuing intense dispute over the leadership of science in the Soviet Union, a dispute which was never completely resolved, even though the Communist Academy eventually disappeared.

The Communist Academy (called the Socialist Academy from 1918 to 1923) had from its first days been considered a counterbalance to the "bourgeois" influence of the old intelligentsia. The unanswered question was whether or not it would supplant the older Academy. In its first years the Communist Academy was considered the leader only of the "communist" scientific institutions, which were carefully distinguished from organizations still not under the Party's complete control, such as the Academy of Sciences.[78] After the 12th Party Congress in 1923 the Communist Academy greatly expanded its activities and created institutes in the natural as well as the social sciences.

[77] *Sobranie zakonov i rasporiazhenii raboche-krest'ianskogo pravitel'stva SSSR*, Moscow, 1924-32 (No. 3, 1927), art. 34; and Fed'kin, *Pravovye voprosy*, p. 35.

[78] The Communist Academy was not strong in the natural sciences, but it contained many talented Marxist theoreticians of the social sciences, such as N. Bukharin, E. Preobrazhenskii, D. B. Riazanov, and G. L. Piatakov. Leonard Schapiro commented: "The intellectual activity of the [Communist] Academy during this period was the golden age of Marxist thought in the USSR. A number of stimulating works appeared under the auspices of the Academy, in which the leading Marxists of the party, writing from different points of view, attempted to develop the principles of Marxism in conditions applicable in Russia. Very few of these intellectuals were destined to survive the more rigorous control . . . after NEP had been abandoned." Schapiro, *The Communist Party of the Soviet Union*, New York, 1960, p. 343.

The discussion of the administration of scientific research continued through 1924 and into 1925. On July 12, 1924 the Special Temporary Committee presented the Council of Peoples Commissars of the Russian Republic with a report calling for its own elimination and the creation of a new coordinating body in science on the all-Union level. A partisan of this proposal was Academician V. A. Steklov. In reply the republic governments objected strenuously, reacting from a combination of nationalism and bureaucratic jealousy.[79] In January 1925 the Scientific Administrations of the separate republics met in their third all-Union conference and insisted on retaining their planning powers in science. Their resolution maintained that:

1. . . . general direction of all scientific research work in the USSR must be concentrated exclusively in the Commissariats of Education of the union republics.

2. Institutions of an all-Union nature located on the territory of individual republics must be subordinate to the Commissariats of Education of these republics with respect to the direction of their scientific-research work.[80]

The Scientific Administration of the Ukrainian republic was particularly active in denying any supreme role to all-Union planning organs in science—and with a specific intent. The Ukrainians suspected the Russians of wishing to usurp the republic's control over their scientific institutions, and, in particular, the Ukrainian Academy of Sciences. The Ukrainian Academy had been founded when the Ukraine was free of the Bolsheviks in November 1918, and had continued its rather precarious existence since that time. The Ukrainians, therefore, insisted that the all-Union planning of science should be performed by the Scientific Administrations of the individual republics when they assembled for all-Union meetings.

[79] The resistance of the republics to the formation of an all-Union planning body in science is cited by F. N. Petrov, the head of Glavnauka, in "K voprosu o planovoi organizatsii nauchno-issledovatel'skoi raboty SSSR," *Nauchnyi Rabotnik* (December 1927), pp. 8-19.

[80] Fed'kin, *Pravovye voprosy*, pp. 296-97.

The extent to which these complaints by the union republics influenced the central government and Party organs is unknown, but one thing is clear: the much talked about all-Union planning body in science was not created in the wake of the 1924 Constitution, as had been expected; the problem remained unsolved. The reasons the Soviet authority on the subject, Fed'kin, gives for this failure to create a director of science in the 1920s are somewhat unconvincing, but provide certain clues:

> Whenever anyone proposed the formation of a special governmental organ, a Committee or a Ministry, other people objected that such an organ would be a superfluous, intermediate, bureaucratic department between the scientific institutions and the government and even between the scientific institutions and the ministries.
>
> Whenever anyone proposed giving the responsibilities for planning the most important scientific research to the Academy of Sciences, other people energetically insisted that this would convert the Academy from the greatest scientific center of the country to a mere office on scientific affairs.
>
> The proposals for the organization of a general governmental organ—a committee or Commissariat of Science—in later years did not receive the support of the directing bodies.[81]

In particular, the thesis that no central planning organ in science was created because of the objections of the officials on the republic level seems weak. As a matter of fact, as will be seen below, the republic organs had lost much of their influence already; the coordination of science was being taken over by all-Union committees, but by several conflicting ones, rather than by a single supreme body.[82] The federal nature of the

[81] *Ibid.*, p. 298.
[82] TsIK took over direct control of a number of important educational and scientific institutions, several of which were located in republics other than the RSFSR. These institutions under TsIK included the Communist Academy, the Marx–Engels Institute, the Museum of the Revolution of the USSR, the Central

union was largely a myth; the Communist Party was a control instrument transcending nationalities or local governments. The fate of those officials who objected to the Party policy was illustrated by the criticism and eventual arrest of Aleksandr Shumskii, the Ukrainian republic's Commissar of Education, who was, incidentally, in charge of scientific research in the Ukraine. Why, then, did not the Soviet Union create during the first five-year plan some sort of all-Union Commissariat of Science? An important reason was the lack of any genuinely competent group of scientists who were in favor of harnessing science to a plan. Any committee or commissariat which would direct the most important lines of research in the country would have to enjoy the support of the leading scientists of the nation. There was no doubt who those dominating scientists were; they were the members of the Academy of Sciences. Even if the Academy itself did not assume executive powers in science, the leaders of any committee which did would either have to be academicians or carry equal prestige. The most advanced theoretical research in the USSR was being conducted in the Academy, or under the control of academicians; the universities and other institutions had been so diluted by the proletarian floods that research quality had declined. But in 1927 the Party still did not trust the Academy, and the mistrust was returned in full measure. The creation of a supreme science committee would have to await the answer to this question: Would the Academy become a truly Soviet institution or would it have to be replaced?

*

To its most enthusiastic proponents the Russian Revolution was not merely a political and economic upheaval, but an all-encompassing transformation of social and intellectual life as

Publishing House of the Peoples of the USSR, the Institute of Orientalists, the Leningrad Eastern Institute, Sverdlov Communist University, Stalin Communist University of the Toilers of the East, Tashkent Central-Asian State University, and Tashkent Central-Asian Communist University. Fed'kin, *Pravovye voprosy*, p. 299.

well. Just as the revolutionary society would produce new
forms of literature and art, so would it produce a novel scientific research program. This new program called for a specific
conception of the relationship between science and technology,
a methodology for the planning of science, and organizational
bodies for the nationwide administration of science.

The principle of the unity of theory and practice, derived
from Marx's reaction against speculative philosophy, acquired
in the Soviet Union specific meanings for the organization of
scientific research: the leaders of all research laboratories were
to direct the work of their institutions toward the fulfillment of
needs on the level of applied science. Such an interpretation
of the principle of the unity of theory and practice was particularly appropriate in Russia at the end of the 1920s, as the
entire nation embarked upon the most rigorous industrialization
program in history. Pure science seemed to Party leaders a
luxury with no justification in a nation of shock-workers. Furthermore, Russia's traditional strengths in science were more in
the field of theory than practice, and redressing the balance
seemed necessary. These conditions of Russia's existence in the
twenties were more important in orienting the planners toward
applied science than the Marxist principle of the unity of
theory and practice, although Marxism provided a convenient
rationalization. Events in later years would show that once a
successful industrialization program had been executed, fundamental research would have to receive compensation for its
deprived years.

Before ossification of Soviet society under Stalin reached an
advanced state in the thirties Soviet theorists and political
leaders made several interesting approaches to the problems of
science policy and planning. Their most important contributions were their commitment to science as a natural resource
and their framing of relevant questions concerning the promotion of science. Bukharin's identification of the aspects of
science which might be planned was also of value. Similarly,
the suggestion for the creation of a Commissariat of Science

was an early acknowledgment of the possibility for a government to determine science policy on a nationwide scale. But both in the areas of methodology and organization, only tentative efforts were made. Furthermore, those aspects of science which seem to be most amenable to planning do not relate to the core of science; it is possible under certain conditions to plan *for* science, but not to plan science itself. Despite the great enthusiasm for a new science, relatively little was actually accomplished in the Soviet Union in the initial industrialization period toward the goal of creating a new foundation for scientific research.

As long as the Academy of Sciences remained aloof from Soviet political life, Soviet policies for science could not be implemented. The Academy in 1927 was thus both an irritant to the Communist Party as an exception to the rule that all Soviet institutions contain a controlling Party organization and also as an obstacle to the new science policies. The reform of the Academy was, consequently, a project of great importance to the Party.

CHAPTER III

THE SIEGE OF THE ACADEMY

THE BESIEGED: *Science is alone and the routes to its achievement are alone. They are independent from the ideas of man, from his aspirations and wishes, from the social tenor of his life, from his philosophical, social, and religious theories. They are independent from his will and from his world outlook—they are primordial.* / Academician V. I. Vernadskii[1]

THE BESIEGERS: *A member of the Academy of Sciences must be not only a representative of science but also a servant of the Soviet Government.* / I. M. Gubkin, Supreme Economic Council[2]

During the years between the end of the Civil War and the beginning of rapid industrialization, many Soviet citizens continued their lives essentially as in the prerevolutionary period. The major difference for the peasants was the beneficial one of having more freedom in their use of the land than ever before or since. The workers were inevitably directly involved in the rhetoric of proletarian revolution, but their factory jobs were not much different from those of previous times. The professionals who were educated before 1917, always uneasy in the Soviet setting, could continue their occupations so long as they did not express active opposition to the state. To be sure, Soviet Russia in the mid-twenties was an authoritarian state where the

[1] V. I. Vernadskii, "Ocherednaia zadacha v izuchenii estestvennykh proizvoditel'nykh sil," *Nauchnyi Rabotnik* (July-August 1926), p. 8.
[2] Ermakov, "Bor'ba kommunisticheskoi partii," citing TsGAOR, f. 3316, op. 23, d. 791, l. 22.

political freedoms of Western democratic nations were absent, but there is no evidence that these freedoms were consciously desired by anything approaching a majority of the Russian people.

The violent change that occurred with the beginning of industrialization and collectivization will always be causally connected with Stalin. Whether that change was a result of Stalin's free will or was required by the geopolitical realities of the Soviet Union in the late twenties is one of the most controversial questions among historians of the Soviet Union; it would be presumptuous to attempt to answer it in this study devoted to one rather narrow aspect of Stalin's cultural policy. As far as the government's policy toward scientists is concerned, it should by now be clear that, just as in the case of industrialization policies, there were different alternatives toward science and scientists which might have been followed. The cultural revolution beginning in 1929, when the old specialists were often either forced into overt conversions of Soviet loyalty, or displaced, was not inevitable. The Russian Revolution was not placed in deep freeze at the end of the Civil War and thawed out intact in 1928. If the more moderate economic policies of the 1920s had been continued, a similarly more moderate attitude toward intellectuals seems quite possible, if not likely.

But given Stalin's adoption of the most ambitious economic programs, it becomes difficult to imagine the continuation of a tolerant attitude toward the old professionals. To link the cultural and economic policies of the Soviet Union at this particular point in time is not simply a version of economic determinism but an observation on the psychological nature of revolutions. The periods of greatest stress in revolutionary countries of the twentieth century, whether Russia, China, or Cuba, have not been periods when intellectuals could avoid being involved. The first demand of the political leaders has been cooperation in the immediate pragmatic goals of the revolution, as they define them. The more grave the economic or other difficulties, the more the leaders have insisted on participation. A coldly rational view would probably admit that the maintenance of a small center of disinterested theoretical research would in the end benefit the government more than the forced enlistment of all scientists in industrial tasks. A retrospective view illustrates that the Academy of Sciences performed this service for the Soviet government, but more in spite of it than because of it. The capitulation of the Academy to Stalin's cultural revolution was, to the end, a partial achievement.

The call for a new charter

The active campaign for the reorganization of the Academy of Sciences began in 1926 when the question of a new charter for it arose.[3] The charter was the weakest spot in the Academy's defense against Soviet criticism. Adopted in 1836 in a form that differed little from the charter of 1803, it was a tsarist document; its first sentence still contained in 1926 the statement that the Academy of Sciences was "the most important learned estate [*soslovie*] of the Russian Empire." Other references also had meaning only in the old regime. For example, the president of the Academy had to be chosen from the "first four classes" of the imperial table of ranks, and pensions were assigned to academic workers on the basis of ranks achieved; elsewhere the charter referred to the emperor, the Holy Synod, and the Governing Senate. A new charter was obviously needed, although it need not be changed radically. A new charter which was essentially the same as the old one, but with the necessary terminological substitutions, could have served many more

3 When I did research for this study in Moscow and Leningrad I unsuccessfully attempted to gain permission to work in the archives of the Academy. I then used several sources, both published and unpublished, which do cite the pertinent archives. In each case when such materials are used, both the secondary and primary citations are given. Note 2 above is an example. The sequence of events in Ermakov's dissertation clarified the abundant but fragmentary information published in the Soviet press in these years.

years if the Academy had been allowed to remain aloof from the task of "socialist construction," but this permission was not to be granted. The 14th Party Congress in December 1925 adopted a program of rapid industrialization; all layers of Soviet society, all organizations and institutions, were obligated to assist in expanding material production. The 1836 charter of the Academy described the old sanctuary of theoretical research, while the industrial planners demanded a charter which would remold the Academy into an office for scientific and technological aid for industrialization.

Exactly from what quarter the initial demand for a new charter came is not known; Soviet sources admit, however, that the reform movement arose outside the Academy itself. Ermakov, who had access to the Leningrad and Moscow regional (*oblast'*) archives, as well as the Academy archives, commented, "It ought to be mentioned that the initiative for working out a new charter did not come from academic circles. They still were not conscious of the necessity of reforming the old methods of work and the organization of the Academy."[4]

The communist critics focused their attention on the disagreements among the academicians in order to gain a hearing for their proposed reforms. In particular, the academicians of the second department, the department of Russian language and literature, had retained a reputation for conservatism throughout the period of the Revolution and the New Economic Policy. The critics asked for a reduction of the department's influence. The second department had been founded by the members of the Imperial Russian Academy when their organization merged with the Academy of Sciences in 1841; the parent organization under its last president, the reactionary A. S. Shishkov, had attempted to preserve the purity of the Russian language and had supported outdated linguistic theories. By means of the system of academic elections, whereby each department had the sole right to nominate academicians

[4] "Bor'ba kommunisticheskoi," p. 127.

for vacant chairs, the members of the second department had preserved some of the flavor of the tsarist period.[5] The Commission of Slavic Scholarship of the department was founded on the former Petrograd Slavic Society, a center of Pan-Slav sentiment. Academician V. M. Istrin was particularly well known for his strong conservative sentiments. The political tenor of the department did not, however, prevent it from performing valuable scholarly research.

The political differences within the Academy eased the task of communist critics in destroying the Academy's structure, as defined by the old charter. S. Voronov wrote that even the other members of the Academy considered the members of the second department "diehards" (*zubry*); Academician Sobolevskii, himself a member of the department, wrote that it was "polluted to an impossible extent."[6] Militant Marxists called for a merger of the first and second departments and a reform in the system of elections to prevent the preservation of reactionary groups.

President Karpinskii's position from the beginning of the reorganization period was that of a conciliator. The octogenarian scientist himself much preferred the traditional patriarchal Academy, with as much autonomy as possible, but he was willing to yield to Party pressure in an effort to achieve some sort of modus vivendi between the Academy and its Soviet environment. He always avoided unpleasant conflicts. (This passivity was explained by one of his acquaintances as the result of a lifelong heart defect.)[7] From the Party's standpoint Karpinskii was a valuable figurehead. He had been freely elected to head the Academy in 1917 and possessed international scientific authority (the French Academy awarded him its Cuvier Prize). In the Soviet Union Karpinskii helped plan

[5] For the rules governing elections, see *Sbornik postanovlenii i rasporiazhenii otnosiashchikhsia do imperatorskoi akademii nauk*, St. Petersburg, 1869, pp. 39-44.

[6] For a critical Soviet discussion of the second department, see S. Voronov, "Iz proshlogo," pp. 135-49.

[7] Michael Kitaeff, "Akademiia nauk SSSR," Russian Archives, Columbia University, p. 30.

the distribution of Ural industry, originated the idea of the Donets Basin, and discovered the Ishimbaevo oil deposit, which became the basis of the "Second Baku." As long as he held the position of president the appearance of the Academy's reforming itself on its own initiative could be maintained.

In November 1926, evidently heeding the warnings of the Party, Karpinskii decided to support the demand for a new charter. Rather than broach the subject in the General Assembly, he invited a few academicians to his home, where he privately explained the need for a new charter.[8] The concern of the academicians was that their unrestricted right to choose the members and officers of the Academy be maintained and that the General Assembly continue to be the governing body of the Academy. Perhaps by yielding to the Party on minor points the essential traditions of the Academy could be preserved. The meeting appointed a commission for reporting on a new charter to the General Assembly, headed by Academician I. Iu. Krachkovskii. On February 5, 1927 Krachkovskii gave his first report to the Academy as a whole and urged adoption of a new charter.[9] On May 31 a group of academicians attended a meeting of the Council of Peoples Commissars, at which the new project for a charter was discussed. The details of this meeting are unknown, but the government's demands were probably incorporated into the draft charter. On June 7 Academician Ol'denburg presented the completed charter to the General Assembly, where it was discussed and finally approved.[10]

The 1927 charter

The new charter reflected the wishes of the Party in several

[8] Arkhiv AN SSSR, f. 208, op. 2, d. 256, l. 29, cited by Ermakov, "Bor'ba kommunisticheskoi," p. 127.

[9] Arkhiv AN SSSR, f. 1, op. Ia, d. 176, l. 74, cited by Ermakov, "Bor'ba kommunisticheskoi," p. 127.

[10] *Protokoly AN SSSR*, 1927, p. 153, cited by Ermakov, p. 127. The charter may be found in *Sobranie zakonov i rasporiazhenii SSSR* (No. 35, 1927), art. 367.

important ways but did not bring the Academy under Party control. The Academy retained its sovereign rights in the selection of its members, even though the Party gained a significant toehold in the nomination procedure.

The charter altered the internal organization and legal status of the Academy. Since 1925 the Academy had been an all-Union organization,[11] but was now, in addition, directly under the jurisdiction of the Council of Peoples Commissars, which had the power to approve or disapprove Academy work plans. At this time the Academy had no work plans (the first appeared in 1930). Another ominous development was the imposition over the Academy of a typical collective council, or *sovet*, replacing, but not eliminating, the old president and permanent secretary. This new organ, called the presidium of the Academy to the present day, consisted of the president, two vice-presidents (previously there was only one; the new one was to direct "planning and organization" matters), the permanent secretary, and the secretaries of both departments. Academicians Karpinskii and Ol'denburg continued to occupy the most important positions of president and permanent secretary, and there was no immediate change in the administration of the Academy.

The new charter also eliminated the advantageous position of the humanities. The troublesome second department, Russian language and literature, was united with the third department, the historical-philological sciences, to form one department. Thus, there were now only two departments in the Academy, the physical-mathematical and the humanities, and each had equal weight; future changes would shift more and more power to the natural sciences and technology. The Party no doubt considered the academicians in the humanities less reliable than those in the natural sciences. By combining the two departments the influence of suspect academicians was

[11] See the resolution of TsIK and Sovnarkom SSSR, "O priznanii Rossiiskoi Akademii Nauk vysshim uchenym uchrezhdeniem Soiuza SSR," *Sobranie zakonov i rasporiazhenii SSSR* (No. 48, 1925), art. 351.

lessened, although in the General Assembly each member continued, as before, to have one vote.

Events of the next few years illustrated that the most significant changes effected by the 1927 charter concerned the election of new members, the total number of which the charter increased from 45 to 70. Only through such a decided increase in membership did it seem possible to change the political orientation of the Academy. Half of the 44 members in 1928 had been elected before 1917, and few even of the newer members favored a basic reform of the Academy.[12] The actual process of electing new members remained as defined in the 1836 charter—secret balloting by the full members, with a two-thirds vote required for election—but the right of "nominating" candidates was given, according to article 17 of the charter, to "social organizations and institutions." Furthermore, article 31 provided that henceforth all meetings of the General Assembly would be public.[13] The new election clauses also provided that the elections would be preceded by a public declaration of the candidates' qualifications by special commissions consisting of academicians and scientists from all the union republics. The purpose of these provisions was ostensibly to prevent the self-perpetuation of particular viewpoints that had occurred in the old second department, but was actually to pressure the Academy into accepting communist academicians. In 1929 twice as many members would be elected as in the entire period 1917-28; the candidates would be nominated not only by the General Assembly but also by organizations completely outside the Academy. Thus, the Party was erecting a system for flooding the Academy with communist members without technically taking away its right to choose its own members. The Academy did not have to accept the Party candidates (and, indeed, would refuse to do so at first) but its ac-

[12] The death in 1928 of Academician V. L. Omelianovskii, a microbiologist, left one chair vacant.

[13] Certain meetings of the Academy had always been public. The 1836 charter stipulated that the annual ceremonial meeting was open to all persons interested in science. Many other meetings, however, were closed.

tions were now exposed to the Party propaganda organs which would keep close account of which candidates were successful.

Another clause in the charter provided that academicians must not only demonstrate their scientific competence but also "assist the socialist reconstruction of the USSR." Furthermore, members could be deprived of their academic chairs if their activities harmed the interests of the USSR.[14] This clause was aimed directly at the émigré academicians Struve and Rostovtsev, whom the Academy still carried on its rolls as full members. The same clause would one day be used against several of the members who voted to accept it.

Despite all of the changes brought about by the 1927 charter, the Academy was still a relatively free organization—certainly much more so than any other prominent institution in the USSR. Many of the changes of the new charter were potential restrictions on the Academy's autonomy, but throughout 1927 and 1928 the Academy continued to direct its own activities, albeit under increasing attack. As long as the Academy lacked a primary party organization it was master of its internal affairs. According to a Soviet source, in 1928 there were only two members of the Communist Party of the more than a thousand people working in the Academy, and both of them were scientific "workers," not members.[15] Even as late as 1930 the organization of Marxist scientists, VARNITSO (about which much more will be heard), could boast of only eight members in the Academy.[16]

Additional evidence of the Academy's enduring unique position was the new charter's statement that publications of the Academy were not subject to censorship, a privilege no other press in the Soviet Union enjoyed.[17] Last, the charter author-

14 "Ustav AN SSSR," in *Sobranie zakonov* (No. 35, 1927), art. 367, p. 713.
15 *VII vsesoiuznomu s'ezdu sovetov akademiia nauk SSSR*, Moscow–Leningrad, 1935, p. 207.
16 On VARNITSO, see Fed'kin, *Pravovye voprosy*, p. 176. The abbreviation stands for the Association of Workers of Science and Technology for the Assistance of Socialist Construction.
17 "Ustav AN SSSR," in *Sobranie zakonov* (No. 35, 1927), art. 367, p. 717.

ized the importation of foreign books for the Academy, free from customs or censorship regulations.

Elections of new members

Under the new charter the Academy continued its old existence, although a line of demarcation had been crossed; elections would soon be held to expand the Academy to its new membership and the pressure to admit communists was mounting. At the 15th Party Congress in December 1927 the Party adopted a two-pronged program of collectivization and rapid industrialization. At first, the pace of collectivization was not forced, but as Stalin outmaneuvered his colleagues in the next several years, collectivization became increasingly intense, and the cultural and social revolution remained in step.

At the beginning of 1928 the Politburo of the Central Committee of the Communist Party specifically took up the matter of reforming the Academy of Sciences by appointing a special commission for the direction of the academic elections, consisting mainly of members of the Leningrad Party organization.[18] Almost all the Academy's institutions and personnel were located on territory under the jurisdiction of the Leningrad regional committee of the Party (*obkom*). The Leningrad Party organization had been headed since December 1925 by S. M. Kirov, whom Stalin had sent there to replace G. E. Zinoviev. The Leningrad special commission spent all of 1928 and the first part of 1929 directing the election campaign for the Academy.

[18] This information comes from Ermakov, "Bor'ba kommunisticheskoi partii," p. 133, who obtained his data from the Archives of the Marx–Engels–Lenin–Stalin Institute (so named at the time he used the archives), f. 17 (*Materialy Leningradskogo obkoma partii*), op. 21, d. 2674, l. 114. There is no reason to doubt the Party's determining role in reforming the Academy, although Ermakov may be guilty of overemphasizing the extent to which the reform was planned in advance. The Party probably made many decisions as events developed, rather than following a plan. Ermakov wrote that the "preparation for the elections and the very elections themselves were under the firm attention and control of the party organs, the Soviet press, and the social organizations." Ermakov, *ibid.*

The Academy was rudely informed in April 1928 that the Soviet government did not consider the 1927 charter adequate for reforming the Academy. Two resolutions of the Council of Peoples Commissars, on April 3 and 6, introduced important changes to the charter without going through any of the customary legal procedure of review and approval by the Academy itself.[19] Most important of all, the total number of full members stipulated in the charter was raised from 70 to 85, meaning that the membership in 1928 of 44 would be nearly doubled. The Council of Peoples Commissars also established the disciplinary specialties of the new chairs in such a way that Marxist candidates would be logical choices. Four chairs were established in "socio-economic" sciences, a description which would cover almost any Marxist political or economic specialist. Two additional chairs were established in philosophy, clearly marked for dialectical materialists. Four other seats carried the designation, "technological sciences," the first posts in the Academy reserved for engineers. The obvious goals of the increase in seats were: (1) speed the influx of membership under Communist Party controls; (2) increase the importance of applied sciences; (3) increase the importance of dialectical materialism; (4) reduce further the influence of the older academicians.

In addition to the membership changes the resolution strengthened Party control over the election procedure by stipulating that the special commissions which reported to the General Assembly would give their conclusions *only* on the candidates whom they had chosen as worthy of admission to membership.[20] The 1927 charter had required the commissions to report on all candidates, regardless of whether or not the commissions approved them. This rather minor change was one more step in the reduction of the General Assembly's control over the election procedure.

19 "Ob izmenenii st. 18 i 26 ustava Akademii Nauk Soiuza SSR," and "O spiske kafedr Akademii Nauk Soiuza SSR," *Sobranie zakonov* (No. 22, 1928), arts. 197, 198.
20 *Ibid.* (No. 22, 1928), p. 415.

Academician Ol'denburg dutifully announced to the press the vacancies in the Academy on April 14, 1928, as he was required to do, both by the charter and the recent resolutions of the Council of Peoples Commissars. Ol'denburg stated that the Academy would receive nominations for the following chairs:[21]

Physics-Mathematics Department		Humanities Department	
mathematics	3	history	6
physics	2	socio-economics	4
chemistry	6	philosophy	2
technology	4	orientology	3
geology	4	European languages	
biology	4	and literature	3
	23		18

In addition, the recent death of Academician V. L. Omelianovskii had created another vacancy; this made a total increase in membership of 42 in one year, a change in personnel equal to that usually occurring in 15 or 20 years.

After Ol'denburg's formal declaration of the vacancies, the complex election procedure was announced. For two months scholarly institutions, social organizations, and individual scholars were invited to mail nominations to the Academy. The nominations would then be printed in the newspapers, and all organizations and individuals were invited to send in criticism and praise of the candidates to the Academy. Then the Academy would form 11 special commissions, one for each discipline, which would narrow the field of candidates before presenting them to the academicians for voting. These commissions would contain not only members of the Academy itself, but also representatives of each union republic, to demonstrate the "all-Union" character of the Academy, and, simultaneously, to counter the Academy's opposition to Party candidates. The

[21] "Khronika," *Nauchnyi Rabotnik* (July 1928), p. 76.

actual vote would then be a two-step process. First, the candidates would be elected in each of the two departments and
then pass to the final election in the General Assembly. Those
who received no less than two-thirds of the votes of the academicians present received full membership.[22]

On April 17 the office of the Leningrad regional Party organization (*obkom*) asked the department of the secretariat
of the Party's Central Committee in charge of assigning personnel (*Orgraspred*) to select an individual as the political secretary for the future party organization in the Academy of Sciences, and on May 17 called on all "social organizations" to
nominate candidates for membership in the Academy.[23]

Certain communists feared that the campaign against the
Academy would overreach itself and destroy the value of the
foremost learned organization in the country. At the first all-
Union conference of the association of Marxist scientists, VAR-
NITSO, April 23-26, 1928, Professor Lengnik, who favored the
reform of the Academy, remarked:

> If we approach the Academy of Sciences from the point
> of view of Marxist analysis, then, of course, we must come to
> a negative conclusion regarding it, but, nevertheless, it seems
> to me, all the sections of the Academy of Sciences other than
> the social sciences are in good order. We would make a great
> mistake if we gave up the whole Academy of Sciences as a

[22] This procedure was stipulated by the 1927 charter and the April 3 and 6,
1928, resolutions of Sovnarkom. The procedure was discussed in I. K. Luppol,
"K vyboram v akademii nauk, SSSR," *Nauchnyi Rabotnik* (November 1928),
p. 3.
[23] Arkhiv IMELS, f. 17, op. 21, d. 2674, l. 114; and d. 2675, l. 48, cited by
Ermakov, "Bor'ba kommunisticheskoi partii," p. 134. The fact that Ermakov did
not identify the person selected to be Party secretary of the Academy's new Party
organization makes one wonder if he were not Bukharin, whom Ermakov studi-
ously avoided. Bukharin was the Party candidate who received the greatest
backing in the election campaign and won the largest number of nominations
of over 200 candidates. S. Belomortsev, "Bol'shevizatsiia Akademii Nauk,"
Posev (November 18, 1951), p. 11, says that Bukharin and Enukidze, the
secretary of TsIK, represented the Party's and the government's interests in
negotiations with the Academy over the elections. Evidently Bukharin's difficulties with Stalin, developing in the summer of 1928, but not openly declared
until the spring of 1929, did not harm his position in the Academy's affairs.

bad job, and did not utilize the great resources of the Academy, in spite of all those mistakes and unfavorable traits which the Academy of Sciences embodies.[24]

The Academy labored to slow down the process of electing new members; the prospect of doubling the size of the Academy in a few months was extremely distasteful to most of the old guard, to whom membership was a mark of arduously earned distinction in scholarship and research and achieved only upon the death of another academician. The Academy pointedly refused to take up the question of the elections until September 1927, and then an academic committee contended that the Academy might be able to fill 25 vacancies in three years "if suitable candidates are found."[25] The members of the militant organizations of communist scientists protested such a slow pace. The government indicated by its resolutions in April that the elections were to be held soon, in 1928 if possible.

In March 1928 the Fourth Plenum of the Central Council of the Section of Scientific Workers sharply criticized the work of the Academy. At that meeting the colorful and caustic D. B. Riazanov (Gol'dendakh), the head of the Marx–Engels Institute, asked for the liquidation of the Academy of Sciences "in general," basing his stand on the view that academies had been replaced by large institutes as loci of research.[26] In 1928 the Academy was still not thought of as a network of institutes across the country, as it later became, but as a society of individual scientists centered in one city, even though the Academy had long since established institutes and observation stations in various locations on the territories of the present Soviet Union.[27] Many of the new research institutes, such as Riazanov's own, were completely outside the Academy's framework.

[24] "Stenograficheskii otchet 1 vsesoiuznoi konferentsii VARNITSO," *VARNITSO* (No. 2, 1928), p. 36.
[25] Ermakov, "Bor'ba kommunisticheskoi partii," pp. 133-34.
[26] *Ibid.*, p. 135.
[27] The Academy created or acquired numerous institutions outside St. Petersburg—Vil'na University Observatory (1832), Tiflis Physical Observatory (1883), Sevastopol' Biological Station (1892), Odessa, Ekaterinburg, and Irkutsk Observatories (1899), Constantinople Archaeological Institute (1894).

The plenum did not call for the dissolution of the Academy, but instead published a criticism of its activities.[28] The report accused the Academy of failing to produce significant studies in economics, sociology, history, philosophy, and in most other fields under the second department. In particular, no scholars were writing from the standpoint of Marxism. Then—in a direct threat—the plenum called for the Academy to prove itself in the coming elections:

> The scientific workers of the USSR are following with resolute attentiveness the elections in the Academy of Sciences, since the result, one way or another, will predetermine the future position of the Academy among the other scientific institutions of the USSR, its role and significance in the economic and cultural construction of the Soviet state.[29]

The Soviet challenge was now in the open—Did the Academy wish to play a leading role in Soviet science? If so, it must elect Marxist candidates. If not, it must be ready to be replaced by the growing network of Marxist institutes. I. K. Luppol, a follower from student days of the dialectical materialist philosopher, A. M. Deborin, one of the leading Marxist candidates for the Academy, commented that the plenum had "considered its comradely and professional duty to warn the Academy and to remind it that on this question the Section of Scientific Workers completely agrees with . . . the opinion of Soviet society. We think that the Academy of Sciences of the USSR cannot fail to heed this opinion most carefully."[30] Later, as the elections drew closer, Luppol observed, "The Academy of Sciences stands as if before an examination. It is expected to demonstrate that it is in step with Soviet society."[31]

[28] See *Nauchnyi Rabotnik* (July 1928), pp. 102-103.

[29] "Rezoliutsii IV plenum tsentral'nogo soveta sektsii nauchnykh rabotnikov," *Nauchnyi Rabotnik* (July 1928), p. 103.

[30] I. K. Luppol, "IV plenum tsentral'nogo soveta (sektsii nauchnykh rabotnikov soiuza rabotnikov prosveshcheniia SSSR) o rabote akademii nauk SSSR," *Nauchnyi Rabotnik* (July 1928), p. 21.

[31] Luppol, "K vyboram," p. 5.

Meanwhile, the prerevolutionary technical intelligentsia were falling under suspicion elsewhere in the Soviet Union. For 10 years the government had encouraged noncommunist specialists to work closely with the regime, but it now began to accuse them of "wrecking" activities. Early in 1928 governmental security organs claimed to have discovered a plot by such technicians at Shakhty, in the Donets Basin, aimed at overthrowing the government. The trial of the "saboteurs" occurred in May 1928; the conclusions which the prosecutor, Andrei Vyshinskii, drew from the trial were that the Soviet government could no longer trust "bourgeois" experts and that technical organizations must examine their ranks.

The government permitted the nomination of candidates to the Academy to extend into August. By that date 135 different organizations had proposed 201 men for 42 vacancies.[32] The following 10 candidates, predominantly Party favorites, received the greatest number of nominations:[33]

	number of nominations
N. I. Bukharin	37
M. N. Pokrovskii	31
D. B. Riazanov	31
A. N. Bakh	25
G. M. Krzhizhanovskii	21
V. A. Obruchev	21
N. M. Knipovich	20
A. M. Deborin	19
D. N. Prianishnikov	19
N. I. Vavilov	19

The members of the secretariat of the Leningrad Party regional committee (*obkom*) discussed the nominees at three

[32] Arkhiv AN SSSR, f. 2, op. I-1928, d. 89, ls. 5, 14-16, cited in Ermakov, "Bor'ba kommunisticheskoi partii," pp. 136-37.
[33] Luppol, "K vyboram," p. 4.

meetings, on August 13, September 20, and October 22, and selected certain ones for approval in the Party press.[34] Literally hundreds of articles discussing the merits of the candidates appeared in print; VARNITSO and the Section of Scientific Workers were especially energetic in backing Marxist candidates. On the other hand, the Academy strove to promote the candidates who, it felt, had earned membership by stint of scholarly achievement. When the Party journalists asked for the removal of the candidacy of the historian M. K. Liubavskii, who, they said, represented "bourgeois" historiography, the academicians stoutly defended him at every step of the election process.

According to one worker in the Academy who later emigrated to the West, Academicians Ol'denburg and Platonov discussed the selection of candidates privately with Bukharin and Enukidze, the Party and government representatives most intimately concerned with the Academy, and agreed that the approved list of candidates would be a compromise between the Academy's list and the Party's. The compromise would place Liubavskii in the Academy, as well as certain other "rightist" candidates, in return for such Party-sponsored candidates as Bukharin, Krzhizhanovskii, Gubkin, Vil'iams (Williams), and Riazanov.[35] If such an agreement was, in fact, reached, certainly not all the academicians subscribed to it, as subsequent disputes demonstrated. The selection of candidates immediately became a heated issue.

In order to narrow the nominees down to a suitable list for balloting by the academicians, the General Assembly appointed 11 special commissions, each for a different field of knowledge, to review the candidates. Each commission contained four to 10 academicians; one academician could sit on more than one commission, several sitting on as many as five.[36] The Party had

[34] Arkhiv AN SSSR, f. 2, op. I-1928, d. 89, ls. 5, 14-16, cited in Ermakov, "Bor'ba kommunisticheskoi partii," pp. 136, 137.

[35] Belomortsev, "Bol'shevizatsiia akademii nauk," p. 11.

[36] The membership of the commissions is given in *Nauchnyi Rabotnik* (November 1928), p. 83.

not been able to control the selection of the members of the commissions. The history and philosophy commissions were overwhelmingly anti-Marxist in composition; all the members of the philosophy commission had been elected to the Academy before the Revolution.

In fact, the Party candidates who lacked scholarly qualifications would probably have not received favor in a single commission had it not been for the "outsiders," the representatives of the union republics, who carried six votes in their pockets and could use all six in any or all commissions if they chose.[37] The leader of this nonacademic delegation was O. Iu. Shmidt, who was later to become a Soviet academician in his own right and a noted cosmogonist and polar explorer. He was assisted by V. P. Volgin, future permanent secretary of the Academy, and the well-known historian. Volgin, who was born in Kursk and educated in Moscow, was a delegate, appropriately enough, in view of the entire absurd procedure, of the Tadzhik republic. The outsiders' six votes gave them enough power to swing the vote in most but not all of the commissions.

From October 10 to 21 the commissions endeavored to select a list of candidates, but the academicians and the outsiders soon came to a stalemate. The first controversial issue was the question of how many candidates would be chosen for the 42 vacancies. Neither the charter nor the government's decrees had stipulated this number. The old guard now proposed to include as many names as possible on the ballots so that the General Assembly could freely choose in the secret vote. The outsiders insisted that only 42 names be put on the ballots, one name for each position. It would be incorrect, Shmidt and his colleagues maintained, to place more than 42 names on each

[37] The "outsiders" consisted of 13 members, that is, six delegates and seven substitutes. They were, from:
the RSFSR: O. Iu. Shmidt, V. P. Miliutin, F. N. Petrov
the Ukrainian SSR: Iu. I. Ozerskii, M. I. Iavorskii
the Transcaucasian SSR: S. M. Ter-Gabrielian, I. K. Luppol
the Belorussian SSR: V. M. Ignatovskii, E. B. Pashukanis
the Uzbek SSR: L. K. Martens, P. M. Kerzhentsev
the Tadzhik SSR: I. A. Sevast'ianov, V. P. Volgin

ballot because that would allow academicians to choose members in completely different fields; mathematicians would be
deciding the fate of biologists, and so forth.[38] Backed by the
Party and all its subservient organizations, the outsiders won
this important dispute, and the special commissions, whose
work was open to public view and whose membership was
known, recommended only 42 candidates for 42 vacancies.
The outsiders' case had been aided by academic tradition,
according to which the departments of the Academy had
usually recommended only one or two candidates for each new
position. (The old rules stated that the maximum number of
candidates for each position was three.)

The task of choosing 42 candidates was not simple. Several
academicians, such as Ipat'ev, the chairman of the commission
on chemistry, attempted to act as mediators between the two
rival groups. Ipat'ev resented Party dictation, but nevertheless
wanted to avoid a sharp conflict between the Academy and the
Party. As a respected scientist as well as an administrator for
the government (he was a member of the State Planning
Commission and the Supreme Economic Council), Ipat'ev had
authority in both camps. Under his leadership the chemistry
commission agreed on a list of six candidates that included the
Party stalwart A. N. Bakh; the others were A. E. Chichibabin,
A. E. Favorskii, N. Ia. Dem'ianov, N. D. Zelinskii, and V. A.
Kistiakovskii.[39] Ipat'ev also eased the situation in the technology commission, chaired by Academician Kurnakov. The
outsiders insisted that V. R. Vil'iams, of the Timiriazev Academy, be approved by the commission despite the opposition of

[38] Luppol, "K vyboram," p. 7.

[39] In his memoirs Ipat'ev said his commission had a quota of eight candidates and that the bitterest dispute was over the choice between Professor A. A.
Iakovkin and L. V. Pisarzhevskii for the eighth seat. The academicians, said
Ipat'ev, favored Iakovkin, while the outsiders insisted on Pisarzhevskii, on the
grounds that the Ukrainian republic should be represented. According to
Ipat'ev, under his leadership the commission approved Pisarzhevskii by a small
majority. Ipat'ev's memory must be at fault on this point. His commission had
a quota of only six; Pisarzhevskii was not among the final slate of selected candidates. Pisarzhevskii was elected to the Academy in 1930, not 1929. V. N.
Ipatieff, *The Life of a Chemist*, Stanford, 1946, p. 462.

most of its members. The academicians' charge that Vil'iams had not published any significant research received unexpected support when Professor Prianishnikov of the Timiriazev Academy, who was himself a candidate, asked Ipat'ev to remove Vil'iams from the list, since the Timiriazev Academy itself did not feel that Vil'iams deserved membership in the Academy of Sciences.[40] Ipat'ev then dissuaded Shmidt from continuing the struggle over Vil'iams' nomination, adding that "later, when the number of academicians was again increased, he could be elected more easily."[41]

Academician V. I. Vernadskii was anything but a conciliator; his family was already known for the strength of its opinions. His father, I. V. Vernadskii, a liberal professor of political economy at Kiev and Moscow Universities in the 19th century, had debated systems of agriculture with Chernyshevskii, the noted publicist.[42] Academician V. I. Vernadskii, the son, was an outstanding mineralogist and geochemist of broad cultural and philosophical views. Before the Revolution he had been active in the liberal local government movement (*zemstva*) and the Constitutional Democratic Party. In 1911 he resigned from university teaching in protest against the policies of minister Kasso. He has been described, perhaps not completely correctly, as a believer in the Manchester school of economics, and both before and after the Revolution he opposed communal systems of agriculture for economic reasons. In science, Vernadskii was known throughout the world of geologists for his research into the formation of minerals and his genetic theories of mineral change. In the period 1923-26 he traveled in western Europe, lecturing at the Sorbonne and other institutions, and again in 1927-29 he traveled abroad. In the Soviet Union he had been one of the founders, along with Academician Karpinskii, of the Commission for the Study of Natural Productive Forces (KEPS), and he was highly valued for his

[40] *Ibid.*
[41] *Ibid.*
[42] *Sovremennik*, Nos. 9 and 11, 1857, include references to *Ekonomicheskii Ukazatel'* which were unavailable to the author.

interest in the use of minerals for aiding the industrialization effort.

After the beginning of the campaign to subordinate the Academy, Vernadskii became the leader of the resistance to Party pressure.[43] He felt keenly that the Academy should choose its new members in exactly the customary procedure: on the basis of merit. Vernadskii chaired the geology commission, and managed to restrict selection of his quota to men of recognized ability. He was also a member of several other groups, including the technology commission, where he opposed I. M. Gubkin, an ardent supporter of the Party and a member of the Supreme Economic Council. In this commission Ipat'ev again prevented an eruption by giving an obviously sincere commendation of Gubkin's scientific abilities.[44] Ipat'ev's support swayed the commission and Gubkin was nominated over Vernadskii's objections.[45]

Vernadskii carried his fight over to the philosophy commission, in which he was also a member, and where all the other members were also disinclined toward compromise. This commission soon became the center of attention of the entire Academy, and the Leningrad Party organization as well. One of the most controversial candidates was A. M. Deborin, the dialectical materialist philosopher who had by this time consolidated his victory over the mechanists even though mechanist philosophy remained strong, especially among natural scientists.[46] Vernadskii based his attack on Deborin on an opposition to Marxist philosophy in general, whether mechanist or dialectical. In a truly audacious display, Vernadskii affirmed that the philosophy of Marx and Engels was growing out of

[43] Kitaeff, "Akademiia nauk SSSR," pp. 42-47, and Ermakov, "Bor'ba kommunisticheskoi partii." Also, Interview, George Vernadsky, East Haven, Connecticut, July 21, 1964.

[44] It seems that Gubkin had saved the Soviet Union from expensive investment in the petroleum industry in the Maikop region by demonstrating that the fields there were poor, contrary to previous reports. Ipatieff, *The Life of a Chemist*, p. 462.

[45] *Ibid.*

[46] See Joravsky, *Soviet Marxism.*

date and that dialectical materialism was only a "survival of Hegelianism."[47] He organized a set of arguments against Deborin and other Marxist candidates that became widely known as the "Memorandum of Academician Vernadskii."[48] His great reputation in geology and his valuable work for the nation as chairman of the Council for the Study of the Productive Forces of the USSR (KEPS) protected him from severe treatment, just as Pavlov's stature preserved him.

In the meetings of the commission Vernadskii voiced his belief that philosophy is always "antagonistic to the science of its time"; to him the philosophical theories of Thomas Aquinas, Hegel, Marx, and Engels seemed equally valueless as approaches to science.[49] He believed science was above class and party conflicts, and expressed his dissatisfaction that in the Soviet Union no other philosophical thoughts except those of dialectical materialism were allowed to come to light. Vernadskii called on his fellow academicians to not only oppose Deborin but elect members "regardless of the circumstances of life in our country and on the basis of the internationalism of science."[50]

The uproar in the Academy itself was accompanied by disturbances in the greater scientific community outside, although relatively little is known about these troubles. One Soviet author referred sketchily to "demonstrations" which are "well-known to all";[51] another referred to the academic "putsch";[52] still another censured disturbances in the Academy, the scien-

[47] Arkhiv AN SSSR, f. 2, op. I-1928, d. 89, l. 397, cited by Ermakov, "Bor'ba kommunisticheskoi partii," p. 140.
[48] "Zapiska akademika V. I. Vernadskogo o vyborakh chlenov Akademii Nauk," *Ibid.*, l. 372.
[49] *Ibid.* In discussing this debate Ermakov interjected, "Academician Vernadskii's absolute lack of understanding of the revolutionary and scientific character of Marxist philosophy led him to the confusion of the reactionary, lifeless, antiscientific philosophy of Aquinas with the eternally living, revolutionary, genuinely scientific, creative Marxist philosophy."
[50] Ermakov, "Bor'ba kommunisticheskoi partii," p. 142.
[51] B. P. Pozern, "Ocherednye voprosy sotsialisticheskogo stroitel'stva i nauchnye rabotniki," *Nauchnyi Rabotnik* (March 1929), pp. 3-10.
[52] V. A. Zelenko, "Osnovnye linii raboty Leningradskogo biuro sektsii nauchnykh rabotnikov," *Nauchnyi Rabotnik* (January 1929), pp. 63-65.

tific institutes, and the universities.[53] This much is known: In late 1928 the Leningrad Bureau of the Section of Scientific Workers called a meeting to discuss candidates for the Academy, and approved 21 persons. However, many of the scientists present felt the choices had been made on purely political grounds and decided to organize a campaign of protest. They collected over 200 signatures, mostly laboratory workers, graduate students, and assistants, who were willing to denounce publicly the selection procedure. Their campaign was immediately attacked by the Party organizations, who, sidestepping the main point, maintained that the campaign was discredited by the presence among the signatures of names "known to no one as scientific workers."[54] Furthermore, the Party sputtered indignantly, the group was "bourgeois-reactionary" in its attitudes and favored "anti-Darwinists" and "anti-social" scientists for Academy membership. Nevertheless, one of the leaders of the Leningrad Bureau of Scientific Workers observed, the incidents served a good purpose by isolating the alien elements of Soviet society: "With their own hands the rightist groups of our scientists have put themselves in an isolated position, and all because they don't possess enough citizenly decisiveness to make a radical appraisal of their social positions."[55]

Within the special selection commissions the remaining Party candidates were railroaded through. The philosophy commission, split between the six votes of the academicians and the six of the outsiders, finally yielded and nominated Deborin for the Academy, although Vernadskii and several others continued their opposition. In November the Academy announced the names of the 42 candidates for the equal number of places in the Academy. Since all these candidates eventually won membership, dominated much of Soviet intellectual life, and have

[53] "Rezoliutsii III vsesoiuznogo s' 'ezda nauchnykh rabotnikov," *Nauchnyi Rabotnik* (April 1929), pp. 40-57.
[54] Zelenko, "Osnovnye linii," p. 64.
[55] *Ibid.*, pp. 64-65.

been the subject of subsequent debate, their names should be listed:[56]

Mathematics: S. N. Bernshtein, I. M. Vinogradov, N. M. Krylov.

Physics: D. S. Rozhdestvenskii, L. I. Mandel'shtam.

Chemistry: A. N. Bakh, A. E. Chichibabin, A. E. Favorskii, N. Ia. Dem'ianov, N. D. Zelinskii, V. A. Kistiakovskii.

Technology: S. A. Chaplygin, V. F. Mitkevich, I. M. Gubkin, D. K. Zabolotnyi.

Geology: V. A. Obruchev, A. D. Arkhangel'skii, A. A. Borisiak, K. K. Gefroits.

Biology: D. N. Prianishnikov, N. I. Vavilov, M. A. Gulevich, M. A. Menzbir, G. A. Nadson.

History: M. S. Grushevskii, M. N. Pokrovskii, D. B. Riazanov, D. M. Petrushevskii, M. K. Liubavskii, N. M. Lukin.

Socio-economics: N. I. Bukharin, G. M. Krzhizhanovskii, P. P. Maslov, S. I. Solntsev.

Philosophy: A. M. Deborin, N. N. Luzin.

Orientology: V. M. Alekseev, B. A. Vladimirtsev, A. N. Samoilovich.

European Languages and Literature: P. N. Sakulin, V. M. Friche, M. M. Pokrovskii.

Despite the presence of the controversial Party candidates, the Academy had valiantly attempted to choose with integrity; 28 of the 42 candidates were already corresponding members of the Academy, chosen for these posts when the Academy had been under much less restraint. Among the 42 were men of very different political views, and many were even opponents of the Sovietization. The Marxists resented the high number of corresponding members as evidence of the Academy's attempt to preserve its old characteristics. The choice of Petrushevskii and Liubavskii,[57] both "bourgeois" historians in the Party's

---

[56] "Khronika," *Nauchnyi Rabotnik* (November 1928), p. 84.

[57] Liubavskii was quite conservative politically; before the Revolution he favored the tsarist government. During the Kasso affair he benefited from the resignations of the other professors.

view, represented victories for the old guard; the presence of Bukharin, Krzhizhanovskii, Deborin, Friche, Lukin, Dem'ianov, Gubkin, Zabolotnyi, M. N. Pokrovskii, and Riazanov was an accomplishment of the outsiders, although this is not to say that these men were not scholars; the Party had, on the whole, proposed its best qualified members.

After the selection commissions had finished their work several of the "outsiders" from Moscow invited the academicians who had worked with them to dine at the European Hotel. The mixed feelings of Ipat'ev, who must have felt less offended about the results of the selection than many of the other members of the old guard, are apparent from his later comments about the occasion: "I doubt if many of the older academicians really enjoyed themselves. It was an excellent dinner and the wines accompanying it were superb. Yet there was somehow the feeling that we were attending a solemn requiem for the old, free Academy."[58] Academicians Ol'denburg and Marr gave optimistic speeches about the future productive work of the Academy. But no one expressed the feelings of the older academicians, except perhaps Academician Krylov, who obliquely defined the situation by referring to the old and the new academies as two men; the old he called "Sire" (*Gosudar'*), the new, "Sir" (*Milostivyi gosudar'*).[59] No one commented on Krylov's subtle distinction.

The issue of the elections was not yet completely resolved, however. The candidates now were destined to pass through the departmental and General Assembly elections, and there the outsiders held no vote. The Party tried to represent these coming elections as mere formalities, since the vacancies and candidates were equal in number, but at the same time obviously feared that they would not be.

At this point the Party launched a new attack on the Academy; it is probably safe to assume that its purpose was to warn the old guard that their continued resistance would lead to serious consequences. On November 16 the Leningrad re-

[58] Ipatieff, *The Life of a Chemist*, p. 462.
[59] *Ibid.*, p. 463.

gional secretariat (*obkom*) upset a beehive of controversy by
calling for public discussion of the participation of academicians in an allegedly anti-Soviet collection of articles published
by a learned circle of émigrés in Prague.[60] In the fall of 1927 a
number of Soviet scholars had received invitations to partici-
pate in writing a collection of articles on archaeology and
Byzantine art from the *Seminarium Kondakovianum* (Kondakov Seminar) in Prague, founded by a group of scholars which
included George Vernadsky, the well-known historian and son
of the academician.[61] The volume was to be dedicated to the
memory of the Russian scholar, Ia. I. Smirnov, who died in
1918.[62] The *Seminarium Kondakovianum* had already published
two scholarly volumes on the same subject and the third was
to be similarly nonpolitical. Eleven Soviet scholars accepted,
including the three academicians, S. A. Zhebelev, V. V. Bartol'd, and I. Iu. Krachkovskii.[63] Zhebelev (1867-1941) had
been elected to the Academy only in 1927, but he was a
product of St. Petersburg scholarship. His specialty was the
political history of ancient Greece and classical archaeology.
Bartol'd (1869-1930) won membership in the Academy before
the Revolution. A man of great erudition, he published over
400 works during his life, most of them on central Asia and
Islam. Krachkovskii (1883-1951), an academician since 1921,
was an equally prolific scholar who concentrated on Arabic
studies.

The Prague collection also contained a contribution by the

[60] The decision of the Leningrad secretariat is in Arkhiv IMELS, f. 17, op.
21, d. 2678, l. 96, cited by Ermakov, "Bor'ba kommunisticheskoi partii," p. 143.

[61] A. P. Kalitinskii was chairman of the board; other members were N. M.
Beliaev, and N. P. Toll'. Toll', an archaeologist, later came to Yale University,
as did Vernadskii.

[62] I am grateful to Laurens H. Rhinelander, Jr., Columbia University, who has
made a separate unpublished study of the Kondakov Seminar. Another source,
with many references, for a discussion of the position of the historians in the
Academy, and which includes the Prague publication and archive affairs, is Fritz
T. Epstein, "Die marxistische Geschichtswissenschaft in der Sovetunion seit
1927," *Jahrbücher für Kultur und Geschichte der Slaven*, vi (No. 1, 1930), 78-
203 and especially 133-40.

[63] The other Soviet scholars who participated were D. V. Ainalov, A. N.
Kube, S. N. Troinitskii, N. P. Sychev, K. K. Romanov, N. V. Malitskii, A. A.
Spitsyn, E. O. Kostetskaia, A. V. Oreshnikov, and G. N. Chubinashvili. Zhebelev
and others had participated in earlier publications of the Prague institute.

outstanding émigré historian of the ancient world, Academician
M. I. Rostovtsev, whom the communists termed "reactionary"
and "anti-Soviet."[64] The collection was, as it promised to be,
nonpolitical; the scholarly merit of the beautifully bound volume, limited to 450 copies, cannot be contested.[65] The ensuing
scandal concerned the introductory article by Academician
Zhebelev, written in honor of Smirnov. The attack which
Luppol, the Deborinite leader of the Union of Scientific Workers, and several other Party activists mounted against Zhebelev
was based on three amazingly innocent statements in the
article. First, Zhebelev said that when Smirnov died on October
10, 1918 "the hard years" (*likholet'e*) had already begun.[66]
Second, he observed that a better place than the Prague institute for honoring Smirnov could not be found, since Smirnov
was the most brilliant of Kondakov's pupils. Third, Zhebelev
said that Smirnov's research method was strictly historical and
philological, "without any kind of divergences toward the
'science of art' [*iskusstvovedenie*], 'sociology,' or any other
similar modish tendencies."[67]

In an unequalled example of sinister pettiness, Luppol declared that Zhebelev's negative attitude toward Soviet authority
had been unmasked by his calling the period after the Revolution "the hard years," that if Prague was the best place to honor
a Russian scholar he did not deserve honors, and, lastly, that
Zhebelev's remarks on the research method of Smirnov were no

[64] This incident is a painfully graphic example of how Russian scholars, bound
together by academic interests, were torn apart by politics. Father and son
Vernadskii lived on opposite sides of the divide, each faithful to his integrity.
Kondakov created a whole school of Russian historians and archaeologists who
were then split by the cutting edge of the Revolution. The most prominent
representatives were Ia. I. Smirnov, D. V. Ainalov, M. I. Rostovtsev, P. P.
Pokryshkin, and S. A. Zhebelev. Some of these scholars stayed in Soviet Russia,
others emigrated. (See G. V. Vernadskii, *O znachenii nauchnoi deiatel' nosti
N. P. Kondakova*, Prague, 1924.) Academician Rostovskii delivered an attack on
the Soviet historian M. N. Pokrovskii at the Sixth International Congress of
Historians in Oslo in September 1928, and thereby attracted a special enmity from
the Soviet regime. See Shteppa, *Russian Historians and the Soviet State*, p. 43.
[65] *Sbornik statei po arkheologii i vizantinovedeniiu, Seminar imeni* N. P.
Kondakova, II, Prague, 1928. Though labeled Vol. II, this was the third of the
series.
[66] *Ibid.*, p. 1.   [67] *Ibid.*, pp. 1ff.

less than an attack on Academician N. Ia. Marr, whose "theory about the necessity of connecting archaeology to sociology is known to all."[68] What would have remained an academic quarrel in a normal society (had it even arisen) took on an ominous tone when Luppol delivered his attack November 21 at the House of Scholars (*Dom Uchenykh*) in Moscow to the local bureau of the Section of Scientific Workers. The Moscow Bureau responded by voting that Zhebelev should be expelled from the Academy on the basis of article 22 of the new charter, a proposal for which not even the autocratic tsarist regime could give precedent.[69] In the same resolution the Moscow Bureau demanded that the émigré Academicians Struve and Rostovtsev also be deprived of formal membership in the Academy. The Leningrad Bureau and VARNITSO followed with their own demands for Zhebelev's expulsion. The VARNITSO statement added that if the Academy intends to have a directing role in science, it must remove all of its members who "besmirch Soviet construction."[70] Under great pressure from the communist organizations, the presidium of the Academy met on November 22 and demonstrated that, in spite of the Soviet-style organization imposed on the Academy by the 1927 charter, it was still an unsubordinated organization. The presidium voted that in view of Zhebelev's 11-year service for the Soviet Union, denial of his membership would be unjust; the presidium did, however, censure him for participation in the publication. Zhebelev publicly apologized before a meeting, saying that when he used the term "the hard years" he had in mind the physical privations of the Civil War period and nothing more.[71]

[68] I. K. Luppol, "Ob otnoshenii sovetskikh uchenykh k uchenym emigratsii," *Nauchnyi Rabotnik* (December 1928), p. 21.

[69] Neither Gorky's deprivation of honorary membership in the *Razriad iziashchnoi slovesnosti* of the Academy in 1902 on order of Nicholas II, nor the blackballing of Mendeleev in 1880 can be considered a precedent for removing a full member from his chair.

[70] "Khronika," *Nauchnyi Rabotnik* (December 1928), pp. 111-14.

[71] *Ibid.*, p. 113. In his public retraction Zhebelev criticized sharply his friend Rostovtsev, the historian, who was in the West. Later Zhebelev wrote Rostovtsev and asked for his pardon. Rostovtsev was greatly grieved by Zhebelev's humilia-

The Prague publication incident was used as a pretext for marshalling opinion against the Academy.[72] The fact that the Leningrad Party organization opened up the public discussion of the affair supports this supposition. Furthermore, the centers of the Academy's opposition to Party control, the election commissions of philosophy and history, fell under suspicion as a result of the affair. Zhebelev himself was a member of both commissions, Bartol'd was a member of the history commission, and Vernadskii, a member of the philosophy commission, was the father of one of the founders of the Prague institute.

The next step in the election process was the departmental elections, which proceeded deceptively smoothly. One reason for the lack of opposition lay in the fact that the outspoken natural scientists (notably Vernadskii and Pavlov) could not vote on the candidacy of those to whom they were most hostile; Deborin and his friends were attempting to enter the humanities department. Nevertheless, Pavlov's temper flared in the Physics-Mathematical elections held on December 5. He opposed the election of D. K. Zabolotnyi, known chiefly for his work fighting the plagues in southern Russia before 1914. The renowned physiologist said he found nothing meritorious in Zabolotnyi's works, and then exploded:

> If such men are recruited into the Academy, then it will be no longer a scientific institution, but God only knows what! Individuals who know nothing about science and do not even know why the Academy exists are endeavoring to change it. Just recently there arrived from Moscow a Georgian whose name I do not recall, I remember only that he had red hair,

tion. Interview, George Vernadsky, East Haven, Conn., July 21, 1964. Zhebelev was later honored in the USSR for administering all the Leningrad activities of the Academy during the siege of Leningrad in World War II.

[72] These were years in which the publication of articles and books by Soviet authors in foreign presses became suspect in the Party's eyes, although in earlier years the practice was widespread. In 1929 the publication in Berlin of Pil'niak's novel, *Red Wood* (*Krasnoe Derevo*), caused a scandal resulting in the author's expulsion from his post as chairman of the all-Russian Union of Writers. Academician Efremov of the Ukrainian Academy of Sciences was also attacked for his publication in the émigré press. See *Nauchnyi Rabotnik* (February 1929), pp. 10-14.

and tried to tell me that he was very much "interested" in the Academy.[73]

Again Ipat'ev served as conciliator, as he himself described:

When I saw that Pavlov's strenuous objections to Zabolotnyi's candidacy would have us deadlocked, I asked permission to speak. I said that since the committee had already publicly announced Dr. Zabolotnyi's candidacy it would be unwise to blackball him in the section now. I reproached Pavlov for not having made known his objections to the committee, whose meetings he had not attended, instead of trying to undo our work at so late a date. Had he spoken earlier, Zabolotnyi could have been eliminated as smoothly as Professor Williams. Thus, for the common good, Dr. Zabolotnyi's election went through.[74]

The Physics-Mathematics department thus elected all of the previously selected candidates, and a week later, on December 12, the humanities department similarly performed its rubber

[73] Ipatieff, *Life of a Chemist*, p. 463. Pavlov chose a formidable target. The red-haired individual was none other than Avel Enukidze, chairman of the TsIK and a member of the Central Committee of the Party. Endearing as Pavlov's olympian disdain of politics may be, it illustrates the difficulty laboratory-oriented scientists had in resisting the Communist Party assault. As Ipat'ev pointed out, Pavlov had not attempted to block Zabolotnyi's election at a time when there had been a better chance of success.

[74] *Ibid.* For the reference to Williams, see pp. 98-99. Boris Nicolaevsky reported that Pavlov also denounced Bukharin during the election process, describing him as "a person who is up to his knees in blood." The tentative date (1926-27) given by Nicolaevsky for this charge is surely a year or two too early. Bukharin is said to have told Nicolaevsky that when he heard about Pavlov's attack he "decided to have it out with him." During Bukharin's visit with Pavlov in the latter's apartment, which was initially embarrassing, Bukharin is supposed to have won the friendship of the physiologist. As Nicolaevsky quoted Bukharin, "We went into the dining room and, as we entered, I noticed that on the walls were cases of butterflies. Pavlov was a collector of butterflies, as was I. I had already sat down at the table when, directly across from me, over the door, I saw a case with an exceedingly rare type of butterfly. And I exclaimed to Pavlov, 'What? You have *this?*' 'So, . . .' Pavlov replied, 'he even knows this.' I inquired where it had been caught, and so on, and he became convinced that I did indeed know it. Thus began our friendship." In later years, Pavlov and Gorky are supposed to have worked with Bukharin in attempting to unite the intelligentsia as a force which would influence Soviet policies, perhaps even as a second political party. See Boris I. Nicolaevsky, *Power and the Soviet Elite*, ed. Janet D. Zagoria, 1965, pp. 14-16, 22.

stamp duty, just as the Party hoped. Many of the members of the department had been intimidated by the threats of re-moving any academicians who "besmirch Soviet construction," knowing that they were much more expendable in the eyes of the government than someone such as Vernadskii. They could not reveal their opposition to the candidates until their votes were indistinguishably mixed with those of the natural scien-tists at the final secret ballot in the General Assembly. Thus the most disliked candidates—Deborin, Lukin, Friche—passed the departmental elections by votes of 16-1, 15-2, and 16-1, respectively.[75]

However, between the departmental elections and the final election in the General Assembly the academicians became somewhat more unified. Pavlov, who evidently had awakened late to the situation in the Academy, now became a leader of the opposition. Ipat'ev, who had demonstrated his ability to prevent open conflict between the Party and the Academy, left on a research trip to Germany and was not present at the elections. Vernadskii continued to advance his memorandum in opposition to Party control of the Academy.

The finale

When the academicians assembled in the General Assembly on January 12, 1929 to cast white or black balls for each candi-date, for the first time since the election campaign began the Academy seemed to have returned to its old traditions. The vote was secret, the Soviet press was momentarily silent, and the outsiders were truly outside. There is no evidence that the academicians had decided as a group which candidates to support and which to oppose; the vote tallies were ragged. Even at this point the academicians disagreed among them-selves on the best action to take. Many who opposed the communist candidates voted for them anyway, knowing that opposition was hopeless and dangerous. Only 30 of 43 acade-

[75] "Khronika," *Nauchnyi Rabotnik* (March 1929), p. 82.

micians were present; some had simply refused to attend. In fact, if there had been two more absentees, and they along with the others had simply stayed in Leningrad away from the meeting, the quorum requirements would not have been met and the elections could not have been held.

The General Assembly blackballed three of the Party candidates, causing a sensation. The most controversial nominee, the philosopher Deborin, who was director of the Institute of Scientific Philosophy, a member of the presidium of the Communist Academy, and assistant director of the Marx–Engels Institute, was voted down by 18 positive and 12 negative votes (18/12), having failed to obtain the necessary two-thirds approval. The art critic, V. M. Friche, chairman of the Russian Association of Scientific-Research Institutes of the Social Sciences (RANION),[76] and director of the Institute of Language and Literature, failed by a tally of 16/14.[77] The historian, N. M. Lukin (Antonov), author of a Marxist history of the Paris Commune and the brother-in-law of Bukharin (who was elected), also failed to gain an academic chair by a vote of 16/14. The geologist and petroleum engineer, I. M. Gubkin, director of the Moscow Mining Academy, was elected by the lowest possible vote, 20/10. Equally irritating to the Marxists, the allegedly rightist historian Petrushevskii (his political sentiments were actually those of the prerevolutionary Kadet party, a group favoring liberal democracy), opposed by the Party

---

[76] RANION included a dozen or more institutes in the social sciences in which Marxist influence varied. See Joravsky, *Soviet Marxism and Natural Science*, pp. 68-69.

[77] One of the supreme ironies of the Academy's history is that two of the three blackballed candidates were later criticized for deviations, and, therefore, Stalinist historians had to bend double to explain that although Deborin and Friche were defeated by the Academy, it was not for the correct reasons. Thus Ermakov wrote in 1956:

Their failure to be elected is not explained by the fact that the academicians saw anti-Leninist mistakes in the works of Deborin, or a vulgarization of the study of literature by Friche. Their failure to be elected is explained chiefly by that incorrect view which was expounded by Academician Vernadskii in his "memorandum."

Ermakov, "Bor'ba kommunisticheskoi partii," p. 145.

press, was swept into membership by a 29/1 vote.[78] In sum, 39 of 42 candidates were elected to membership.

The elections provoked a paroxysm of rage from the Party organizations. Complaints and threats poured in from RA-NION, the Institute of Red Professors, Moscow State University, the Association of Workers of Science and Technology for the Assistance of Socialist Construction (VARNITSO), the Central Aero-Hydrodynamic Institute, the Society of Militant Dialectical-Materialists, and the various bureaus of the Section of Scientific Workers. RANION said the elections had demonstrated that even yet there were "nestled deeply" in the Academy "reactionary tendencies of the prerevolutionary period, when faithful to the orders of the tsarist government and motivated by its own caste-like secludedness, the Academy did not permit revolutionary thinkers such as Timiriazev, Sechenov, and others to enter into it. . . ."[79] Sverdlov University called for the replacement of the Academy as the center of Soviet science,[80] and Moscow State University suggested that the replacement be accomplished by breaking the Academy into separate institutes, none of them more important, evidently, than the already existing non-Academic institutes.[81] The Moscow Bureau of the Section of Scientific Workers also believed that the moment had arrived for the replacement of the outmoded Academy by institutes of a new type: "The reorganization of the Academy must be conducted along the lines of an association of scientific-research institutes of the modern Western-European mode."[82] The Institute of Red Professors suggested a purge: "A cleansing of the Academy of all people of no scientific value is necessary. Those academicians who do not agree with the political statements of the reactionaries must openly and directly disassociate themselves from them and ask if it is possible to work with them anymore."[83]

[78] The voting statistics are from "Khronika," *Nauchnyi Rabotnik* (February 1929), p. 89, and (March 1929), p. 82; and Ermakov, "Bor'ba kommunist-icheskoi partii," p. 145.
[79] "Khronika," *Nauchnyi Rabotnik* (March 1929), p. 86.
[80] *Ibid.*, pp. 87-88.
[81] *Ibid.*   [82] *Ibid.*   [83] *Ibid.*, p. 87.

Under this intense pressure, the presidium of the Academy buckled. The leaders realized that continued resistance would destroy the Academy; a reelection of the blackballed candidates seemed the only solution. Academician Ipat'ev gloomily remarked,

> The veteran academicians knew that the decision would have a vital bearing on the Academy's future; its present members would probably end their days as pensioned servants and a new Academy would be created. Struggle with the Soviet authorities was useless; with might making right the will of the rulers was not to be resisted.[84]

Apparently agreeing with this viewpoint, the presidium submitted a request to the Council of Peoples Commissars to grant the Academy an exception from its charter, so that it might have a second vote on the rejected candidates.[85] The exception was needed since articles 16-18 of the charter required each election to be preceded by discussion in the press, meetings of the special commissions, and the departmental elections.

This request could not be sent to the Council of Peoples Commissars without the approval of the General Assembly. On January 17, 1929 an extraordinary session was called to discuss the presidium's resolution and to take up the problem of the blackballed three. The session became the scene of a very heated debate; the tradition of one academician not attacking another was discarded.[86] Academician Pavlov so violently denounced any procedure which would violate the charter that some observers said that he lost control over his emotions.[87] President Karpinskii favored reelection, but showing the strain that led him to request retirement later in the

---

[84] Ipatieff, *Life of a Chemist*, p. 465.

[85] TsGAOR, f. 374, op. 1, d. 5359, ls. 163, 164, cited in Ermakov, "Bor'ba kommunisticheskoi partii," p. 146, and "Khronika," *Nauchnyi Rabotnik* (February 1929), pp. 92-93.

[86] TsGAOR, f. 3316, op. 23, d. 763, l. 119, cited in Ermakov, "Bor'ba kommunisticheskoi partii," p. 147, and "Khronika," *Nauchnyi Rabotnik* (February 1929), pp. 92-93.

[87] TsGAOR, f. 3316, op. 23, d. 763, l. 119, cited in Ermakov, "Bor'ba kommunisticheskoi partii," p. 147.

year, he remarked that his assignment was "worse than back-breaking penal labor."[88] Newly elected Academician Petru-shevskii, a historian of medieval England and a longtime associate of Paul Vinogradov, affirmed the Party's fears by immediately joining the old guard and emphatically opposing the reelections. Another new academician, A. D. Arkhangel'skii, a geology professor at Moscow University, believed that the problem would best be solved by amending the charter to permit the reelection. When the question of the reelection was put to a vote, in which a majority would carry, the Academy approved sending the presidium's request on to the Council of Peoples Commissars by a vote of 28-9, with four abstaining.[89] The hard core of resistance remained, but with the Academy growing in size it was losing its effectiveness.

The Council of Peoples Commissars approved the Academy's "request" on February 5, and the General Assembly was called to meet on February 13 in order to revote on the three troublesome candidates. The end of the battle was signalled when 15 academicians announced that they would plead diplomatic illness, according to academic tradition. Again, if two more academicians had joined the protesters the elections could not have been held because of quorum requirements.[90] This event probably would have led to expulsion of the schismatics so that the election could proceed. Nevertheless, the meeting was the largest such assemblage ever held in the Academy; 54 academicians attended, including the newly elected communists, Bukharin, Krzhizhanovskii, Riazanov, Pokrovskii, and Gubkin. The three blackballed candidates were firmly, but not proudly, elected to office by the following votes: Deborin, 52/2; Lukin 52/1, and one withheld; Friche, 51/2, and one withheld.[91]

The election struggle was over. The date of capitulation, February 13, 1929, is the best date to designate the turning point in the history of the Sovietization of the Academy,

---

[88] *Ibid.*, l. 117.   [89] *Ibid.*
[90] "Khronika," *Nauchnyi Rabotnik* (March 1929), p. 83, gives the attendance.
[91] *Ibid.*

although much opposition remained. Appropriately enough, 1929 was the year of the "great break," or *perelom*, which Stalin called for on "all fronts of socialist construction."[92] The line of resistance on the scientific front had yielded and the gains were soon consolidated. The next elections occurred in January, 1930; during the next two years 30 more academicians were elected.[93] Many of their names were already famous in Soviet history, or soon would be—A. V. Lunacharskii, former commissar of education; V. P. Volgin, the Marxist historian who almost immediately became permanent secretary of the Academy; L. V. Pisarzhevskii, a founder of electrochemistry in Russia; V. P. Vil'iams (Williams), the soil scientist, who fulfilled Ipat'ev's prediction concerning his admittance; S. G. Strumilin, dean of Soviet economists; I. G. Aleksandrov, designer of the Dnieper hydroelectric power plant; S. V. Lebedev, inventor of Soviet synthetic rubber; N. N. Semenov, future Nobel prize-winning chemist;[94] S. I. Vavilov, future president of the Academy.

The encroachment of the Party and its subservient organizations left a legacy of resentment among many of the academicians. On the same day as the reelections Academician Ol'denburg gave his report of the activity of the Academy for 1928, in which he commented:

At the present moment, the Academy is the object of a great

[92] See Joravsky, *Soviet Marxism and Natural Science*, p. 233. He discusses the *perelom* in Chapter 16, "The Great Break for Natural Scientists." Joravsky cites the quote from Stalin's article marking the twelfth anniversary of the Bolshevik Revolution, "God velikogo pereloma," *Pravda*, November 7, 1929, p. 2.

[93] 1930: A. V. Lunacharskii, V. P. Volgin, L. V. Pisarzhevskii
    1931: V. P. Vil'iams (Williams), S. A. Zernov, B. A. Keller, N. S. Derzhavin, A. S. Orlov, S. G. Strumilin
    1932: A. A. Baikov, I. G. Aleksandrov, I. P. Bardin, E. V. Britske, B. E. Vedeneev, A. V. Vinter (Winter), G. O. Graftio, M. A. Pavlov, S. V. Lebedev, N. N. Pavlovskii, I. V. Grebenshchikov, A. A. Chernyshev, K. I. Shenfer, S. I. Vavilov, N. N. Semenov, A. N. Frumkin, A. A. Bogomolets, V. V. Adoratskii, V. V. Osinskii, M. A. Savel'ev, A. I. Tiumenev, I. I. Meshchaninov, A. A. Rikhter

[94] Many years later Academician Semenov promoted the greatest reform of the Academy since that which occurred in 1927-32; his proposals in several important respects restored the form of administration that existed before the Academy's Sovietization. N. Semenov, "Nauka segodnia i zavtra," *Izvestiia*, August 9, 1959.

deal of attention, and, unfortunately, not often benevolent attention. We recognize that in social criticism there is much that is correct, but we have complete justification for saying that there is also a great deal that is untrue, based on inadequate knowledge of our work.[95]

*

From late 1926 to early 1929 the crucial issue in the controversy surrounding the Academy of Sciences was the admission to membership of communists or candidates backed by the Communist Party. The campaign to achieve this goal was directed by the leaders of the Leningrad Party organization. Resistance was widespread in the Academy, and was most visibly led by V. I. Vernadskii and I. P. Pavlov, both scientists of great international reputations. Vernadskii's research was furthermore of signal importance to the Soviet Union's industrialization program; Pavlov's was better known abroad than that of any other Soviet scientist.

Academician Vernadskii's "Memorandum" and his urgings of systematic resistance to Party coercion were the single greatest obstacles to the entrance of the communist members. In the 11 commissions which chose the 42 candidates the Party managed to overcome the obstacles through mere pressure, since the deliberations of the commissions were public; not all the academicians were willing to disclose their hostility toward the Marxist candidates. In the elections scheduled for the General Assembly, however, the balloting was secret and the Party obviously worried about the outcome.

The purpose of the Kondakov Seminar affair was to frighten the academicians into submission. Seizing on a few innocent phrases in a publication with no political goal, the Party organizations threatened the expulsion of Academician Zhebelev and simultaneously cast suspicion on Academicians Vernadskii, Bartol'd, and Krachkovskii. The fact that Vernadskii's only connection with the Prague publication was through his son

[95] *Otchet o deiatel'nosti akademii nauk SSSR za 1928 g.*, Leningrad, 1929, p. xix.

mattered little to the Party stalwarts. The important thing, to them, was to demonstrate to the academicians that their positions were no longer inviolable. Henceforth the Party would attempt to hold the Academy to the political docility already imposed on the rest of Soviet society.

The Party's subjugation of the Academy through threats rather than direct action achieved a considerable victory in obtaining the election of all but three of the Party candidates. That election, though in a certain sense a rebuff to the Party, was even more a signal of eventual triumph. For while the Party could not have retained the old Academy had all Party candidates been rejected—and consequently would have been forced to the extremely difficult alternative of replacing it— the denial of only three was an act which could be undone. While the entire Academy might well have been wrecked by the wholesale imposition of communists by simple fiat, few academicians were willing to abandon their scientific careers as a result of a squabble over three candidates. To compare the situation in 1929 to that in 1905, when almost the entire Academy did threaten resignation in protest to the actions of the tsarist government, is not justified, since all the academicians in 1905 could have found rewarding careers outside the Academy but still in their native land. In 1929 there was no such alternative. Emigration was perhaps barely possible, but a life amounting to house arrest, or even actual imprisonment, was much more likely. The dilemma of the academicians in 1929 was an extremely harsh one: a continuation of their careers and the pursuance of their research interests might balance on their casting of votes. In this light the ultimate election of all the Party candidates is not surprising.

In retrospect it is clear that the academicians did not conduct a well-coordinated resistance to the Party's effort to gain control of the Academy. Absorbed in their research, many of them did not attend the meetings of the early selection committees, and then only slowly awoke to the Party's subjugation of the Academy. Pavlov tried to stop Zabolotnyi's election after missing several meetings where his voice would have been more influential. Other academicians left on expeditions and foreign trips and missed the elections entirely, even though they could have cancelled the elections on the basis of quorum requirements if they had been present but refused to vote. Academicians Vernadskii and Pavlov were unaware of the political realities of the Soviet Union, did not even know who the governmental leaders were, but courageously, and perhaps more nobly, resisted nonetheless. But why pinpoint the mistaken tactics? The sole achievement which a more coordinated resistance would have attained would have been the replacement of the Academy by other organizations. In the end, the academicians, the Soviet Union, and science would have been the losers.

The tactics of the Party at first glance appear to be shrewdly chosen. Under the old charter the academicians could have stopped the inflow of communist members. Therefore, the first step of the reform campaign was a change of the charter, which contained antiquated sections which no one could defend, and a simultaneous change of the election procedures.

But in the absence of full access to the Party archives, one should not conclude that the Party's campaign against the Academy was as smooth or as well coordinated as may appear. Certainly there were hitches in the reform program; the rejection of the three candidates by close votes was probably not foreseen by the Party. And the Party itself must have contained more divisions of attitudes about the Academy than one could discern either from the press of that time or from accounts of later Soviet historians, who usually portray the Party as a decisive, united force. We do know that the Party contained very different attitudes toward science and scientific institutions in the mid-twenties and those differences must have been latently present several years later. Indeed, signs of anxiety about the lasting effects of the Party's campaign in science and indecision about future actions toward the Academy can be discerned even at the height of the renovation of the Academy.

Several communist scholars warned their colleagues not to lose all faith in the Academy, not "to give it up as a bad job." On the other hand, other communist scholars (Riazanov, for example, if we are to credit the reports given by later writers) and many less enlightened militants favored the total replacement of the Academy by the Communist Academy or other institutions. Thus a division between Party moderates and radicals in policy toward the Academy probably existed throughout the reform period. The major difference seems to have been the question of the retention of existing academicians, most of whom were educated before the Revolution, as the leading figures in the natural sciences. The answer to that issue, despite the violence of the subordination of the Academy, was in favor of the moderates. The very coercion which the Party exercised in gaining the reelection of its candidates was an indication that the Academy was to be retained.

The elections of Marxists to membership in the Academy was far from the last act of the drama, however. The goal of the Party was not merely the capitulation of the Academy but its complete seizure and renovation. Science in the Soviet Union was to be established on a different basis; the organizational forms, the research emphases, and the direction of science were to be radically changed. The resistance of the old academicians to these changes might be even greater than to the election of Communist Party members to Academy chairs, for these projected alterations would affect the aspects of the academicians' lives most dear to them—their scientific research. The next few months in the life of the Academy indicated that the Party did not intend to approach these crucial issues until a further softening of resistance in the Academy had been achieved.

CHAPTER IV

THE SEIZURE OF THE ACADEMIC STRUCTURE

Some people took advantage of the fact that the working class of the Soviet Union looks upon science and scientific workers with such great love . . . and converted the Academy into a sanctuary for counter-revolutionary work against Soviet power. / Iu. Figatner, 1930 Chairman, Purge Commission[1]

Violations of socialist legality toward scientific workers occurred [during the Stalin period]: administrative pressure and the restriction of freedom of scholarly criticism, illegal repressions of certain scientists, violations of labor rights, and so forth. / G. I. Fed'kin, 1958 Soviet Jurist[2]

In the long struggle leading to the elections at the end of 1928 and the reelections in February 1929, the academicians had never been threatened with arrest or physical violence. The threat of expulsion alone directed against Academician Zhebelev was extremely traumatic to the academicians and other workers in the Academy, among whom the tradition bestowing unique status upon a full member of the Academy of Sciences retained much of its potency. Yet outside the walls of the Academy the use of the purge against non-Party organizations was already a practice of the government. A typical Soviet procedure in taking control of other prerevolutionary institutions

[1] Iu. Figatner, "Proverka apparata akademii nauk," *VARNITSO* (February 1930), p. 75.
[2] Fed'kin, *Pravovye voprosy organizatsii nauchnoi raboty v SSSR*, p. 25.

was to impose communist members and simultaneously expel or arrest older members. With the first step already undertaken in the Academy, the Party did not wait long to initiate the second.[3] In 1929 the members of VARNITSO were told to reconsider the value of all faculty members of Soviet educational institutions on the basis of three points: (1) the scientific value of the candidate, (2) his pedagogical talents, (3) his socio-ideological "physiognomy."[4]

The purge

The Leningrad Party regional committee (*obkom*) ordered a purgative trial for the Academy in July 1929, when it established a special governmental commission, headed by Iu. Figatner, a veteran of many "inspections" (*proverki*) in his position in the Commissariat of Workers' and Peasants' Inspection (RKI).[5] Appointed to assist Figatner as members of the commission were Academicians Komarov, Fersman, and Ol'denburg; Professors Nikiforov and Kiparisov from the Section of Scientific Workers of the Academy; Professor Vorob'ev from the executive committee (*ispolkom*) of the Leningrad city soviet; three workers from factories in Leningrad, and representatives of the Leningrad section of the Workers' and Peasants' Inspection.[6] The commission proceeded to check the general performance of the Academy. In July and August the

[3] Academician Ipat'ev had a high opinion of Lenin's and Dzherzhinskii's judgment in technical affairs, and he believed that, had these two lived, the old intelligentsia could have retained their positions. He noted that Dzherzhinskii praised engineers like Khrennikov, Berezkin, and Svitsyn, but that immediately after his death these men were arrested. He pointed out that the first famous trial, the "wreckers of the Don Basin," did not occur until July 1927, a year after Dzherzhinskii's death. (These views are contained in V. N. Ipat'ev, *Personal Papers*, Vol. III, Ipat'ev High Pressure Laboratory, Northwestern University.) Ipat'ev obviously placed too much emphasis on Dzherzhinskii's and Lenin's passing and not enough on Stalin's machinations. As Joravsky, *Soviet Marxism and Natural Science*, p. 235, comments, by late 1929 the earlier shouts against the bourgeoisie were "joined by a more poorly defined threat, by obscure, unexplained acts of terror." The new terror bore Stalin's trademark.

[4] *VARNITSO* (July 15, 1929), p. 6.

[5] Arkhiv IMELS, f. 17, op. 21, d. 2681, l. 280; d. 2682, l. 3; cited by Ermakov, "Bor'ba kommunisticheskoi partii," pp. 157-58.

[6] *VARNITSO* (February 1930), p. 73; also TsGAOR, f. 374, op. 1, d. 535, l. 40; cited by Ermakov, "Bor'ba kommunisticheskoi partii," pp. 157-58.

inspectors called the employees of the Academy to more than 10 meetings in which they submitted each other to "socialist criticism."[7]

Academician Ol'denburg, a member of the inspection commission, could not tolerate the ignoble spectacle in which he was participating. An ambitious man, he became increasingly pathetic as he tried, first, to accommodate himself to the Sovietization of the Academy, and then failed to follow through because of his conscience. Ol'denburg since the early 1920s had relied on the theory that cooperation with the Soviet government and preservation of the traditions of the Academy were simultaneously possible. He was unsuccessful in his attempt to balance these forces, and he incurred the criticisms of both sides in the struggle over the independence of the Academy. During the inspection Ol'denburg submitted a letter of complaint to Academician Komarov in which he said it was impossible to publish an article "objectively describing the situation in the Academy . . . the press now is devoting itself not to a correct description of the situation, but is interested only in settling personal accounts and in voicing criticisms which cannot be substantiated."[8] Ol'denburg, supposedly one of the inspectors, was already himself falling under suspicion. Within a month he would be removed from his position as permanent secretary "for obstructing the reconstruction of the Academy of Sciences,"[9] but not before making a desperate final attempt to rationalize the purge.

Figatner delivered to his superiors an indignant report on the inspection. Never before in his long experience of checking Soviet institutions, he said, had he found such "an asylum for alien elements hostile to Soviet power . . ."; most of these "aliens," he continued, "had nothing to do with science."[10] The

---

[7] *Ibid.*, pp. 153-54.
[8] Arkhiv AN SSSR, f. 277, op. 2, d. 491, l. 6, cited by Ermakov, "Bor'ba kommunisticheskoi partii," p. 156.
[9] *Ibid.*, p. 169.
[10] See Figatner's own description of the Academy in Figatner, "Proverka apparata," *VARNITSO* (February 1930), p. 73. Also see "Chistka apparata akademii nauk: pochemu nuzhna byla chistka," *Izvestiia*, August 30, 1929, p. 4.

Academy was filled with "former landowners, senators, gentlemen of the court, ministers of religion, princely scions."[11] Moreover, he charged that the institutions of the Academy were characterized by lack of planning, by genuine chaos. The work of the Asiatic Museum (headed by Academician Ol'denburg) and the research of the Commission for the Study of Natural Productive Forces (KEPS, headed by Academician Vernadskii) were particularly purposeless, he continued.[12] The atmosphere in Pushkin House (*Pushkinskii Dom*, directed by Academician S. F. Platonov) and the Tolstoi Museum (also under Platonov) was "pre-revolutionary." The Academy was so backward in its studies, Figatner remarked, that the scientists in the Zoological Museum (directed by Academician A. A. Bialynitskii-Birulia) were still combating Darwinism. Figatner's assistant from the Section of Scientific Workers, Professor Nikiforov, enjoyed exposing what he considered the ludicrous activities of several Academic organizations.[13] He commented that the importance of the research of Pushkin House could be easily evaluated by noting its pride over determining that the aunt of Fedor Tiutchev, the aristocratic poet of the 19th century, had previously been called Maria Pavlovna, but that actually her name was Maria Petrovna.[14] Equally absurd in a socialist and atheistic state, thought Nikiforov, was the very existence in the Academy

[11] TsGAOR, f. 374, op. 1, d. 535, ls. 41-42; cited by Ermakov, "Bor'ba kommunisticheskoi partii," p. 154.

[12] Lunacharskii four years earlier praised the work of the Asiatic Museum, especially its work in the Sanskrit, Turkish, and Georgian languages, as providing the necessary basis for Soviet policies toward minority linguistic groups. See A. V. Lunacharskii, "K 200-letiiu," pp. 99-112.

[13] Nikiforov's comments are contained in "Iz otcheta lokal'nogo biuro SNR akademii nauk," *Za sotsialisticheskuiu rekonstruktsiiu Akademii Nauk SSSR* (No. 1, 1930), p. 3.

[14] Pushkin House did much more than worry about Tiutchev's relatives. In 1929 its scholars presented 24 papers, published volumes 53, 54, and 55 of their current series, made six expeditions for the collection of literary materials, and arranged three exhibits in their exhibition halls. Their work concerned not only Pushkin and Tiutchev, but Korolenko, Griboedov, Lomonosov, Chekhov, and others. Devoted to honoring previous literary figures, Pushkin House's work lacked originality, but remains very significant in literary history. See *Otchet o deiatel'nosti Rossiiskoi akademii nauk za 1929*, I, Leningrad, p. 227. For a more complete account of Pushkin House's history and activities, see *Pushkinskii dom, AN SSSR, 1725-1925*, Leningrad, 1925.

of a "Commission for the Scholarly Publication of the Slavic Bible" (directed by Academician A. I. Sobolevskii). The Institute of Buddhist Culture (Academician F. I. Shcherbatskoi) was engaged in the study of the "idealistic conceptions of Buddhism," accused Nikiforov, and had invited representatives of the Buddhist priesthood to help with this work.[15]

When Figatner and his inquisitorial assistants visited the library of the Academy, one of the largest libraries in the Soviet Union, they asked the scientific secretary of the library, F. A. Martinson, to name some of the Marxist classical works. No doubt spared any such confrontation since grammar school, the flustered Martinson was able to name only *Das Kapital*; according to Figatner, he could not give the titles of any works by Engels, Lenin, or Plekhanov. Martinson's name, therefore, was placed on the list of suspects. His ignorance, declared Figatner, could be explained by his studies at orthodox seminaries in Riga and St. Petersburg, and by his employment before the Revolution at the Tsarskoe Selo *realschule* under the shadow of the throne.[16]

Martinson was only one of many workers in the Academy whom Figatner damned for past activities or associations. He asserted that many people with questionable backgrounds had sought employment in the Academy after the Revolution because, as one of them answered, "It gave shelter."[17] Figatner allowed no room for the possibility that these people might have become loyal Soviet citizens; the Academy was a center "for counter-revolutionary work against Soviet power."[18] Among the refugees whom the fanatical Figatner hunted down were "Citizeness" Durnovo, daughter of the tsarist Minister of Internal Affairs and chief of the secret police; Citizen Rostovtsev, former personal secretary to Tsarina Alexandra Fedorovna, wife

[15] The Buddhist Institute had been founded only the year before. The various sections of the Institute were devoted to the study of Tibet, India, Mongolia, China, and Japan. In the first year the Institute began studies of the cultures of these countries and projected an encyclopedia of Buddhism.

[16] Figatner, "Proverka apparata."

[17] *Ibid.*, pp. 74-75.

[18] *Ibid.*

of Nicholas II; Citizen Shinkevich, assistant minister of the Ministry of Internal Affairs under Dmitri Tolstoi; Citizen Gergens, allegedly the author of reactionary political literature before the Revolution; Citizen Shidlovskii, former tsarist governor of Arkhangel'sk and prison inspector of Ekaterinoslav, and many others.[19]

Even the impassive historian of these events must ask himself if such charges should be dignified by repetition. These accusations based on activity during the tsarist regime and on kinship could not by any stretch of the imagination have justified Figatner's conclusions.

Acting on the basis of these conclusions, the governmental security organs proceeded with the purge, starting in September 1929. According to Academician Fersman's official report, given in December, 128 workers were taken into custody and another 520 were fired.[20] In the administrative office of the Academy, 11 of 99 workers were seized; in the office of the secretariat, four of 15 employees; in the library, 36 of 149;[21] in Pushkin House, four of 29. The arrested employees included the professor of Russian history, S. V. Rozhdestvenskii, the Pushkin scholar, I. V. Izmailov, and B. N. Molas, Ol'denburg's

---

[19] *Ibid.*

[20] "Khronika," *Nauchnyi Rabotnik* (January 1930), pp. 96-97. See also Belomortsev, "Bol'shevizatsiia akademii nauk." On the subject of the purge Ermakov, "Bor'ba kommunisticheskoi partii," p. 154, cites TsGAOR, f. 374, op. 1, d. 535, ls. 41-42. There is some variation in the statistics of the purge, perhaps because it was a continuing process; for other figures, which are not necessarily contradictory, see "Chistka apparata akademii nauk," *Izvestiia*, September 4, 1929, p. 3.

[21] The large proportion in the library was a result of the archive affair, which had already occurred. (See p. 126.) Fersman's report is not completely clear. In Russian, he said "Vsego v Akademii sniato s raboty 128 chelovek i 520 rabotnikov Akademii postanovleno ne schitat' v shtate. Po upravleniiu delami Akademii iz 99 chelovek sniato 11, po sekretariatu iz 15—4. Bol'she vsego sniato sotrudnikov v biblioteke Akademii nauk—iz 149 uvoleno 36, v Pushkinskom dome iz 29 uvoleno 4." "Khronika," *Nauchnyi Rabotnik* (January 1930), p. 96.

[22] Belomortsev said that Rozhdestvenskii and Molas died in prison camps. He added that of 106 men arrested with him from the Academy, five were executed, 15 died in labor camps, and eight were rehabilitated. Many of those who served their prison terms were not permitted to return to their native cities. Belomortsev, "Bol'shevizatsiia akademii nauk," p. 11, and Belomortsev, "Zhertvy 'dela' akademii nauk SSSR," *Volia*, Munich (No. 10, 1952), pp. 24-

assistant.[22] The purge at first did not affect the academicians directly. After Figatner reported on his commission's work to the Academy, Ol'denburg addressed his fellow members with a piteous and tortured statement of approbation:

Today the first step has been taken on a very difficult road, and the commission itself and all of you realize very well how difficult, how laborious and complicated its work has been. . . . The commission was absolutely necessary so that we could work in the proper way. . . . Every person is aware of that seriousness and attentiveness with which the commission fulfilled its obligations. . . . I believe that it is necessary that each person understand and feel this because, of course, it will be difficult for many people after the work of the commission, just as it was difficult for others before. . . . Nothing genuine and great can be created without certain sacrifices. . . .

The members of the commission, with maximum attention and impartial will, genuinely aided the Academy of Sciences, and in this case we can only be appreciative of that profound attention which all the members of the commission displayed. I think that all the academicians present will join me in these words.[23]

But the purge had not yet run its course. It received additional impetus when, during the course of the inspection, Figatner announced the discovery of "illegal archives" in the Academy library. Some of the workers in the library, Pushkin House, and the Archaeographical Commission reportedly informed Figatner's inspection team about the presence of important historical documents in the Academy, contrary to Soviet law requiring that all such materials be reported to the

28. Molas's name is variously cited as Molas, Mollas, Molis, and Malas; compare Belomortsev, "Bol'shevizatsiia akademii nauk," with Ipat'ev, *Zhizn' odnogo khimika: vospominaniia*, 2 vols., New York, ii, 451. Molas is the form given in the Academy's annual reports.

[23] S. Voronov, "Iz proshlogo i nastoiashchego akademii nauk," *Novyi Mir* (May 1930), pp. 146-47.

government.[24] These archives, under the care of Platonov, contained the following materials, according to the reports of the inspectors: the original abdication of Nicholas II, and Grand Prince Michael's refusal to assume power; the archives of the central committees of the Social Revolutionaries, the Mensheviks, the Kadets, and the Octobrists; the diaries of Konstantin Romanov (66 volumes); the Valuev and Dzhunkovskii archives; a small archive of the son of Konstantin Romanov, Oleg, consisting mostly of his verses; and a collection of correspondence between several princely families.[25] Some of these valuable materials, said Figatner, were smuggled abroad before the commission learned of them.[26]

The affair of the illegal archives was utilized, as were all misdemeanors, real or imagined, of the Academy, to stir up the "indignation" of Soviet society against the Academy, the "island of treason."[27] The Soviet press brushed aside the assertions of several academicians, led by the forcible Vernadskii, that the documents were in the Academy by accident, and had probably been forgotten by the curator, Platonov.[28]

VARNITSO sounded the now customary call for a complete renovation of the Academy. The Voronezh local adopted a resolution aimed at specific academicians, demanding the "im-

---

[24] "Khronika," *Nauchnyi Rabotnik* (December 1929), p. 88.

[25] Figatner, "Proverka apparata."

[26] *Ibid.*

[27] Concealing documents in the Academy library was neither an innovation nor necessarily an expression of tsarist sentiment. Before the Revolution, Lenin sent illegal Bolshevik documents from abroad to workers in the Academy library, who concealed them there. See Kniazev and Kol'tsov, *Kratkii ocherk istorii akademii nauk SSSR*, p. 59.

[28] According to one source, Ol'denburg reported at least some of these archives to the Soviet government several years earlier, but was told to leave them where they were. (*The London Times*, March 2, 1934, p. 16.) Ermakov said that Academician Vernadskii told Academician Komarov by letter that the whole archive affair was a mistake. Ermakov, "Bor'ba kommunisticheskoi partii," p. 157, cited from Arkhiv AN SSSR, f. 277, op. 2, d. 99, l. 1. The very large archives of the Academy contained historical and political references as well as purely scientific material, since the Academy included both types of departments. Anyone looking for such materials would surely find them, although, admittedly, the find was a big one. The same sort of archive scandal, though less spectacular, occurred in the Ukrainian Academy of Sciences; see "Khronika," *Nauchnyi Rabotnik* (May-June 1930), p. 90. Such a parallel in the two academies is more than a coincidence.

mediate expulsion" and "calling to account" of "Ol'denburg
and Platonov as openly conscious culprits in the conceal-
ment of these important counter-revolutionary political documents. . . ."[29]

Ol'denburg now fell into disgrace and was forced to resign
his post as permanent secretary, although he managed to continue his work in the Academy, no doubt partly because of his
abject apologies.[30] The permanent secretary's position was temporarily taken by Academician V. L. Komarov (1869-1945).
Komarov was a botanist who was known for his work on the
flora of Manchuria, physical geography, and for his interest in
the history and administration of science. He would later spend
the last nine years of his life as president of the Academy.
Ermakov described Komarov as "one of the first academicians
to join in the struggle for reconstruction, fully conscious of its
socio-political significance."[31] Komarov's political profile was
not that simple. He was in high standing with the Party because he had given refuge in 1905 to several fugitive Bolshevik
leaders. At that time Komarov made no distinction between the
Bolsheviks and other groups struggling against autocracy. After
the Revolution his political position permitted him to pursue an
unusual policy, which was described by a former worker in
the Academy:[32]

> Komarov's viewpoint on academic matters and on relations
> with the Soviet regime amounted to the following: if full
> autonomy could not be achieved, then it was better to be
> directly subordinate to the Kremlin than to be dependent on
> Party functionaries in academic caps. . . . In short, it was a

[29] *VARNITSO* (January 15, 1930).
[30] In August 1932 he was named chairman of the commission for the study of
the history of the Academy. The following year he died, after the Academy
honored him on the 50th anniversary of his scholarly activity. See *S. F. Ol'denburg: K piatidesiatiletiiu nauchnoobshchestvennoi deiatel'nosti, 1882-1932.*
Speeches at the Academy of Sciences on February 1, 1933, honoring Academician S. F. Ol'denburg. Leningrad, 1934.
[31] Ermakov, "Bor'ba kommunisticheskoi partii," pp. 154-55.
[32] Kitaeff, "Akademiia nauk SSSR," Russian Archives, Columbia University,
pp. 31-32.

matter of selling oneself at the highest price possible and obtaining the maximum of at least outward respect.

On November 14, 1930, 15 more workers in the Academy were arrested; this group included the first academician, S. F. Platonov, the prominent historian of Russia, who is said to have predicted his arrest a year earlier.[33] Then at the end of January 1931 Academician E. V. Tarle, also a historian, was incarcerated, shortly after his return from abroad. On February 5 and 18 more arrests followed, including Academician N. P. Likhachev, a historian and student of iconography.[34] Also arrested was Academician M. K. Liubavskii, the noted historian of west Russia and the Grand Duchy of Lithuania.

According to several sources, the arrested scientists were sorted into definite categories for punishment:[35] members of the first category were expelled from the Academy and forbidden to take jobs elsewhere; those of the second category, including Platonov, were exiled and disappeared; those of the third category, including Tarle, were exiled but later resumed their academic positions.[36] Tarle, who had once been a Menshevik, after his return became one of the USSR's best-known historians, winning the Stalin Prize three times.

[33] Belomortsev, "Bol'shevizatsiia akademii nauk," p. 11; for the charges against Platonov, see p. 251.

[34] *Ibid.*

[35] These categories are based on the testimony of Dr. Nicholas Poppe, former corresponding member of the Academy, as recorded by Alexander Vucinich, *The Soviet Academy of Sciences*, Stanford, 1956, p. 10. The evidence is supported by E. Kh. Zankevich, *K istorii sovetizatsii rossiiskoi akademii nauk*, Munich, 1957, p. 41, and *Izvestiia*, September 4, 1929, p. 3. However, there is a lack of clarity in these reports over the exact meanings of the different categories.

[36] The exact fates of the purged academicians cannot be determined; Belomortsev, who was one of the workers imprisoned, said that four academicians were sentenced to exile in August 1931, and that their destinies were as follows: Platonov was sent to Samara (Kuibyshev) where he soon died (BSE says in 1933); M. K. Liubavskii went to Ufa where he also died; N. P. Likhachev went to Astrakhan and also is said to have perished there; Tarle went to Alma-Ata, from whence he returned in two years. (Belomortsev, "Bol'shevizatsiia akademii nauk," p. 12.) The large number of historians who were given severe punishments can be partially explained as a result of the dictatorship of the Marxist historian M. N. Pokrovskii. Professor Vernadsky believes that Platonov might have returned from exile also had not he died before the discrediting of Pokrovskii. Interview, George Vernadsky, East Haven, Conn., July 21, 1964.

The examination of personal backgrounds was completed by the end of 1929, but the Academy's report for 1930 indicated that the purge might later be renewed. V. P. Volgin commented in the report:

Among the scientific workers of the Academy as it was on January 1, 1930, we have, of course, many people with very high scientific qualifications. We must conduct ourselves very carefully in relation to this wonderful Academic wealth. But at the same time we must be fully conscious of the fact that these people, principally hostile to socialist construction, people organically incapable of accepting the new conditions of the Academy, are for the Academy—even in conditions of their actual neutrality—heavy ballast, interfering with its movement forward.[37]

And a year and a half after the purge began, A. Samoilovich wrote that the renovation of the staff of the Academy "cannot be considered completed."[38] Some "heavy ballast" still remained.

Reorganization of the Academy

The increasing demands for a reorganization of the Academy, intensified by the archives affair, were accompanied by an increased resignation of the old guard to the loss of their academic freedom, as well as an increase in their fear to resist. Nevertheless, they realized that, contrary to what the press said, Soviet society as a whole was not united against them; the public indignation over the discovery of the archives and the demonstrative meetings of the Sections of Scientific Workers

[37] *Otchet o deiatel' nosti akademii nauk SSSR za 1930 god*, Leningrad, 1931, p. xiii.
[38] A. Samoilovich, "Rekonstruktsiia vsesoiuznoi akademii nauk," *Front Nauki i Tekhniki* (April-May 1931), p. 69. On March 3, 1931 the presidium of the Academy expelled D. B. Riazanov (Gol'dendakh), the disgraced former head of the Marx–Engels Institute. (See *Vestnik Akademii Nauk* [March 1931], p. 50.) His fate is unclear, although Joravsky cites the available information in his *Soviet Marxism and Natural Science*, p. 377, note 73.

were mostly artificial. The academicians yielded not because they feared the wrath of society but because they feared the fury of the Party. In view of the purge and the multiple threats the fact that Vernadskii and a few other scientists continued to resist at all is quite remarkable.

Soon after the election of the communist academicians, the Academy took up the problem of basic reorganization; on March 7, 1929 the General Assembly appointed an organizational committee, headed by Academician Fersman and consisting of a diverse group: Gubkin, Bakh, Arkhangel'skii, and Bartol'd.[39] The committee split almost immediately between those academicians who supported a radical reorganization and those who did not. Only after the purge of the Academy in the fall was the committee able to proceed with its work, and even then its deliberations were entangled with difficulties. The chairman of the committee, A. E. Fersman (1883-1945), a member of the Academy since 1919, was a mineralogist and geochemist, and belonged to that same important group of geologists as Karpinskii and Vernadskii who were beginning to unite practical and theoretical work before the Revolution. Fersman was a student of Vernadskii, who won much attention by his expeditionary work in the Urals, Mongolia, central Asia, and other remote areas. As a result of the expeditions he became involved in the administration of scientific research and the management of institutions. Fersman lost the respect of some of the other academicians by his role in Figatner's commission and his compliance with the Party's desires. Academician Ipat'ev described him as a man

who could adjust himself to any environment, while he had a surprising gift of speech which enabled him to phrase the most ordinary ideas so skillfully that among many people he passed as a scientist of great promise. . . . My opinion of him was shared by many mineralogists and his closest associates. A careerist, he was quite willing to debase himself before

[39] Arkhiv AN SSSR, f. 1, op. 1. d. 251, l. 12; cited by Ermakov, "Bor'ba kommunisticheskoi partii," p. 152.

higher officials, provided it furthered his career. He and others like him were eagerly welcomed by the Bolsheviks.[40]

This description is too harsh. Fersman himself resigned as vice-president of the Academy over the purge, and Academician Vernadskii, an opponent on the subject of reorganization, had a very high opinion of his scientific ability.[41] Certain academicians appear simply to have chosen at a relatively early date to work with the Party and the Soviet government; some of them undoubtedly were sincere. Another example was A. F. Ioffe (1880-1960), a very able physicist who tutored a generation of Soviet scientists.

On October 30, 1929 Fersman delivered to the General Assembly his radical "Reorganization Project for the Academy of Sciences," thereafter known as the "Fersman Project." His reform plan was postulated on a new charter for the Academy and a new structure for its institutions. Fersman emphasized that the period of the Academy's isolation from society had ended; a new Academy was emerging which bore the responsibility for participating in the socialist reconstruction of the economy. The old insularity of the individual laboratories and commissions must be destroyed, he said, by amalgamating them into enormous scientifically organized institutes. The Academy's tradition of uniqueness and intellectual superiority could be maintained, Fersman rationalized, by giving the Academy "special functions, not given to other institutions."[42] To draw up the reorganizational plan he recommended an extra meeting of the General Assembly at the end of 1929, to be attended both by the academicians and by representatives of other scientific institutions.[43] Fersman thus would continue the policy of bringing in observers from the outside who legally possessed none of

[40] Ipatieff, *Life of a Chemist,* p. 434.

[41] Figatner, "Proverka apparata," and Zelenko, "Rekonstruktsiia vsesoiuznoi akademii nauk," p. 58. Fersman may in fact have been forced to present his "project."

[42] Arkhiv AN SSSR, f. 2, op. I-1929, d. 126, l. 5; cited by Ermakov, "Bor'ba kommunisticheskoi partii," pp. 158-59.

[43] *Ibid.*

the academic privileges, and yet would give them consultative rights which, under the circumstances, usually amounted to demands.

The Fersman Project met the expected opposition of the academic old guard, but their forces had been intimidated by the purge and diluted by the election of Marxist academicians. Academician V. M. Alekseev, a Sinologist, caustically remarked that Fersman's proposal for a special reorganizational meeting of the General Assembly was a "political act having no significance for science other than a negative one."[44] Academicians Krachkovskii, Zhebelev, Bartol'd, and Vernadskii also opposed the project, asserting that Fersman intended to reform the Academy far too hastily. Vernadskii warned, futilely, that the new organization must provide for "freedom of scientific research and opportunity for individual initiative."[45]

This group of protesters could not prevent the reorganization, although they still had hopes to influence it. The General Assembly approved the Fersman Project on the same day that Fersman presented it—October 30—and appointed a new committee to draft a more concrete reorganization plan based on Fersman's principles (A. E. Fersman, V. L. Komarov, M. N. Pokrovskii, A. N. Krylov, V. I. Vernadskii, A. M. Deborin, F. Iu. Levinson-Lessing, S. F. Ol'denburg, and S. I. Solntsev).[46] The presence on the committee of such men as Vernadskii and Levinson-Lessing, who had consistently opposed the subjugation of the Academy, was an indication of the General Assembly's continuing reservations concerning the reform.

Unable to stop the reorganization plan, at the same meeting several members took up the purge of the Academy then in progress and called for an explanation by Academician Fersman, a member of Figatner's commission. The General Assembly asked for a report by Fersman at the next meeting,

---

[44] Arkhiv AN SSSR, f. 2, op. I-1929, d. 1, l. 38, cited by Ermakov, "Bor'ba kommunisticheskoi partii," pp. 161-62.

[45] *Ibid.*

[46] Arkhiv AN SSSR, f. 1, op. 1, d. 251, l. 21, cited by Ermakov, "Bor'ba kommunisticheskoi partii," p. 162.

followed by a general discussion of the commission's activity. The Party directly answered this challenge to its authority, illustrating once again the falsity of its stated intention of permitting the Academy "to reform itself." The Leningrad regional committee (*obkom*) anticipated the Academy's inquiry into the purge by discussing Figatner's work on December 4. The regional committee's complete approval of the purge was a warning to the Academy that no criticism of it would be tolerated.[47] Fersman gave his report on the purge to the General Assembly during the December meeting, but, in view of the Party's previous action, the purge was presented as an accomplished fact.[48]

Fersman's reorganization committee continued its work, holding meetings on November 14 and December 18, but could not come to agreement since Vernadskii and several other members of the commission continued to resist Fersman's suggestions. In particular, they objected to the increasing involvement of outsiders in the Academy's affairs, maintaining that the present trend would convert the Academy into a "Peoples' Commissariat of Science."[49] On the other hand, Fersman and his supporters asserted that they could not carry through the reorganization project so long as the committee contained such obstinate members. On the first day of the extraordinary meeting of the General Assembly in December, which Fersman had called for in his project, Academicians Krzhizhanovskii, Deborin, and Fersman were designated to draw up a new and more workable membership for the reorganization committee and to present it to the General Assembly two days later.[50]

47 Arkhiv IMELS, f. 17, op. 21, d. 2644, l. 181, cited by Ermakov, "Bor'ba kommunisticheskoi partii," p. 163.
48 "Khronika," *Nauchnyi Rabotnik* (January 1930), pp. 96-97.
49 Arkhiv AN SSSR, f. 2, op. I-1929, d. 1, l. 59; cited by Ermakov, "Bor'ba kommunisticheskoi partii," p. 163.
50 Arkhiv AN SSSR, f. 2, op. I-1929, d. 95, l. 138, cited by Ermakov, "Bor'ba kommunisticheskoi partii," p. 164. According to Ermakov the new membership, as appointed on December 20, consisted of Academicians Bakh, Marr, Ioffe, Deborin, Arkhangel'skii, representatives of the Communist Academy, and of other scientific institutions. The new committee also included Bukharin, accord-

This meeting, from December 18 to 20, came at a moment when tension in the country as a whole was approaching new limits as a result of the ruthless agrarian program which collectivized over half of the peasant households in a five-month period.[51] The same calendar period was significant in the history of the Academy.[52] It was at the December meeting that the General Assembly definitely decided to draft a new charter, promoted, in particular, by Academicians Krzhizhanovskii and Gubkin. Furthermore, the Academy learned that it had been transferred from the jurisdiction of the Council of Peoples Commissars to that of the "Scientific Committee" of the Central Executive Committee (TsIK), headed by A. V. Lunacharskii.[53] This shift put the Academy in the anomalous position of being under the direction of a man who was currently trying to become a member; Lunacharskii was elected to the Academy in January 1930.

The debate over the reorganization project continued heated. The aged President Karpinskii, whom Ipat'ev described as "an idealist, and a man so honest as to be indeed rare," felt exceedingly uncomfortable in his position; he had always permitted Ol'denburg, now no longer at his right hand, to run most of the affairs of the Academy.[54] He offered little resistance to the Party's reorganization of the Academy. "There are good times and there are bad times," he once remarked. "We are entering a bad period and must bear everything patiently. Fighting the

---

ing to "Khronika," *Nauchnyi Rabotnik* (January 1930), p. 96. Ermakov's omission of Bukharin was not a typographical error. The new committee was of little significance, as things turned out, because the government stepped in within a few days to direct the reorganization. See p. 136.

[51] Schapiro, *Communist Party of Soviet Union*, p. 384.

[52] Ermakov, "Bor'ba kommunisticheskoi partii," p. 164, calls this meeting the turning point in the reorganization of the Academy. This could hardly be the case, since the fate of the Academy was determined after the influx of new members in early 1929. After that time the reorganization was inevitable. The old guard could not muster a one-third vote after January 1929.

[53] The transfer was a result of the abolishment of the Department of Scientific Institutions (*Otdel nauchnykh uchrezhdenii*) under Sovnarkom. The change was announced in "Khronika," *Nauchnyi Rabotnik* (March 1930), p. 88.

[54] See Ipatieff, *Life of a Chemist*, p. 434.

regime is not in my line. . . ."[55] Karpinskii maintained courteous, but often strained, relations with Party and government officials throughout the turbulent year of 1929, but now he asked that the Academy free him from the post of president.[56] As a result of the purge and the general stress the Academy was having some trouble filling all administrative positions. The new members did not yet have sufficient prestige within the Academy to hold office, while the older members now refused. In March 1929 the two men who had been nominated to hold the positions of the vice-presidencies, Vernadskii and Levinson-Lessing, "categorically" refused, pleading "inability" in administrative work and an overloaded scientific schedule.[57] Anxious to preserve the semblance of the old Academy, however, the Marxist academicians joined with the old guard in asking Karpinskii to remain as leader of the Academy throughout the reorganization period, and Karpinskii assented.

Before Karpinskii could accomplish much toward drafting a new charter, the Soviet government dropped the mask of "reform by the Academy" completely; the chairman of the Scientific Committee of the Central Executive Committee, Lunacharskii, sent the Academy a telegram flatly stating that the charter would be drawn up by a governmental committee rather than by a committee of the Academy.[58] This telegram merely illustrated beyond any doubt what was already clear enough—the Academy was no longer its own master.

The new governmental committee contained some academicians, but none of the members of the old guard. The chairman was the newly elected historian V. P. Volgin; his assistants were Academicians Krzhizhanovskii, Gubkin, Komarov, Fersman, and Deborin, as well as representatives of the all-Union Council of Trade Unions (VTsSPS), the State Planning Commission, the Supreme Economic Council, the Section of Sci-

[55] Kitaeff, "Akademiia nauk SSSR," Russian Archives, Columbia University, p. 30.

[56] Ermakov, "Bor'ba kommunisticheskoi partii," p. 164.

[57] "Khronika," *Nauchnyi Rabotnik* (April 1929), p. 102.

[58] TsGAOR, f. 3316, op. 22, d. 1095, l. 2; cited by Ermakov, "Bor'ba kommunisticheskoi partii," p. 166.

entific Workers, the Communist Academy, and the Central Executive Committee.[59]

During one of the committee's first meetings in February 1930 Academician Bukharin presented a report on the basic changes to be enacted in the new charter.[60] First, he said, the Academy must be given tasks closely related with socialist construction. Second, the organization of the Academy should be modified by decreasing the General Assembly's influence compared to the departments. The most important of the two departments, he continued, is that of the physical-mathematical sciences, which he suggested renaming the department of natural sciences. The second (humanities) department should be renamed the social sciences department. Third, he concluded that the role of "social organizations" and graduate students in the Academy should be increased.

Academician Vernadskii, not a member, attended the meeting of the governmental committee on February 28, 1930 and gave his last formal argument against governmental control of the Academy: "The government must be legally limited in its relationship with the Academy"; it must "be careful about dismissing from scientific work . . . workers for reasons . . . of political security or ideological suspicion." Vernadskii did not deny the validity of a great revolution in the relationship between science and government; he himself favored such a flourishing of science by means of the active support of the government, but "a social experiment of our scale can be successful only if people are attracted to it who have knowledge, talent, and an intelligence adapted to science, as well as great desire."[61] Lunacharskii and Gubkin criticized Vernadskii's views, insisting that a Soviet scientist must be a servant of the Soviet government. Vernadskii did not retract his opinions, but capitulated to superior forces; he stated that he no longer intended to oppose his "Vernadskii Memorandum" to

[59] *Ibid.* Bukharin was probably a member also.

[60] "Khronika," *Nauchnyi Rabotnik* (March 1930), p. 87.

[61] TsGAOR, f. 3316, op. 23, d. 791, ls. 36-42; cited by Ermakov, "Bor'ba kommunisticheskoi partii," p. 167.

the work of the governmental committee. Although he resigned from his headship of the Council for the Study of Productive Forces (SOPS), he submitted to the reorganization of the Academy and worked faithfully in his academic field until his death in 1945. He occupies an illustrious position in the geological sciences, especially in geochemistry and biogeochemistry; in 1943 he received the Stalin Prize.[62] The reason Vernadskii did not follow the historian Platonov, whom he defended, to exile was undoubtedly his much greater value to the Soviet industrialization program. Vernadskii, like Pavlov, was one of those distinguished scientists inherited from the old regime who were permitted to commit occasional heresies. As Zankevich remarked, this tolerance was harmless for the Party: "The young people could be told that it is difficult for an old scientist to 'overcome the vestiges of capitalism.' "[63]

The 1930 charter

The governmental committee drafted the new charter in March 1930. One very controversial point was the requirement of political orthodoxy for honorary members. The necessity for such conformity among the regular members of the Academy had a precedent in the 1927 charter, but nothing had been said about the political views of honorary, or even of corresponding members. Honorary members were as a rule distinguished foreign scientists elected on the basis of scientific achievement alone; to consider the political beliefs of such men would mean hampering ties between the Soviet Academy and the academies of other nations, since honorary members were important channels of such communications. Academician Levinson-Lessing opposed a political clause, but Volgin defended

[62] The BSE does not mention Vernadskii's resistance to the Sovietization of the Academy, but does mention that he sometimes "expressed idealistic viewpoints."

[63] Zankevich, *K istorii*, p. 51. Voronov praised Pavlov's scientific achievements helping socialism, but noted that he was "hopelessly hardened in his sociopolitical development at the level of the pre-February epoch." S. Voronov, "Iz proshlogo," p. 144.

such a requirement.[64] Volgin's view triumphed, and the members agreed to insert a clause in the charter stating that scientists who have displayed a "hostile attitude toward the revolutionary movement of the proletariat" could not be elected to honorary memberships.[65]

The new charter of the Academy, approved by the Assembly on April 4 and by the Central Executive Committee on May 23, was a document directed toward two goals: the linking of the Academy to industrialization and the reduction of the influence of the academicians in their General Assembly. The first goal, by now a familiar theme of the Soviet reorganization of the Academy, was formulated in the second paragraph of the charter, which directed the Academy to "fulfill the needs of the socialist reconstruction of the country and the further growth of the socialist social order."[66] The work of the Academy was now (legally) fully subordinated to Soviet goals. As Volgin commented, "The idea of the closest ties of the work of the Academy of Sciences with socialist construction runs like a red thread through the whole new charter."[67]

The second goal, the diminishing of the influence of the academicians, especially the old guard, in the General Assembly, was achieved by several means. The most obvious was the stipulation that, henceforth, election to full membership in the Academy could be achieved by a simple majority vote in the General Assembly. Any chance for further resistance by the old guard to new communist members was simply erased. Furthermore, honorary members, corresponding members, and directors of academic institutes were given consultative votes in the meetings of the General Assembly. A two-thirds vote was still required in departmental elections, but the Party had

[64] Arkhiv AN SSSR, f. 2, op. I-1930, d. 17, cited by Ermakov, "Bor'ba kommunisticheskoi partii," p. 173.

[65] *Sobranie zakonov i rasporiazhenii SSSR* (No. 30, 1930), art. 336, p. 566.

[66] *Ibid.*, p. 564.

[67] *Otchet o deiatel'nosti akademii nauk SSSR za 1930 god*, Leningrad, 1931, p. ii.

already demonstrated its ability to control these. The General
Assembly's influence was further diminished by shifting more
and more of its functions to the two departments, which were
now named "mathematics and natural sciences" (MEN) and
"social sciences" (ON). These departments were in turn broken
down into "groups" on disciplinary lines, in which representatives of scientific workers had full voting rights. The Party was
now able to control the institutions of the Academy at every
level.

The system of control was concentrated in the hands of the
secretaries of the presidium and the departments. V. P. Volgin
(1879-1962), Marxist historian, revolutionary, former president
of Moscow University, and one of the founders of the Institute
of Red Professors, was named permanent secretary of the
Academy in early 1930. The position of permanent secretary
was the only one in the presidium without a definite term of
office.[68] In each department a departmental secretary was ready
to comply with orders from the presidium's secretary. Thus the
position of Academic secretary was the seat of power, as it had
been during the early years of the Academy when Schumacher
purchased expensive bookcases for his library with Academy
funds, promoted his relatives, and perverted the purposes of
Peter's Academy.[69]

The power of the permanent secretary was illustrated by his
control of the Academy's publications. According to article 58
of the charter the Academy's press was henceforth under the
control of a new "Editorial-Publication Council." The chairman
of the council was the veteran Party member, Volgin. The
Academy thus lost its free press, the last in the Soviet Union.

[68] Volgin's policies in the Academy were so harsh that finally even President
Karpinskii demanded that he be removed. In 1935 Volgin was dismissed as an
extremist and his post was taken by Academician Komarov. However, in World
War II the government restored Volgin to favor as vice-president of the Academy. He held that position until 1953. Kitaeff, "Akademiia nauk SSSR," pp. 32,
54, 62.

[69] The tradition of secretarial control had never really died. Many academicians considered Ol'denburg too domineering. See Ipatieff, *Life of a Chemist*,
p. 434. There is, of course, a real difference between Schumacher's use of the
powerful office for personal ends and Volgin's use of it for political ones.

Before the formation of the Editorial Council the support of any full member of the Academy was usually considered sufficient reason for the publication of a book. The new council, however, could disregard the academicians if it wished; it judged material on the basis of its "scientific character, methodological content, topicality, and correspondence to the needs of socialist construction."[70] The charter still contained a perfunctory nod to the previous rights of the Academy by stating that publications of the Academy which carried the permanent secretary's signature were exempt from governmental censorship. This statement was largely meaningless, since any such publication had, in fact, already passed through a form of censorship.

Graduate study in the Academy

The Academy of Sciences had not been responsible for the formal education of students since the reform of 1803. Outstanding graduate students worked with academicians on invitation, but they received their recognized educations and degrees from the regular universities, not from the Academy. After the Revolution the government abolished all advanced academic degrees as symbols of capitalistic inequality, so the Academy was no longer dependent on the universities. Superior students simply stayed on in the universities or the Academy and received informal educations; during the first few years the Academy contained primarily scholars inherited from the prerevolutionary era. However, after 1925 the government established a more formal program of graduate study (*aspirantura*) in the universities, and workers in the Academy were once again dependent on outside institutions for formal degrees. The Academy found this system unsatisfactory for two reasons. First, the quality of university education was poor during the early years, and second, the graduates of the universities contained many Young Communist League and Com-

[70] A. S. Orlov, "Akademiia nauk u poroga 1932 goda," *Vestnik Akademii Nauk* (No. 10, 1931), col. 28.

munist Party activists. The Academy was anxious to preserve its special status as a calm island of research endeavor no matter how passionately the political winds blew outside its walls. The dissatisfaction of the Academy with the new crop of graduates is apparent in Academician Fersman's statement:

When a young scientist began working in the Academy, it was necessary to bring him in from the outside; he had not received his education in the Academy; his habits and inclinations were formed outside the Academy. The outside sources of academic personnel were the higher educational institutions, mainly the universities. Such a system was, beyond any doubt, unsatisfactory from the standpoint of the Academy, especially during these times. This is a result of the peculiarities of university education and university institutions.[71]

Therefore the Academy decided to establish a system of training students which would preserve both its high standards of scholarship and its insulation from political strife. In December 1925 Academicians A. A. Bialynitskii-Birulia, the director of the Zoological Museum, and P. P. Sushkin and F. Iu. Levinson-Lessing asked the General Assembly to establish a system for preparing "probationers" (*praktikanty*) in the museums of the Academy. The General Assembly, and later the Council of Peoples Commissars, approved the request and in 1926 the Academy established the new institute, directed by Sushkin.[72] The Academic institutions choosing probationers, which seem to have included some not strictly museums, had absolute power over the selection of the students who would enter the Academy. The entering students were already graduates of other educational institutions; their duties in the Academy were to study their specialties, assist the academi-

[71] Quoted in "Podgotovka nauchnykh kadrov i akademiia nauk," *Vestnik Kommunisticheskoi Akademii* (Nos. 35-36, 1929), p. 382.
[72] G. A. Kniazev and A. V. Kol'tsov, *Kratkii ocherk istorii akademii nauk SSSR*, p. 86.

cians, and execute an independent project of work. By 1928 there were 30 such probationers.

The Party had meanwhile become concerned with the state of higher education throughout the country. There were far fewer qualified technical personnel in the Soviet Union than the industrialization program required. In 1929 in the RSFSR there were only 2,368 graduate students (*aspiranty*), and only 143 of these were in the engineering sciences.[73] Another defect, in the Party's view, was the scarcity of Party members among technical personnel. In 1929 it was estimated that there were 24,000 "scientific workers" in the Soviet Union, most of them with prerevolutionary educations, of whom only seven or eight percent were members of the party.

The Central Committee therefore decided to enact essential reforms in graduate study. On July 12, 1928 a plenary meeting of the Central Committee adopted a resolution concerning the preparation of technical specialists, based on a report which Molotov had presented to the plenum.[74] The resolution lamented the insufficient number of specialists, especially engineers, and called for improvement in the quality and ideological training of new technicians.

In March 1929, shortly after the first elections of Party-sponsored academicians, the Academy decided that something would have to be done about training personnel to meet the expanding Academy's needs. Furthermore, Academician Sushkin had recently died, and the affairs of the Institute of Probationers were in general disorder. Two Academic subcommittees took up the question of graduate study (*aspirantura*) in March and April 1929. The two groups, one in Moscow and the other in Leningrad, came to opposite conclusions. The split was the inevitable one between the old and the new factions. The Leningrad subcommittee met on March

[73] "Podgotovka nauchnykh kadrov i akademiia nauk," pp. 381-82.
[74] "Ob uluchshenii podgotovki novykh spetsialistov," *Pravda*, July 13, 1928, p. 3.

13 and decided that the system of probationers should remain essentially as it had been, with certain changes in numbers and administration; the Academy should prepare "scientific workers specifically for institutes of the Academy, and in order to establish scientific 'schools' around individual academicians."[75] Academicians Ol'denburg, Ioffe, Bartol'd, Krachkovskii and even Komarov all agreed that the Academy had no responsibility to train scientists for the country as a whole. The Academy was a preserve for research by the most talented scientists in the country, both teachers and students, and any attempt to transform it into a university would interfere with this research for knowledge. The Leningrad subcommittee decided, therefore, that the Academy should ask the government to permit an increase in the number of probationers to 80, to extend the period of study to four years, and to give each student a stipend of 90 rubles a month.[76] The probationers would be completely in the charge of individual academicians, who would also select them. Every academician would have one to three such students, each chosen initially for a period of one year. If a student demonstrated appreciable talent, he might be invited to remain with the academician for an additional three years. Upon graduation the students would become "co-workers" of the Academy. The students and co-workers would be connected to the Academy through the person of the academician under whom they worked.

The Moscow subcommittee had very different ideas, based on the Party's policy toward graduate study. On April 8, Academicians Arkhangel'skii, Bakh, Gubkin, and Lazarev discussed the problem and decided that the Institute of Probationers should be completely disbanded and replaced by a regular system of graduate study similar to that in all other educational institutions. The graduates of the Academy would be considered equal to university graduates from the stand-

---

[75] Arkhiv AN SSSR, f. 277, op. 3, d. 79, ls. 2-3; cited by Ermakov, "Bor'ba kommunisticheskoi partii," p. 182.
[76] "Khronika," *Nauchnyi Rabotnik* (April 1929), p. 103.

point of placement, and would work in universities, research institutes, and industry throughout the country. The Moscow group concluded that the graduate students in the Academy would be held responsible for dialectical materialism to the same extent that all other Soviet students were.

The Academy was again torn by dissension. Fearing the enforcement of such ideological restrictions on their studies, the probationers of the Academy tried to assert their independence by adopting a resolution citing the "uselessness of the study of Marxist–Leninist methodology for them," and insisting that they should remain true to the Academic "traditions."[77] Many of their academician-teachers also believed at this time, before the purge, that the Academy occupied a unique position; they expected their probationers to be exempt from the ideological requirements enforced in other institutions. The General Assembly discussed the contradictory reports on May 15, but failed to reconcile the two factions.

The Party proceeded with its plans to reform higher education. On June 26, 1929 the Central Committee ordered the improvement of graduate study in Soviet institutions by (1) establishing uniform rules of admittance, (2) requiring greater participation of "social organizations" in choosing candidates, (3) increasing the ideological content of graduate studies, and (4) increasing the number of Party and Young Communist League members in graduate study.[78] This decree also contained a section particularly important for the Academy: "The Leningrad Party regional committee . . . is directed to assign forty Communists in the current year to scientific work in the institutions of the Academy of Sciences."[79]

[77] Arkhiv AN SSSR, f. 203, op. 1, d. 192, l. 36; cited by Ermakov, "Bor'ba kommunisticheskoi partii," p. 181; also see K. V. Ostrovitianov's criticism of the students in his "O perspektivakh i metodakh raboty sektsii nauchnykh rabotnikov," *Nauchnyi Rabotnik* (July-August 1929), pp. 3-10; also, S. Romanova, "Nekotorye vyvody iz chistki v akademii nauk," *Izvestiia*, September 10, 1929, p. 2; and "Podgotovka nauchnykh kadrov i akademiia nauk," *Vestnik Kommunisticheskoi Akademii* (Nos. 35-36, 1929), p. 383.

[78] "O nauchnykh kadrakh VKP(b)," *Pravda*, p. 6, August 18, 1929.

[79] *Ibid.*

The reform of the Academy now passed into its most un-bridled stage—the purge. The probationers and academicians had no chance of preserving the old system of training. On October 9 the Leningrad Party regional committee directed the final dissolution of the Institute of Probationers and the establishment of the normal Soviet system of graduate study.[80] The Academy lost even the unrestricted right to select its own students, since the admission board, established October 30, included not only representatives of the Academy but also delegates from the Central Bureau of the Section of Scientific Workers, the Communist Academy, and a representative of the Leningrad Institute of Marxism.[81] Candidates for admission were required to submit recommendations from institutions where they previously studied and from Party or Party-sponsored organizations.

Graduate study in the Academy was open to students of both sexes under 35 who had already completed work in a university or similar institution. The period of study was three years; students would receive no less than 170 rubles a month, almost double what the Academy had asked for.[82] The Party's policy toward graduate study in the Academy could well serve as a description of its policy toward the entire Academy and, indeed, of all of Soviet education and science: the denial of freedom was combined with generous material support. Apparently the Party did not consider these policies contradictory.

The higher educational institutions in the Soviet Union favored students from worker or peasant families over those with middle or upper class backgrounds. In the early 1920s this preference had been very marked, but on July 10, 1926 the Council of Peoples Commissars ruled that children of the intelligentsia could be educated on an equal basis with those of workers.[83] Therefore, of the 112 students admitted to

[80] Arkhiv IMELS, f. 17, op. 21, d. 2682, l. 178; cited by Ermakov, "Bor'ba kommunisticheskoi partii," p. 184.
[81] The academicians on this admission board were Komarov, Favorskii, Samoilovich, Marr, Deborin, and Arkhangel'skii.
[82] "Khronika," *Nauchnyi Rabotnik* (October 1929), p. 83.
[83] *Nauchnyi Rabotnik* (September 1926), p. 97.

graduate study in the Academy in 1929-30, only 60 percent came from worker and peasant families,[84] and these were so poorly prepared that the presidium of the Academy was forced to create, on May 21, 1930, a special "preparatory department" to which only students from worker and peasant families would be admitted.[85] After a period of intensive preparation the students in the preparatory department would embark upon regular graduate studies. Despite this extraordinary measure, which reminds one of the effort of the 18th century Academy to establish a university by buttressing it with a *gymnasium*, the Academy found it increasingly difficult to acquire graduate students with adequate preparation. The numbers continued to grow nevertheless. In 1931 the graduate students in the Academy reached a total of 370.[86] The following year the Academy liquidated the "preparatory department," expelled 69 students because of their inadequate education, and raised entrance requirements.[87] The attempt to restrict education in the Academy by social origin was, on the whole, unsuccessful.

Rise of Communist Party strength in the Academy

The establishment of graduate study brought large numbers of Communist Party members inside the Academy. Almost one-half the students admitted to study in 1929 and 1930 were

[84] Ermakov, p. 186. Volgin gave slightly different figures, saying that in February 1931, 11 percent of the *aspiranty* were from peasant families and 20 percent from worker families. (*Otchet o deiatel'nosti akademii nauk SSSR za 1930 g.*, p. xiv.) Another source says that of the first class of 125, 13 were workers, 33 peasants, and 59 of the "service class." On a national breakdown, 72 were Russian, 22 Jews, five Ukrainians, two Belorussians, and 12 of Caucasian nationalities. "Podgotovka nauchnykh kadrov i akademiia nauk," *Vestnik Kommunisticheskoi Akademii* (Nos. 35-36, 1929), pp. 381-85.

[85] There was also established in the Academy in 1930 a Pupils' Institute (*Institut Uchenichestva*) for younger (17-20 years) students. Its relationship to the preparatory department is unclear. See V. A. Zelenko, "Rekonstruktsiia vsesoiuznoi akademii nauk," *Nauchnyi Rabotnik* (November-December 1930), pp. 50-66.

[86] A. S. Orlov, "Akademiia nauk," col. 28.

[87] Ermakov, "Bor'ba kommunisticheskoi partii," p. 187. TsIK SSSR passed a resolution on September 19, 1932, demanding higher entrance requirements to educational institutions. See "O podgotovke nauchnykh kadrov i vysoko-kvalifitsirovannykh spetsialistov," *Sobranie zakonov i rasporiazhenii raboche-krest'ianskogo pravitel'stva SSSR* (No. 68, 1932), art. 409.

members of the Party. Although very few of these students ever became members of the Academy, they worked closely with the newly elected communist academicians in drawing the Academy into the sphere of the Party's activities; the much debated political insularity of the Academy had been eliminated. A. Iarilov surveyed the change and commented:

> *Aspirantura* rejuvenated the Academy, smothered the odors of the long-ago moribund past, which had previously been assiduously cultivated in it. *Aspirantura* tied the Academy with direct, vital, and durable links not only with the trade union organizations, but also with the Party, and with VARNITSO.[88]

The lonely pair of Party comrades who had worked in the Academy in 1928 were joined by almost 350 other communists by late 1933.[89] This group included the following members or corresponding members of the Academy: V. V. Adoratskii, N. I. Bukharin, V. P. Vil'iams, V. P. Volgin, I. M. Gubkin, A. M. Deborin, S. A. Zernov, B. A. Keller, G. M. Krzhizhanovskii, N. M. Lukin, A. V. Lunacharskii, N. Ia. Marr, V. V. Osinskii, L. V. Pisarzhevskii, A. A. Rikhter, M. A. Savel'ev, S. G. Strumilin, and N. M. Tulaikov.[90]

The local committee (*mestnyi komitet*) of Academic workers, which corresponded to the Party-dominated factory committees among Soviet industrial workers, became the primary unit of the professional union in the Academy. The duties of the local committee, a former member of a biological institute has reported, were educational and cultural work, socialist propaganda, improvement of labor efficiency, and control over vacations for scientific workers at resorts and sanatoriums.[91]

---

[88] A. Iarilov, "Staraia i novaia akademiia nauk," *Front Nauki i Tekhniki* (July-August 1931), p. 55.

[89] Kniazev and Kol'tsov, *Kratkii ocherk*, p. 94.

[90] E. Kh. Zankevich, *K istorii sovetizatsii Rossiiskoi akademii nauk*, p. 39, cited from *VII-mu vsesoiuznomu s'ezdu sovetov akademiia nauk SSSR*, Moscow–Leningrad, 1935, pp. 207-208. The list also included Riazanov until his expulsion in March 1931.

[91] Zankevich, "K istorii," p. 42.

The committee also worked with the local organization of the Marxist scientists, VARNITSO, in reorganizing the Academy; in 1931 the Academy underwent both an organic and a spiritual transformation. At great expense the Academy was molded into a vast, centralized scientific organization unique in world history. During this process the fact that the Academy was purged and coerced was not so remarkable as the fact that within its battered framework it preserved the seeds of fruitful research.[92]

A logical question concerning the Academy in this period might be: Why did not more academicians flee to the West? Many of them traveled to international scientific congresses or foreign universities to teach or study, spoke foreign languages, had friends abroad, and with little difficulty could have remained there. No easy answer can be found, but perhaps one should remember, in addition to all the obvious ties holding a person to the land of his birth, that these men had already lived in the Soviet Union over a decade; its authoritarian aspects were not new to them, nor did these controls in every case restrict their research. When several academicians did flee, the reasons they gave were personal, as will be seen below, and not any general unwillingness to live and work under the controlled conditions of the Soviet Union. Their primary motivations were not, as is often supposed in the West, a belief that science could flourish only in conditions of freedom.

Academician Ipat'ev, the administrator of much of Soviet chemical industry, learned that he was in great danger of arrest; dozens of rumors circulated around Leningrad that the secret police (GPU) was following his activities. He later said that he

heard a rumor that . . . the gradual arrest and elimination of the following men had been agreed upon: Spitalsky, Kam-

[92] The important question of the effect of police control on scientific creativity will be discussed later; see pp. 150-51 and 204-209. In sum, my view is that science is much more resilient than commonly thought; oppression definitely limits creativity, but the results are probably more selective and less pervasive than outside observers have judged.

zolkin, Kravets, Fokin, and Ipatieff [sic]. I had dismissed the statement as a rumor, possibly to frighten us into better productivity; but now this prophecy was being fulfilled. Early in 1929 Spitalsky had been arrested, six months later Kamzolkin, the director of industrial chemistry in Gosplan, and now in November, Kravets. The future looked none too pleasant. . . .[93]

By 1930, he said, the "desire to leave my native land became overwhelming."[94] But Ipat'ev admitted that the terror which drove him personally out of Russia had not smothered creativity in general:

The hardest thing about my departure from Russia was to break with this institute [Laboratory of High Pressures] which I had created. But I was partially consoled by the knowledge that I was leaving a fine center of research, independent and vigorous enough to continue its work without my guidance. The quality of the papers which have been published by the Institute since I left speaks for itself. . . .[95]

And yet, during the very time that these papers were published, more arrests occurred in the Academy, even of some of the researchers in the Laboratory of High Pressures.

Ipat'ev remained abroad after he went to the International Power Congress in Berlin in June 1930. He later accepted employment at the Universal Oil Products laboratories in the United States, owned by the American Chemical Society, where he was initially quite critical of the research in his field. In the United States he became a professor at Northwestern University, where he built another high pressures laboratory, and was eventually awarded the Willard Gibbs Medal of the American Chemical Society for his discoveries. In 1939 he was elected to membership in the U. S. National Academy of Sciences. He received worldwide fame for his research in the

[93] Ipatieff, *Life of a Chemist*, pp. 486-87.
[94] *Ibid.*, p. 494.
[95] *Ibid.*, p. 472.

high pressure catalysis of petroleum, necessary for the production of high-octane gasoline in World War II.[96]

While Ipat'ev was in Berlin he met a fellow academician, A. E. Chichibabin who was also fleeing the Soviet Union. Chichibabin and his wife advised the Ipat'evs to stay abroad indefinitely, since the terror in their country had increased in the short period since Ipat'ev left. Chichibabin's reasons for leaving were also primarily personal. He had compromised himself by defending several arrested scientists, and his only daughter, a student of chemistry, was killed by a shower of sulphuric acid while "on practice" in a factory. Chichibabin blamed the tragedy on the poor working conditions in Soviet industry and maintained that his daughter's life would have been saved by proper medical treatment. Interestingly enough, when Chichibabin and his wife asked for permission to go abroad, the Soviet government quickly gave them permission even though the purpose of the "visit" must have been known.[97]

✿

The years 1929 and 1930 were the most turbulent in the over two centuries of existence of the Academy of Sciences, worse even than the later period of the great purges of the 1930s, which marked the peak of Stalin's sanguinariness in the country as a whole. With the eventual Soviet conversion

[96] Ipat'ev was constantly pressured to return to the USSR, even by Soviet Ambassador to the United States, Troianovskii. (See p. 248 of the Ipat'ev Papers, Vol. III, Northwestern University.) In 1965 Ipat'ev was posthumously rehabilitated in the Soviet Union. A Soviet source praised his work and added the remark that before his death in 1952 he was preparing to return to the Soviet Union. There is no known evidence of a planned return. See Harry Schwartz, "A Defector Wins Praise in Soviet," *New York Times*, August 22, 1965, p. 18; and "Ipatieff Back in News," *Chemical and Engineering News*, September 6, 1965, p. 168.

[97] Ipat'ev Papers, III, 16-17. In December 1936 the Academy voted to expel Academicians Ipat'ev and Chichibabin from membership because of their emigration to the West. Academician Komarov said the men had violated the charter of the Academy by taking anti-Soviet positions. When the Academy voted on Ipat'ev's expulsion, of 62 academicians present, six abstained from voting. The old guard was still in existence and still could afford to dissent despite the ubiquitous practice of unanimous votes elsewhere in the Soviet Union and even though Ipat'ev's own son and daughter publicly denounced him. *Ibid.*, p. 252.

of the Academy promised by the election of the first communist Academicians, the Party, or perhaps Stalin himself,
decided to hasten that transformation by ejecting the personnel
who might hinder its plans for the complete subjugation and
subsequent renovation of the Academy. The governmental
commission, headed by the veteran police official Figatner,
directed a purge of the entire academic staff. While Figatner's
claim that the Academy was a center of counterrevolutionary
activity was merely an ignominious and feeble rationalization
for his actions, there is little doubt that the Academy contained
large numbers of people who would have preferred another
type of government. As one of the few isolated and nonpolitical
institutions in Soviet Russia after the Revolution, the Academy
had indeed attracted people who sought shelter. But the Academy was in no sense of the word, so far as one can determine
from available information, including the evidence advanced
by the Party, a locus of actual counterrevolutionary activity.
Its worst sin was political aloofness, not political opposition.
Yet in the Soviet Union in the year of the "great break," such
aloofness was a major transgression in itself, incurring disgrace
and loss of position, if not worse.

While the purge proceeded, the small group of academicians
who supported the Party's plans for the Academy initiated a
basic reorganization of its structure and goals. Academician
Fersman's "Reorganization Project" was an effort to bind the
research in the Academy more closely to the industrial economy, and to create a new type of large research institute. The
Fersman Project provoked a great deal of controversy and opposition among the other academicians which was overcome
only when the Soviet government intervened to impose a new
charter upon the Academy. The 1930 charter drew the Academy closer to the industrialization effort, imposed censorship
on the Academy's press, reduced the significance of the General Assembly, and stipulated that even honorary members
must meet political qualifications. It did not, however, accom-

plish a basic reorganization of the individual research institutions within the Academy, a task deferred temporarily.

Another important issue in 1929 and 1930 was the training of graduate students. Although the Academy had not considered education of students one of its major functions for over a hundred years, the decline of intellectual standards and the requirement of political loyalty among university students in the twenties had forced the Academy to initiate a training program even before the Party attempted to make of the Academy a particular form of higher educational institution. Thus the Institute of Probationers provided the Party with a valuable precedent for the institution of a normal Soviet system of graduate study in the Academy. This system (*aspirantura*) has been a characteristic of the Academy to the present day.

The greatest immediate effect of including graduate students in the Academy was to increase the role of the Communist Party in academic affairs. The graduate students were by far the youngest of all the personnel of the Academy and were often the most militantly Soviet. They quickly established the strident atmosphere of agitation and propaganda (*agitprop*) in the previously placid research laboratories of the Academy.

The major task of the Party in the Academy after the purge and the enactment of the 1930 charter was not one of acquiring control but of using that control to give a new direction to the Academy's activities. The Party's plans to reorganize the existing Academic institutions, to create new ones, and to accomplish the planning of science now unfolded.

CHAPTER V

THE NEW DIRECTION

The ideologues of Menshevism do not stop barking that the great construction of industrial giants in the USSR is very similar to the erection of Egyptian pyramids, and that the leadership of our party is similar to that of the pharaohs. . . . The pyramids of the pharaohs are the materialization of unproductive labor, symbols of gods and tsars, ancient bastilles of the soul, like the Gothic cathedrals of the middle ages. . . . Our colossi are the great tools of productive labor. / N. I. Bukharin, 1931[1]

The reconstruction of the individual research bodies within the Academy began on March 13, 1930, when the Central Executive Committee (TsIK) confirmed a new presidium. Neither Academicians Ol'denburg, the permanent secretary for the past quarter of a century, nor vice-president Fersman were members of the new presidium. Ol'denburg had lost his position in October 1929 during the purge, and Fersman resigned his office several weeks later, stating that he could not give the Academy the leadership it needed.[2] The members of the new presidium were A. P. Karpinskii (president), G. M. Krzhizhanovskii, V. L. Komarov, N. Ia. Marr (vice-presidents), and V. P. Volgin (permanent secretary). Karpinskii and Komarov were the only presidium members who did not belong to the Party.[3] This new presidium, which granted consultative

[1] *Vsesoiuznaia konferentsiia po planirovaniiu nauchnoissledovatel'skoi raboty,* pp. 15-16.

[2] Ermakov, "Bor'ba kommunisticheskoi partii," p. 169.

[3] Komarov never became a member of the Party, although from 1936 to

votes in its meetings to invited representatives of the Bureau of Scientific Workers, proceeded to enact sweeping organizational changes in the Academy.

Liquidation and amalgamation of existing institutions

The first step in the reorganization of the Academy was the liquidation of those institutions that the communists considered "out-of-date," such as the Russo–Byzantine Historical–Lexicographical Commission (called simply the Byzantine Commission), the Commission of Slavic Scholarship, and the Commission for the Scholarly Publication of the Slavic Bible.[4] The disappearance of these centers of study was a serious blow to Byzantine and Slavic studies. The Byzantine Commission was a postrevolutionary descendant of several earlier commissions of the Academy studying Byzantine influences on the Kievan Rus' and Russo–Byzantine relations of the period from the 9th to the 12th centuries. The Byzantine Commission was founded and first directed by Academician F. I. Uspenskii, who died in 1928. Another noted Byzantinist who had worked with the Commission was V. G. Vasil'evskii.[5] The Commission had sponsored the publication of numerous studies.[6] The Commission of Slavic Scholarship, under the leadership of Academician A. I. Sobolevskii, was an outgrowth of the Petrograd Slavic Society and studied the Slavic peoples from a historical, literary, and ethnographical standpoint. The Commission sponsored several scholarly journals or monographic series.[7] The Com-

---

1945 he was president of the Academy. Nesmeianov became in 1951 the first president of the Academy who was also a member of the Party. His successor, Keldysh, was a member of the Central Committee of the Party.

[4] The Russian titles of these organizations cannot be felicitously translated: *Russko-Vizantiiskaia Istoriko-slovarnaia Komissiia; Slavianskaia Nauchnaia Komissiia; Komissiia po Nauchnomu Izdaniiu Slavianskoi Biblii.*

[5] See V. G. Vasil'evskii, *Trudy*, Petrograd, 1915, Leningrad, 1930. Other academicians who were members of the commission were: V. M. Istrin, I. Iu. Krachkovskii, N. Ia. Marr, and S. F. Ol'denburg.

[6] Since 1894 the Academy had published the series *Vizantiiskii Vremennik.*

[7] The Academy published since 1900, *Pamiatniki staroslavianskogo iazika;* since 1911, *Entsiklopediia slavianskogo iazika;* since 1931, *Obozrenie trudov po slavianovedeniiu.*

mission of Slavic Scholarship was probably somewhat guilty of its critics' charge of "hurrah-patriotism and clerical tendencies."[8] The Slavic Bible Commission, also directed by Academician Sobolevskii, was preparing the publication of the Slavic Bible in all its textual variants, and collecting Biblical themes and illustrations from iconography and versification. This valuable work found no place in a socialist Academy, although the Commission had continued its research on these topics for over a decade under Soviet power.

The second step consisted of the amalgamation of many smaller laboratories and commissions into the new type of immense research institute. In fact, one could say that the principal organizational feature of the reconstruction of the Academy was consolidation. The gigantomania which led the Soviet Union to create state farms (*sovkhozy*) of 250,000 acres led them in the same period to establish enormous centralized research institutes. The idea of research in specialized institutes, as distinguished from research in universities or the conventional academies, was relatively new. The Soviet planners considered consolidation the trend in the West also, but a trend in which they would soon lead.

Academician Ol'denburg was an opponent of many aspects of the Sovietization of the Academy, but he was a strong supporter of the idea of specialized institutes; he once commented, "If the eighteenth century was the century of academies, while the nineteenth was the century of universities, then the twentieth century is becoming the century of research institutes."[9] Ol'denburg believed that mass education was antithetical to deep research for knowledge; consequently, the influx of large numbers of students to the universities resulted, in his opinion, in a conversion of their function from research to pedagogy. The specialized institutes, developed first in Germany, were assuming the major responsibility for research.

[8] S. Voronov, "Iz proshlogo," *Novyi Mir* (May 1930), p. 143.

[9] S. F. Ol'denburg, "Vpechatleniia o nauchnoi zhizni v Germanii, Frantsii i Anglii," *Nauchnyi Rabotnik* (February 1927), p. 89.

Bukharin, on the other hand, interpreted this same phenomenon as a change in the nature of scientific progress. He said that scientific achievement in the 18th and 19th centuries depended primarily on increasing *mechanical* efficiency and the application of generally known principles to industry; the result was the Industrial Revolution. Now, he believed, history was moving into a new era in which future progress depended much less on the individual inventor and his machine shop, or the individual scholar and his study, and much more on the large, organized research laboratory.[10] Academician N. I. Vavilov, a future foe of Lysenko, agreed that they were witnessing a revolution in world science which demanded new methods: "New scientific disciplines are being created, the applied sciences are developing into a fertile scientific class. We are observing a great upsurge of scientific creativity. From the work of solitary scientists we are shifting to collectivism. Modern institutes and laboratories—they are, so to speak, 'factories of scientific thought.' "[11]

The process of amalgamation not only complied with the Academy presidium's ideas on the administration of scholarly research but also, by reducing the number of administrative posts, permitted the control of the most important institutes by Marxist academicians, who were still quite scarce. At the end of 1929, the year of the election of the first communist to an Academic chair, Komarov observed:

> The Academicians–Marxists among the new members and the new worker–Marxists who took the places of those expelled during the purge have already influenced the coordination and execution of new tasks in spite of their relatively small numbers and short duration of stay in the Academy. . . . There can be no doubt that by the renovation and revivification of the Academy (both in personnel and methods of work) the Academy may now develop scientific research

[10] *Vsesoiuznaia konferentsiia po planirovaniiu nauchno-issledovatel'skoi raboty, 1-ia,* Moscow–Leningrad, 1931, p. 20.
[11] "Khronika," *Nauchnyi Rabotnik* (March 1929), p. 86.

on the basis of planned work and in coordination with the
actual problems of socialist construction.[12]

The renovators concentrated at first on the social sciences.
Academic Secretary Volgin carefully noted which institutions
were headed by communist academicians; in the 1930 General
Report on the activities of the Academy he wrote that "Marxist leadership was guaranteed" in that year in eight of the
Academy's institutes, museums, and commissions.[13] Eight different bodies concerned with Russian language and literature
were combined to form larger institutions. Those organizations,
which Figatner called "prerevolutionary in spirit" (the Pushkin
House, Tolstoi Museum, and the Commission for the Publication of Pushkin's Works), were forged together into the
Institute of Modern Russian Literature, headed by the communist Academician Lunacharskii. A number of smaller bodies
in the literary field—the Commission for the Publication of the
Classics of Old Russian Literature; the Dialogic Commission;
the Commission for Compiling an Explanatory Bibliography
for Old Russian Literature; the Commission for the Collection
of Materials on the Old Russian Language; and the Dictionary
Commission—were combined into two larger commissions devoted to the study of the Russian language.[14]

[12] *Otchet deiatel' nosti akademii nauk SSSR za 1929 g.*, p. iv. This speech
is also quoted in "Khronika," *Nauchnyi Rabotnik* (February 1930), p. 92.
[13] The bodies were: the Japhetic Institute (headed by N. Ia. Marr); the
Museum of Anthropology and Ethnography (N. M. Matorin); the Institute of
Modern Russian Literature (A. V. Lunacharskii); the Archaeographical Commission (M. N. Pokrovskii); the Commission on the History of Knowledge
(N. I. Bukharin); the Museum of Books, Documents and Letters (A. S. Orlov);
the Institute for the Study of the Nationalities of the USSR (N. Ia. Marr);
the Institute of Oriental Studies (S. F. Ol'denburg). Ol'denburg's inclusion,
which may seem rather surprising, was evidence of his increasing orthodoxy
after his earlier disgrace. In November, 1930, a brigade of inspectors from
communist organizations outside the Academy gave the highest grades to the
Archaeographical Commission, the Museum of Anthropology and Ethnography,
the Seismological Institute, and the Japhetic Institute, thus illustrating that
the effects of Marxist leadership in three of four of these bodies were immediately visible. The Archaeographical Commission, headed by Pokrovskii, was
considered the best organized of all. See A. N. Samoilovich, "Rekonstruktsiia
vsesoiuznoi akademii nauk," *Front Nauki i Tekhniki* (April-May 1931), pp.
70, 73.
[14] See *Otchet o deiatel' nosti akademii nauk za 1930 god*, pp. v, vi and
Samoilovich, "K reorganizatsii," p. 71.

Four previously separate bodies which Figatner and his examining board had censured for "idealism" and "purposelessness"—the Asiatic Museum, the Institute of Buddhist Culture, the Turkic Office, and the College of Orientalists—were combined into one "Institute of Oriental Studies," devoted to current social problems of the East, studied from the standpoint of Marxism.[15] This reorganization was a disastrous blow to the Academy's study of oriental religions, especially the Institute of Buddhism, which had attracted much scholarly attention under its director, Academician F. I. Shcherbatskoi.[16]

The consolidation of the institutions in the humanities rode roughshod over the objections of the scholars, as is obvious from the close connection of the renovations with the purge. In the natural sciences, however, the reformers were more cautious; when scientists in this department protested strenuously the sweeping consolidation, the presidium sought a temporary compromise. Volgin admitted that the natural scientists, particularly the geologists, displayed a remarkable degree of individuality, maintaining that the enormous institutes would hamper their research. By the end of 1930 the presidium relented; Volgin told the Academy that there were exceptions to the principle of amalgamation, as long as everyone continued to recognize the need for some sort of overall coordination.[17] The legitimate reasons for exceptions, he said, were the existence of new departments of science which needed to be given the fullest opportunity for quick and independent development, and the "psychological" nature of some scientists who insisted on maintaining their individualism.

The compromise organizational form announced by the presidium was the "association," described as "that incomplete form of assimilation which is especially characteristic of the system of institutions in the Department of Mathematical and

[15] The Institute of Oriental Studies (Institut Vostokovedeniia) later became the Institute of the Peoples of Asia (Institut Narodov Azii).

[16] See *Nauchnyi Rabotnik* (November 1928), pp. 84-85, for a report on the proposed encyclopedia of Buddhism.

[17] *Otchet o deiatel'nosti akademii nauk SSSR za 1930 g.*, p. vi.

Natural Sciences."[18] The associations represented a most delicate compromise; they were supposed to unite separate but
related research organs in networks sufficiently coordinated to
permit all of them to work on the same complex problems, but
sufficiently independent to permit the individual academicians
to feel uncoerced. Time showed that this was an impossible
assignment; the associations tended to fulfill the one goal to
the extent that they did not fulfill the other.[19]

The geologists, who initially suggested the idea of the association, created the first such organization. The Geological
Association consisted of the informal union of the following
institutions, all of which retained their own identities: the
Geological Institute, Petrographic Institute, Paleozoological
Institute, Mineralogical Institute, Geochemical Institute, and
Soil Institute. The chemists immediately followed the example
of the geologists by the creation of an association composed of
the Laboratory of General Chemistry, Laboratory of High Pressures, Laboratory of Organic Synthesis, Colloidal–Electrochem-
ical Laboratory, Laboratory for the Research and Synthesis of
Vegetable and Animal Matter, the Institute for the Study of
Platinum; and the Institute of Physical–Chemical Analysis. A
further degree of complexity in coordination was achieved in
1931 when a "crossing association," the Geochemical Association, was formed of selected institutes in both the Geological
and the Chemical Associations. Thus, several institutes were in
more than one association, and the conception of the association as a future amalgamation seemed more and more unrealis-
tic. Other associations soon followed; the biological sciences
alone formed three separate associations.

Creation of new institutions

At the same time that the presidium was amalgamating
smaller bodies into larger institutes, it created other entirely

[18] *Ibid.*

[19] The associations seem to have been abandoned in the late 1930s. The
Chemical Association was disbanded in 1938. Letter to the author from N. A.
Figurovskii, Director of the Institute of the History of Natural Sciences and Tech-
nology, Academy of Sciences, Moscow, June 1961.

new institutions.[20] Between 1927 and 1933, 29 major organizations appeared in the Academy, some based on amalgamations, others entirely new.[21] A number of other small committees and activities, such as meteorological and seismological stations, were also established.[22]

Other new institutions which the presidium organized in this period were the "branches" (*filialy*) and "bases" (*bazy*) in the

[20] See Appendices B and C for charts of the structure of the Academy.

[21] The new institutions are listed below, with indications of their origins if they were formed on the basis of earlier organizations:

Microbiological Laboratory
Laboratory of Genetics (arose from the Bureau of Eugenics existing before 1930 under KEPS)
Institute of Energetics (arose from the Department of Energetics of KEPS)
Channel Coal Commission
Soil Institute (expanded from the Committee on Soil of KEPS)
Institute of Oriental Studies (formed in 1930 on basis of several smaller institutions)
Institute of Language and Thought (formed by combining the Commission for the Study of the Russian Language and the Institute of Japhetic Languages)
Institute for the Study of the Nationalities of the USSR (the former Commission for the Study of the Tribal Composition of the Population of the USSR)
Institute of Slavic Studies
Botanical Institute (before 1930 existed outside the Academy as the Botanical Garden and Museum)
Editorial-Publishing Council
Colloidal-Electrochemical Laboratory
Commission on the Study of Permafrost
Geomorphological Institute (former Industrial Geographical Section of KEPS)
Zoological Institute (former Zoological Museum)
Paleontological Museum (former Paleontological Section of the Geological Museum)
Laboratory of Biochemistry and Animal Physiology
Demographic Institute
Museum of the History of Religion
Economics Office
Committee of Scientific Consultation and the Propaganda of Scientific Achievements
Pacific Ocean Committee
Seismological Institute
Institute of Physical-Chemical Analysis (formerly part of KEPS)
Institute for the Study of Platinum and Other Noble Metals (formerly a part of KEPS)
Biogeochemical Laboratory
Geochemical Institute
Salt Laboratory
Laboratory of Evolutionary Morphology
See Supplement and Appendices B and C.

[22] For information on the organization of the Academy see Iablokov, V. S.,

distant regions of the Soviet Union. Branches and bases can be defined as local complexes of scientific-research institutions belonging to the Academy, established for the purpose of studying local scientific phenomena. As they grew older, however, these institutions tended to shed their narrow restrictions and become centers of broad research.

The first such institutions were established in 1932. In that year the Urals Branch in Sverdlovsk, headed by Academician Fersman, and the Far Eastern Branch in Vladivostok, led by Academician Komarov, began their scientific investigations. The Kazakh Base in Alma Ata and the Tadzhik Base in Stalinabad began operations at approximately the same time.[23] The branches and bases became quite important in the total organization of Soviet science, growing to a total of 12 after World War II. They were the origins of the Academies of Sciences in the Republics of Georgia, Uzbekistan, Armenia, Azerbaidzhan, Kazakhstan, Tadzhikistan, and Turkmenistan. As each center grew larger it seems to have acquired, in ascending order, the titles "base," "branch," and "republic academy."[24]

---

220 let Akademii Nauk SSSR; spravochnaia kniga, Moscow–Leningrad, 1945; P. G. Shidlovskii, "Sotsialisticheskaia rekonstruktsiia akademii nauk," *Vestnik Akademii Nauk* (No. 7, 1933), pp. 20-26; B. N. Molas, "Struktura akademii nauk SSSR," in A. E. Fersman, ed., *Akademiia nauk soiuza sovetskikh sotsialisticheskikh respublik za desiat' let (1917-27)*, Leningrad, 1927; V. P. Volgin, *Akademiia nauk SSSR za chetyre goda 1930-33*, Leningrad, 1934; S. F. Ol'denburg and E. F. Karskii, eds., *Nauka i nauchnye rabotniki SSSR, Chast' II, Nauchnye uchrezhdeniia Leningrada*, Leningrad, 1926; and the yearly reports of the Academy, *Otchety o deiatel'nosti akademii nauk SSSR, 1927-35*, Leningrad (15 vols.). The names of the various institutes, laboratories, commissions, etc., changed so often that accurate identification is difficult. Also, some bodies which the Academy planned to create never actually appeared. One of the most convenient sources for information on the date of origin of the many academic bodies and the dates of the numerous changes in names, although it must be used with some caution, is Dimitry Krassovsky and Robert Vosper, "The structure of the Russian Academy of Sciences from its beginning to 1945; a guide for bibliographers," *Kentucky University, Margaret I. King Library, Occasional Contributions*, no. 39, Lexington, 1952. This source does not list, however, the dates of foundation of all of the antecedent organizations.

[23] See Fed'kin, *Pravovye voprosy*, p. 95, and A. K. Kulieva, "Rol' akademii nauk SSSR v razrabotke plana vtoroi piatiletki"; *Uchenye zapiski turkmenskogo universiteta* (No. 8, 1956), pp. 181-88.

[24] On the other hand, some branches such as those at Sakhalin and Arkhangel'sk, have been reorganized into institutes of the Academy. (See

The branches possessed their own presidiums, whose chairmen were chosen by the General Assembly of the all-Union Academy. Despite this formal subordination to Leningrad, and later Moscow, in actual practice the branches and bases became rather independent. The governmental planners often deplored this lack of coordination.[25]

Both pragmatic and ideological arguments motivated the establishment of branches of the Academy throughout the country. The advantage of such centers for exploring natural resources and local phenomena need not be elaborated. Moreover, the communist planners viewed such centers of research and scholarship as steps toward the Marxist utopia in which the differences between urban and rural areas would be eliminated. G. I. Lomov, a member of the Party Central Committee, proudly announced at the 1931 planning conference:

We are creating completely new cultural centers in the countryside. Around them we will concentrate culture in its entirety, by means of them we will eliminate that gulf between the city and the countryside which right now still exists, but which in the process of socialist construction must disappear.[26]

The creation of the new institutes, bases and filials resulted in the transformation of the Academy from a small society located in Leningrad to an enormous national scientific net-

---

Fed'kin, *Pravovye voprosy*, p. 98.) President Nesmeianov announced in 1955 that since the goal of the branches has been fulfilled, i.e., the study of regions with peculiar natural or national characteristics, no more branches would be established. (See *Vestnik Akademii Nauk SSSR*, 1955, no. 3, p. 17.) In the 1961 reform of the Academy the branches were transferred to the regional economic councils, although the Academy retained a vague advisory role. (See "O merakh po uluchsheniiu koordinatsii nauchno-issledovatel'skikh rabot v strane i deiatel'nosti akademii nauk SSSR," *Pravda*, April 12, 1961, p. 1; and Nicholas DeWitt, "Reorganization of Science and Research in the U.S.S.R.," *Science*, cxxxiii [June 23, 1961], p. 1,987.) The Academy's power was again increased by a further reform in 1963. See D. A. Senior, "The Organization of Scientific Research," *Survey* (July 1964), pp. 19-35; and James M. Swanson, "Reorganization: 1963," *Survey* (July 1964), pp. 19-35.

[25] For example, see Fed'kin, *Pravovye voprosy*, p. 96.

[26] *Vsesoiuznaia konferentsiia po planirovaniiu nauchno-issledovatel'skoi raboty, 1-ia*, Moscow, 1931, p. 7.

work. Between 1913 and 1932 the staff of the Academy grew from 153 to 1,604, while its budget went from 1,000,000 to 22,000,000 rubles.[27] This growth was just the beginning of the expansion—beyond the limits of this study—which would give the Academy in 1965 a staff of 14,000 in 166 institutes, and the entire Academy system (including the republic academies) a staff of about 50,000 in almost 600 institutes.

Reorganization of KEPS into SOPS

Perhaps the most interesting organizational change of all was the radical reform of the Commission for the Study of Natural Productive Forces (KEPS) which took over a year to enact. The controversial chairman and founder of KEPS, Academician Vernadskii, resigned after his effort to halt the reorganization of the Academy failed. If any one academic body would bear the responsibility for integrating the Academy's research closely with the industrialization program, KEPS was the logical candidate. It was an experienced body; throughout World War I and afterward, KEPS had promoted the exploitation by Russian industry of previously unknown or unutilized natural resources. Large areas of the Soviet Union were still largely unknown, geologically speaking. When the Academy first took up the problem of reorganizing KEPS in March 1929 Academician Ioffe suggested forming some sort of "Scientific State Planning Commission devoted to the study of the country." The Academy appointed a special committee to consider the problem, and released the following statement:

> Our country, despite its many research institutions of all kinds, is still in many respects unexplored. In particular, the great task of studying the distribution of productive forces not only has not been solved, but has not been even started. The creation of a great organization for studying the productive forces of the USSR in the form of a special research

[27] P. G. Shidlovskii, "Sotsialisticheskaia rekonstruktsiia akademii nauk," *Vestnik Akademii Nauk* (No. 7, 1933), p. 20.

institute, devoted to the needs and demands of our national economy—this is one of the urgent and imperative tasks of the Academy of Sciences.[28]

KEPS was combined in 1930 with the old Commission of Expeditionary Researches (KEI) and the Commission for the Study of the Republics into one organization—the Council for the Study of the Productive Forces of the USSR (SOPS), headed by Academician I. M. Gubkin, who was known for his studies of the oil fields of the Caucasus. SOPS was given broad authority to integrate research plans with the national five-year plans. Thus SOPS was not intended to be a mere organ of the Academy, but a planning body of national significance. In the broad lexicon of the Soviet planners, almost any area of knowledge contained "productive forces"; geologists hunting valuable minerals was no more natural a function of the committee than anthropologists and economists studying the workers and peasants as productive elements of society. Consequently, the duties of the new Council included (1) "general direction over the scientific-research activities of all institutions of the Academy in the area of the study of productive forces";[29] (2) "the drafting and working out of projects for the rational use and application of the results of scientific research in agriculture, industry, and socio-cultural development."[30] The Council was designed to tie the work of the Academy more closely to the practical task of industrialization, in contrast to the old KEPS, which the Soviet planners accused of believing in "science for science's sake."

SOPS contained three departments—a Special Planning and Economic Bureau, a Territorial Sector, and a Thematic Sector. The Special Planning and Economic Bureau, with Gubkin at its head, coordinated the work of the Academy with non-Academic institutions, such as the State Planning Commission.

---

[28] "Khronika," *Nauchnyi Rabotnik* (April 1929), p. 102.
[29] *Otchet o deiatel'nosti akademii nauk SSSR za 1930 g.*, p. viii.
[30] Ermakov, "Bor'ba kommunisticheskoi partii," p. 178, lists the duties of SOPS as recorded in the archives of the Academy, f. 1, op. 1, d. 254, l. 27.

The Bureau began its work in October 1931. The Territorial
Sector, headed by Academician N. S. Kurnakov, directed expeditionary work, and was subdivided into several sections,
European, Ural-Siberian, Central-Asian, and others.[31] This sector proved to be by far the most active organ of SOPS, and in
the future years published invaluable information on the natural resources of the Soviet Union. In 1931 alone SOPS sent
107 expeditions to the Soviet Far East, Siberia, Kazakhstan,
Uzbekistan, the Caucasus, and the Crimea.[32] The Thematic
Sector, led by Academician Fersman, dealt with specific subjects of research; its duties were to distribute the assignments
of the national economic organs to the institutions of the Academy, and to ensure that important scientific discoveries were
promoted industrially.

Successful as SOPS was, the grandiose conception of its
activities was never realized. In actual practice, it directed
only the expeditionary work of the Academy, which included
very significant studies of geological formations, hydro-elec-
trical energy sources, soil composition, fauna and flora, and
the economic geography of the districts (*raiony*), regions
(*oblasti*), and republics of the Soviet Union. The study of
man as a productive force was a less fertile venture, although
the Institute for the Study of the Nationalities of the USSR
did coordinate its work with SOPS.

Along with the reorganization of old institutions and the
establishment of new ones, another major task was the drafting of "statutes" for each organization, old and new, in the
Academy. By the end of 1930 every institution in the Academy
possessed an approved statute which defined its goals and

[31] Samoilovich, "Rekonstruktsiia vsesoiuznoi," *VARNITSO* (April-May 1931),
72. Kitaeff's description of Kurnakov's attitude toward the Soviet government
is interesting. "As an intelligent, level-headed person, he could see that any
active attempt to fight it was virtually useless. He kept silent, secluded himself, withdrew into science. In that sense, he was a typical representative of
scientists of that sort. He never engaged in political discussion." Kitaeff, "Akademiia nauk SSSR," p. 21.

[32] Orlov, "Akademiia nauk," col. 25. The value of this work can hardly be
overestimated. By 1957, 98 percent of the USSR had been covered by geological surveys.

structure. Volgin considered such strict definition of responsibilities necessary in order to facilitate the planning of research
work.[33] The drafters of the statutes also tried to reduce what
the Academy's critics called the "guild-like seclusion" (*tsekhov-
shchina*) of its laboratories by creating advisory councils in
each one consisting of scientific workers and representatives
of Party-sponsored organizations.

The new academic atmosphere

To a person who visited the Academy in 1930 or 1931 the
most obvious change from previous years would not be any
organizational reshuffling or greater productivity, but a transformation of the tone of the Academic environment. To the
old guard, the staid Academy seemed scarcely recognizable.
The growing communist faction established a newspaper for
the Academy in April 1930, entitled "For the Socialist Reconstruction of the Academy of Sciences," which directed what at
times seemed more like raucous demolition than reconstruction. Prominent Academicians V. L. Komarov, V. P. Volgin,
A. A. Borisiak, and N. Ia. Marr wrote articles in the paper.
Leafing through the pages of this briefly published paper the
historian can easily sense the strain then existing throughout
the Academy. The Party activists urged young workers to
reveal the discrepancies of their seniors; regular articles listed
the names of Academy employees who were late to work; other
writers condemned the "neutrality" of political belief still prev-
alent in the Academy. An organization both ludicrous and
sinister, the "Light Cavalry," established by the Young Communist League, called on all graduate students and assistants in
the Academy to "intensify the class struggle." The newspaper
advertised the goals of the new organization:

> In the closest contact with the RKI [Workers' and Peas-
> ants' Inspectorate] and under the direction of the Party and
> the Komsomol [Young Communist League] cell group, the

[33] *Otchet o deiatel' nosti akademii nauk SSSR za 1930 g.*, p. ix.

order of the Light Cavalry will strain every effort to aid the reorganization, toward exposing abuses, red tape, wastefulness and everything of an anti-Soviet character.[34]

The Academy became a home for such similarly coarse organizations as the Society of the Militant Godless and the Society of Militant Dialectical Materialists; even some of the proud old generation of academicians, including Ol'denburg, Fersman, and Shcherbatskoi, entered into them.[35]

The injection of politics and ideology into the Academy was also apparent from a speech which Academician Deborin gave to the General Assembly on February 2, 1930, entitled "Lenin and the Crisis of Contemporary Physics." In this speech Deborin maintained that the Leninist writings on science provide the "dependable paths and means of overcoming this crisis," which plagued not only physics but all of science.[36] Dialectical materialism had played no real role in the Academy previously. The philosophical disputes between the Deborinites and the mechanists were familiar to many natural scientists, but the physicists of the Academy had never felt a direct connection between these disputes and their own research. The physicists were among the most international in orientation of the scientists of the Academy; they were fully aware of the implications and controversies surrounding relativity and quantum-mechanical theory, but their attitudes on these subjects were not markedly different from those of scientists in other countries. Even in 1930 ideology was of minor significance in the Academy; Deborin's speech was mainly significant as a harbinger of later developments.[37]

[34] *Za sotsialisticheskuiu rekonstruktsiiu akademii nauk SSSR*, No. 1 (April 1930), p. 1.
[35] "Khronika," *Nauchnyi Rabotnik* (April 1930), p. 88.
[36] *Otchet o deiatel'nosti akademii nauk SSSR za 1929 g.*, I, Appendix, p. 3. The speech is given in its entirety in this reference.
[37] Joravsky, *Soviet Marxism and Natural Science*, p. 295, gives an excellent short analysis of the reasons why the greatest conflicts arose in biology rather than physics, even though Lenin's concerns in science had been primarily over physics. See also my "Quantum Mechanics and Dialectical Materialism," in the *Slavic Review* (September 1966), pp. 381-410; a reference to Deborin's speech is included, p. 383.

The Academy's reformers prided themselves on broadening the contacts of the Academy with the "working masses"; they contrasted the dark and secluded prerevolutionary museums of the Academy with its new institutes, open to the public and almost as involved in educational work as in research. Shidlovskii accused the old Academy of refusing to permit the people to enter its institutions; he wrote that the Academy's library, for example, was accessible only to scholars with special permission and that in 1912 was used only by 400 people who called for a total of 11,000 books, less than one percent of its extensive holdings. The geological museum, he continued, was primarily concerned before the Revolution with the collection of new specimens, and its expeditions continued to amass materials even after the museum was forced to close in 1912 because, as the curators reported, "boxes of specimens, up to thousands of pounds of weight, are blocking not only all the passageways but also are overflowing into the front stairway."[38] Shidlovskii added that this museum, along with several others, had now been converted into a large institute with exhibition halls open to the public.

Shidlovskii's black-and-white contrast between the secluded tsarist Academy and the public Soviet one is not quite borne out by the facts. The rules for the use of the Academy library adopted in 1848 clearly stated that any educated individual could read the volumes in the library, and encouraged a wide use of the library.[39] The Baedeker guide published in 1914 lists the library as being open to the public in the winter on Mondays, Tuesdays, Thursdays, and Fridays from 11 to 3, and lists no restrictions on admission, although the Botanical and Asiatic Museums of the Academy were open only to specialists in those fields. Nevertheless, more than a grain of truth existed in Shidlovskii's criticisms. The tsarist Academy of Sciences was

[38] Shidlovskii, "Sotsialisticheskaia rekonstruktsiia," p. 22. Shortage of funds to purchase display cases and other equipment was the most important reason for the museum's troubles.

[39] *Sbornik postanovlenii i rasporiazhenii otnosiashchikhsia do imperatorskoi akademii nauk*, St. Petersburg, 1869, p. 70.

indeed an intellectually aristocratic institution little interested in the dissemination of popular science. The Academy's library was primarily for scholars, not the general public. The question of whether or not an institution can simultaneously be both mass-oriented and elitist is a perfectly legitimate one, and one which has not yet been answered either in the Soviet Union or abroad.

The planners of the new Academy had long intended to improve the publication and dissemination of scientific literature. Even in 1929, the year of the purge, the total volume of publication continued to increase; in that year the Academy published 209 books, compared to 170 the previous year.[40] The Editorial-Publication Council, created in 1930, began publication of a new journal devoted to "scientific-organizational and scientific-planning problems," *Vestnik Akademii Nauk SSSR*, which has remained to the present day the major journal on the Academy's general activities.[41]

The Academy's relationship with the Belorussian and Ukrainian Academies of Sciences also came to the Party's attention. The Ukrainian Academy had been established by Hetman Skoropadskii on November 14, 1918, and its first president was none other than Academician V. I. Vernadskii, who had gone south during the early part of the Civil War. After the Soviet government regained control over the Ukraine, the Ukrainian Academy was permitted to continue its existence, although the Bolsheviks preferred to ignore its origin.[42] The Belorussian Academy was established considerably later, on January 1, 1929, as an outgrowth of the Institute of Belorussian Culture, whose former head, V. M. Ignatovskii, became its first president; among its first members were the well-known Belorus-

[40] *Otchet o deiatel'nosti akademii nauk SSSR za 1929 g.*, p. vi.

[41] *Otchet o deiatel'nosti akademii nauk SSSR za 1930 g.*, p. 60.

[42] E. Kh. Zankevich, *K istorii*, p. 22. Zankevich points out that the latest edition of BSE incorrectly states that the Ukrainian Academy was founded in 1919 under Soviet power. For a history of the Ukrainian Academy, see N. Polonska-Vasylenko, *Ukrainska Akademiya Nauk* [Institute for the Study of the USSR], 2 vols., Munich, 1955.

sian poets Ianko Kupala and Iakub Kolas.[43] Both academies
passed through crises similar to the all-Union Academy's. In
1928 a commission of the Commissariat of Education of the
Ukrainian republic investigated the Ukrainian Academy and
found serious "defects," including "anti-Soviet reactionary elements masquerading under the slogan of academic freedom."[44]
In May 1928 the Academy was ordered to elect a new presidium, but when the academicians tried to reinstate the old
permanent secretary, A. Iu. Krymskii, the Commissariat of
Education stepped back in and forced the election of Academician Korchak-Chepurkovskii as permanent secretary. The
Ukrainian Academy then bumped along a familiar road of false
charges and purges. Early in 1929 Academician Efremov was
relieved of his administrative duties as a result of his participation in a foreign publication;[45] the membership of the Academy
was doubled by the election of 40 new academicians in the
same year. The unoriginal story of the Ukrainian Academy
even included an archive scandal in the spring of 1930.[46] A
purge followed; justification for the terror, said the Soviet government, was the membership of one academician and several
coworkers in an alleged nationalistic organization, the Union
for the Liberation of the Ukraine.[47] The Belorussian Academy's
day of reckoning came in late 1929 when its permanent secretary, V. U. Lastovskii, was discharged; in the following months
the Belorussian Academy was cleansed of "hostile" and "na-
tional-democratic" elements.[48]

One of the logical ways of coordinating the relations of the
three academies, said the communist members, was on the
basis of "socialist competition"; through friendly rivalry the

[43] *Nauchnyi Rabotnik* (November 1928), pp. 85-86; and (February 1929),
p. 93.
[44] "Khronika," *Nauchnyi Rabotnik* (August-September 1928), p. 92.
[45] "Khronika," *Nauchnyi Rabotnik* (February 1929), p. 93.
[46] "Khronika," *Nauchnyi Rabotnik* (May-June 1930), p. 90.
[47] "Khronika," *Nauchnyi Rabotnik* (December 1929), pp. 92-93.
[48] See "Khronika," *Nauchnyi Rabotnik* (November 1929), pp. 93-94;
(August-September 1930), pp. 88-89; and (November-December 1930), pp.
157-58.

academies could accelerate enactment of the program of reforms and also compete in scientific achievement. In December
1929 and January 1930 the General Assembly of the all-Union
Academy discussed the feasibility of "socialist competition" in
scientific research; Academician Pavlov opposed any kind of
competition among scientists, but was overruled.[49] In February
the all-Union Academy sent delegations to Minsk and Kiev to
draft a formal agreement which representatives of all three
academies signed on March 3. The seven areas of competition
were:

1. The rationalization of the organizational structure of the
   academies and their institutions
2. The degree of planning of scientific research work
3. The role of the academies in the socialist reconstruction
   of the national economy
4. The introduction of Marxist methodology in scientific research work
5. The removal from the academies of mediocre and "anti-
   social" workers
6. The improvement of the qualifications of Academic workers and the preparation of new scientists
7. Work "with the masses" in the area of the cultural revolution.[50]

By May 1, 1930 the academies took upon themselves the
obligation to strengthen bonds with the Communist Academy
and to compose five-year plans of work connected with the
national five-year plans. The agreement included provisions for
rating progress in each of the seven formal areas of competition listed above. On February 2, 1931 a local evaluating

[49] Zelenko, "Rekonstruktsiia vsesoiuznoi," p. 56; also, Arkhiv AN SSSR, f. 2,
op. I-1930, d. 62, l. 2, cited by Ermakov, "Bor'ba kommunisticheskoi partii,"
p. 171. According to "Khronika," *Nauchnyi Rabotnik* (January 1930), pp. 97-
98, the Ukrainian Academy took the initiative in suggesting the agreement on
socialist competition.
[50] Zelenko, "Rekonstruktsiia vsesoiuznoi akademii," p. 56. For a detailed
description of the socialist competition between the academies see "Khronika,"
Nauchnyi Rabotnik (March 1930), pp. 86-87.

committee of the all-Union Academy gave high marks in areas 1, 2, 3, and 5, but noted serious shortcomings in 4, 6, and 7.[51]

The attempt to establish socialist competition between the three academies was, in fact, only one aspect of an overall attempt to transplant "socialist norms" of production from factory labor to scientific research—an attempt which was eminently unsuccessful.[52] Even Soviet observers later noted that some of the statements on socialist competition were overly enthusiastic. For example, one of the requirements of the agreement among all three academies was "to set up individual plans for every worker, precisely fixing the norms of work for each scientific worker," a stipulation which, said Ermakov, discredited the idea of socialist competition.[53]

The concept of socialist competition had not been easily introduced into Soviet factory production, since it seemed very little different from the "exploitative" work norms in capitalistic factories; Lenin felt constrained to point out carefully that

> socialism not only does not eliminate competition, but, on the contrary, creates the opportunity for applying it in a genuinely thorough, massive way. . . . Our task now, when the socialist government is in power—is to organize competition.[54]

The Soviet government enforced competition throughout Soviet industry. The attempted extension of this principle into scientific research failed, however, for a very practical reason: scientific achievement, dependent on long, apparently unproductive labors, cannot be rated within certain previously defined periods of time.

Socialist competition, and its companion principle, the

[51] Samoilovich, "Rekonstruktsiia vsesoiuznoi," p. 70. This committee was the one, already noted, which gave the highest marks to the Archaeographical Commission, the Archives, the Seismological Institute, the Museum of Anthropology and Ethnography, and the Japhetic Institute.
[52] See pp. 47-49.
[53] Ermakov, "Bor'ba kommunisticheskoi partii," p. 172. The requirement of exact norms is in *Kalendar'-spravochnik AN SSSR*, 1931, pp. 71-74.
[54] Lenin, *Sochineniia*, Izd. 3, Moscow, 1929, xxii, 158.

"shock-workers' " movement (*udarnichestvo*) were so heartily disliked by the members of the Academy that they were important in its activities for only a short period of time—at most two years. In October 1930 the Academy announced that 70 employees of the Academy had won the title of "shock-worker," and that seven different institutions had made agreements for socialist competitions among themselves. Under the pressure of Party organizations, the workers of the Academy simply assumed the title of "shock-worker" without appreciably altering their traditional work patterns. By October 1931 over a thousand of the Academy's employees had nominally entered the shock workers' movement.[55] One communist critic observed, "We have cases where the character of the shock-worker obligations are so inconcrete, so broad, that we cannot consider them anything but preliminary declarations."[56] Several institutes simply issued statements that "all work" under their guidance was being conducted according to the principles of the shock-workers' movement.[57]

Political influences on the Academy

In November 1930, the same month in which Academician Platonov was arrested, the trial of the "Industrial Party" was held. Professor Leonid Ramzin, the chief defendant, was convicted of "espionage" and "wrecking" as an "agent of French imperialism."[58] According to the Soviet prosecutor, Vyshinskii, Ramzin's organization was striving for the restoration of capitalism in the Soviet Union.[59]

[55] Orlov, "Akademiia nauk," col. 29.
[56] Stukov, "Vyvody gosudarstvennoi planovoi komissii Gosplana SSSR ob ekspeditsiiakh AN na 1929-30," *VARNITSO* (1929), p. 4.
[57] The Soil Institute early declared all work on an *udarnichestvo* basis.
[58] See Andrew Rothstein, ed., *Wreckers on Trial: A record of the trial of the industrial party held in Moscow, November-December 1930*, New York, 1931.
[59] A. Ia. Vyshinskii, "Delo prompartii," *Nauchnyi Rabotnik* (November-December 1930), pp. 7-25. Academician Ipat'ev, a personal friend of the defendant, was absolutely convinced of his innocence. Ipat'ev cited the fact that Ramzin had no foreign currency when abroad as evidence that he was not in the pay of the French government. (See pp. 11-12 of the Ipat'ev Papers,

The Academy was not drawn into the Industrial Party affair
at first, although it, along with all scientific organizations, was
disturbed by the indirect results. In January 1931 Ernst
Kol'man warned in the journal *Bol'shevik* that the writings of
bourgeois specialists must be examined carefully to separate
the "good from the bad."[60] Kol'man asserted that such apparently innocent information as locations of fisheries grounds,
compiled by bourgeois ichthyologists, might be purposely
misleading in order to enhance the failure of the government's
fisheries plan. The first sign that a member of the Academy
was to be drawn into the net of conspiracy was Rykov's statement on February 16, 1931 to a meeting of engineering workers
that the arrested scholar of the Academy, S. V. Rozhdestvenskii, had testified that his fellow historian Platonov had plotted
to seat Grand Prince Andrei Vladimirovich on the throne.[61]
Then on April 26 another contingent of Academic employees
was arrested and accused of participation in a counterrevolutionary organization which aimed to overthrow the Soviet
government and establish a constitutional monarchy. The members of the new government, the Soviet police charged, were
to include Academician Platonov as prime minister; Academician Tarle as minister of foreign affairs, and Professor Rozhdestvenskii as minister of education.[62]

As was the case with the other charges of counterrevolutionary activities, there is absolutely no evidence to support these
accusations; even Soviet authors have admitted that Platonov
probably knew nothing of his inclusion in the "government."[63]

Vol. III, Northwestern University.) Michael Samygin, on the other hand, considered Ramzin guilty. Samygin, also writing in exile, believed that the Industrial Party was quite influential in the Academy and said Academician
P. P. Lazarev was closely connected with the underground organization. The
goal of the Party, said Samygin, was to convert the Soviet Union into a
technocracy, directed by men of genuine technical accomplishments. Samygin,
"Terror v akademii nauk," Research Program on the History of the Communist
Party of the Soviet Union, Russian Archive, Columbia University, XII (typed).
   [60] E. Kol'man, "Vreditel'stvo v nauke," *Bol'shevik* (January 31, 1931), pp.
73-81.
   [61] Belomortsev, "Bol'shevizatsiia akademii nauk," p. 11.
   [62] *Ibid.*
   [63] Ermakov, "Bor'ba kommunisticheskoi partii," p. 126.

In the post-Stalin period the Soviet government has frequently admitted that trials in the 1930s were often based on fabrications. The accusations against the Academy were merely convenient weapons for use in the process of reconstructing the institution along Stalinist lines.[64]

The submission of the Academy to planning

The Academy of Sciences was, until its Bolshevization and even after, a major center of resistance to the idea of planning science. The academicians believed their freedom to choose their own topics of research could not continue to exist if the State Planning Commission, or any other organ, attempted to integrate the Academy's research with national economic plans. The academicians expressed little interest even in the Academy itself becoming the supreme planning body in science, as a few people suggested; since they doubted that science could be planned *in principle*, discussions of the mechanics of planning seemed irrelevant. No doubt they realized that orders issued by the presidium in the name of the member academicians could be as dictatorial as decisions made by an organ completely outside the Academy.

In the early years of the reform period, the leaders of the Academy did not hesitate to speak out on the subject of planning. In 1926 Vice-president Fersman told a Leningrad meeting of scientific organizations that "the organization of scientific-research under the flag of planning organs is an enormous mistake."[65] The same year Secretary Ol'denburg warned a working meeting of the State Planning Commission: "Do not forget that science is not national, it does not belong to one government, it is international, and it is impossible to

[64] The ludicrousness of the charges is further shown by the accusation that the conspirators carried on negotiations with the Pope. Tarle, not a Christian, may have purposely admitted responsibility for contacts with Rome in order to make the entire proceeding appear ridiculous. Konstantin Shteppa further reported that one of the alleged plotters told him that he was forced to confess. Shteppa, *Russian Historians,* p. 49.

[65] TsGAOR, f. 4394, op. 1, d. 1, l. 101, cited by Ermakov, "Bor'ba kommunist-icheskoi partii," p. 190.

harness it to a plan, for the normal development of science cannot in any way be confined to the too-simple framework of planning."[66]

The first Five-Year Plan (1928-32) did not contain a section listing the work of the Academy, since the academicians still did not consider their research a proper subject for such prognostications. The State Planning Commission did send invitations to representatives of the Academy to attend the planning congresses for this first long-range plan, and the Academy accepted, but its delegates there acted only as observers and technical advisors, not as participants.

The introduction of planning into the Academy proceeded step by step with the admission of the first communist academicians and the general Sovietization of the Academy. As noted previously, the Party presented the Academy with a clear ultimatum before the elections in early 1929; either the Academy would elect the Party candidates or be replaced as the supreme scientific body of the Soviet Union. In either case, the Academy's research work would be subject to the national plans. If the Academy cooperated in the elections it might have a large voice in drawing up its own plans; if it continued its resistance it would become a mere subordinate to the Communist Academy, or to an association of Marxist scientific and scholarly institutes. The members of the Society of Marxist Scientists, VARNITSO, led the ranks of the new Soviet intelligentsia calling for the dethronement of the venerable Academy of Sciences.

As discussed in Chapter III, after a short but spirited resistance the Academy buckled before the demands. It was flooded with communists and the renovation of the nation's supreme scientific body began. Less than two months after the crucial elections, the Academy took up the entangled problem of introducing planning in all its institutions. At the General Assembly meeting from March 4 to 7, 12 special academic

[66] *Ibid.*

committees were appointed to consider planning of work in the different disciplines.[67]

These signs of conversion provoked mixed emotions among the Marxist scientific organizations that had been attacking the Academy; several of them seemed disappointed. Perhaps the ambitions of some politically active scientists had been whetted by the possibility that the Academy of Sciences would have to be replaced; now it was being reformed instead. Or perhaps the militant organizations were aware of how much resistance still resided in the Academy. At any rate, they underscored the incompleteness of the Academy's reconstruction. VARNITSO's mistrust of the Academy was reflected in the resolution of its presidium in May 1929, which called for the drafting of national scientific research plans but added the warning, "The planning of the scientific research work of the whole Union cannot and must not be the affair of the all-Union Academy of Sciences."[68] Even the Communist Party itself seemed doubtful about the Academy's future; a resolution of the Central Committee on May 27, 1929 strengthened the role of the Communist Academy relative to the other institutions in the country; it would henceforth have general "methodological direction" over all governmental scientific organizations in the country.[69] And even as late as April 1931 Iarilov from VARNITSO warned, "it is not without purpose that every day the significance of the Communist Academy as a directing theoretical center is growing."[70]

On the other hand, the academicians believed that, regardless of other changes occurring in the Academy, its scientific preeminence was incontestable. The older academicians justifiably disparaged the Communist Academy's feeble attempts to conduct research in the natural sciences; the newer Marxist

[67] "Khronika," *Nauchnyi Rabotnik* (April 1929), p. 102.
[68] *VARNITSO* (No. 3, 1929), pp. 13-14.
[69] "O meropriatiiakh po ukrepleniiu nauchnoi raboty," *Nauchnyi Rabotnik* (September 1929), pp. 124-25.
[70] *Vsesoiuznaia konferentsiia po planirovaniiu nauchno-issledovatel' skoi raboty, 1-ia,* Moscow–Leningrad, 1931, p. 63.

academicians undisguisedly valued their memberships in the Academy of Sciences over their legally equal status in the Communist Academy. The seizure of the Academy of Sciences by the communists destroyed the *raison d'être* of the Communist Academy, although six years passed before the Academy of Sciences absorbed the fragments of its former Bolshevik competitor, in a fashion similar to the Academy of Sciences' much earlier absorption of the Russian Academy.[71] The Academy of Sciences was an extraordinarily durable organization.

Strengthened by its Bolshevik baptism in 1929, the Academy began asserting its superiority among the other scientific organizations of the country. In April 1930 Academician Borisiak challenged VARNITSO's view that the Academy could not coordinate all scientific research; indeed, the Academy was the logical organization for directing research on the all-Union level:

> The scientific institutions of the Academy . . . must be in agreement with the other scientific-research institutions of the Union. In those areas of science where the Academy of Sciences assumes the responsibility for determining the most important immediate tasks . . . its work . . . often will not coincide with the work of other institutions. In these instances . . . the coordination of the work of these institutions, both among themselves and with the Academy, must take place in special commissions belonging to the Academy.[72]

The Academy's relative position was also elevated by the

[71] A Soviet author described the Communist Academy's demise thus: "In 1936 the Council of Peoples Commissars and the Central Committee of the Communist Party recognized the inconsistency of the parallel existence of two academies—the Academy of Sciences of the USSR and the Communist Academy, and, with the aim of uniting the men of science in one governmental scientific center, decided on the expedient solution of liquidating the *Komakademiia* and transferring its institutions and chief workers to the Academy of Sciences of the USSR." Fed'kin, *Pravovye voprosy*, p. 35. Also, see *Izvestiia*, February 8, 1936.

[72] *Za sotsialisticheskuiu rekonstruktsiiu akademii nauk SSSR*, No. 1 (April 1930).

weaknesses of its competitors. Kol'man noted the distressing fact that until 1931 the Communist Academy still had not converted its Technical Section into a body capable of leading the technological thought of the country.[73] Furthermore, the Communist Academy's reputation was tarnished by "deviations" from the Stalinist position; Deborin, Bukharin, Pokrovskii, and Riazanov had all played much more important roles in the Communist Academy than they had in the Academy of Sciences; transgressions of the Communist Academy, created specifically as a Marxist intellectual counterbalance to "bourgeois" institutions, somehow seemed more reprehensible than those of the understandably backward Academy of Sciences.[74]

Before the Academy could accept any sort of general planning obligations, however, it had to settle the quarrels over planning still raging within its own walls. The mere admission of communist academicians had not solved the problem of how the work of the Academy could actually be programmed. In 1929, after the elections, the academicians were asked to submit work plans for the first time. The results were in many ways comical. Academician Pavlov replied that he found it impossible to compose such a plan because the development of his work would define the problems he later would work on, and he could not yet foresee this development.[75] Academician Vernadskii, then still head of the Commission for the Study of Natural Productive Forces, submitted a one and a half page plan with a few comments about financial and personal problems.[76] The five-year plan of Academician Gulevich was 17 lines long, and Academician Favorskii's was 10 lines.[77] Academician Platonov, chairman of Pushkin House, wrote that his goal was to obtain as many as possible of the following items: bookstands, cupboards, and boxes.[78]

[73] Kol'man, "Vreditel'stvo," p. 80.

[74] Pokrovskii was not officially criticized until after his death on April 13, 1932; in August of that year the Party Central Committee noted "inadequacies" in the study of history.

[75] Arkhiv AN SSSR, f. 103, op. 1, d. 11, l. 44, cited by Ermakov, "Bor'ba kommunisticheskoi partii," p. 202.

[76] *Ibid.*, l. 109.   [77] *Ibid.*, ls. 16-17.   [78] *Ibid.*, l. 127.

A number of academicians made a final attempt to fence off a certain section of scientific research from any planning controls whatsoever. These scientists proposed that the Academy's research be divided into two categories—pure and applied. All the institutions engaged in applied research would be united, for planning purposes, in one large organization named the Mendeleev Institute, while all those doing research in pure science would be combined into a Lomonosov Institute. The work of the Mendeleev Institute would be carefully coordinated with the national five-year plans and would be conducted on the basis of strict programing. The Lomonosov Institute, however, would be a refuge of pure, theoretical science where scientific creativity could flourish in complete freedom from planning controls.[79]

The plan had no real chance to succeed; its "separation of theory from practice," embodied physically, was in direct contradiction to the current interpretation of dialectical materialism. Academician Bakh took the proposal to task in VARNITSO's journal; he maintained that applied research involves the same sort of creativity as pure research, and that if one can plan the former, one can also plan the latter. Even the "bourgeois" scientist Pasteur, Bakh noted, had long ago written that there is no pure science and no applied science, but only applications of science.[80]

The inevitability of planning as a principle was indicated by events early in 1930. The new charter for the Academy, approved by the Central Executive Committee (TsIK) in May, unmistakably stated that planning science was an obligation of all academicians. G. M. Krzhizhanovskii, the new vice-president of the Academy, was also the chairman of the State Planning Commission (Gosplan) and exercised the most important

[79] The names of the academicians who suggested this plan are unknown. The idea must have attracted considerable attention, however, since Academician A. N. Bakh discusses it as a serious proposal in his article, "Vsesoiuznaia akademiia nauk i sotsialisticheskoe stroitel'stvo," *Front Nauki i Tekhniki* (October 1932), p. 22.
[80] *Ibid.*

planning powers in the Academy. To assist him the Presidium
established in April and May a Planning-Organization Commission (POK) under the chairmanship of Academician Marr,
with assistants Komarov and Volgin.[81] The duties of POK were
to direct the compilation of research plans within the Academy
and to coordinate these plans with the overall plans of socialist
construction.[82] The Presidium directed the Commission to draw
up the "general principles of planning" for ratification by the
General Assembly in the fall.

During the discussion of these planning principles the emotions of several of the academicians again flared. At a meeting
of the physicists and mathematicians Academician A. N. Krylov noted that the great mathematician Gauss pondered for
seven years a certain problem and then solved it in a few
moments. Krylov then turned to the proponents of planned science with the comment, "And yet you would compose a systematic plan for mathematics when even Gauss was not able to
work in a planned fashion."[83]

By October 1930, however, the academicians were willing
to consent to the "idea" of planning, even though they continued to debate its methodology. Academician Nadson even
declared that the planning of science is a natural necessity,
and referred to the experiment in the planning of science by
the Americans as an example of its feasibility.[84]

Academician Bakh attacked the problem of methodology
with his suggestion that planning should start from individual
laboratories and build up to the central organs:

> We believe that the basic, initial cell in the process of
> planning should be, first of all, the scientific-research insti-
> tution itself. Keeping in view the plan of economic construc-

[81] *Otchet o deiatel'nosti akademii nauk SSSR za 1930 g.,* p. xi. Iarilov,
"Staraia i novaia," says POK was not established until October 1930.
[82] *Ibid.,* p. 50.
[83] TsGAOR, f. 3316, op. 23, d. 572, l. 387, cited by Ermakov, "Bor'ba
kommunisticheskoi partii," pp. 205-206.
[84] TsGAOR, f. 3316, op. 23, d. 573, l. 250, cited by Ermakov, "Bor'ba
kommunisticheskoi partii," p. 206.

tion for a given length of time, fully informed on the material and personnel resources of the institution, its governing collective can, better than anyone else, decide how to use the potentialities which it possesses for fulfilling the assignments which the country faces.[85]

This approach to the planning of science, known as the "arithmetic sum" method, was also favored by Academician Borisiak, who had this method in mind when he urged the Academy to assert itself in planning science on a national scale. Borisiak believed that the "groups" in the departments of the Academy, established by the 1930 charter, should be the planning initiators; in this way the individuality of brilliant scientists would not be smothered.[86]

The "arithmetic sum" method came under heavy attack from several of the communist academicians at the meeting of the General Assembly in early October 1930. If the Academy was the mere sum of its institutions, these critics maintained, then, in turn, the institutions could be thought of as the sum of its individual academicians, and the old "chaotic" situation would have been restored. Volgin opposed the arithmetic sum method, even though it was somewhat similar to his own defense of planning, on the grounds that "every individual scientific worker always has some kind of good or bad mental plan of scientific work."[87] The General Assembly rejected the arithmetic sum method of planning and decided that "the plans of the separate institutions must be drawn up on the basic lines of scientific-research work."[88]

At the same meeting of the General Assembly on October

[85] A. N. Bakh, "K voprosu o planirovanii raboty nauchno-issledovatel'skikh uchrezhdenii soiuza," *VARNITSO* (No. 3, 1929), p. 1.

[86] A. Borisiak, "K rabote podkomissii po uchrezhdeniiam otdeleniia fiziko-matematicheskikh nauk," *Za sotsialisticheskuiu rekonstruktsiiu akademii nauk SSSR* (April 1930), p. 2. This "arithmetic sum method," the essence of which is that small bodies of scientific workers would determine the basic policies of their institutions, bears some resemblance to the "workers' control" deviations in Soviet factories. There, as in the Academy, centralized control from above became the approved policy.

[87] *Otchet o deiatel'nosti akademii nauk SSSR za 1930 g.*, pp. x-xi.

[88] *Ibid.*

3, 1930 the academicians defined three different types of problems in science to be planned:

1. Comprehensive theoretical problems, "the solving of which, in the final analysis, always proves to have a great influence on practice in the most diverse directions."

2. Problems connected with socialist reconstruction and the five-year plans, "especially the problems of grain and fuel."

3. Problems connected with the cultural revolution, "especially in the national republics and regions [*oblasti*]."[89]

The Assembly affirmed that all three types of problems would be subject to planning; no division of functions along the lines of the suggested Lomonosov and Mendeleev Institutes could satisfy both socialist construction and dialectical materialism.

Volgin gave in his report for 1930 a summary of the way in which the Academy's work plans were to be drafted.[90] The method was one of frequent consultation between high and low levels, but with all final authority resting on the higher levels. Volgin said that the State Planning Commission assigned the task of drawing up scientific research plans to its "Science Section" (*sektsiia nauki*), which at first seemed to be the long-awaited planning body for science. The Science Section held regular meetings to establish the broad outlines of future scientific research. The delegates attending the meetings were representatives of the Academy of Sciences, the Communist Academy, the Lenin Academy of Agricultural Sciences, the Supreme Economic Council, the Academic Committee (*uchenyi komitet*) of the Central Executive Committee, VARNITSO, the Young Communist League, the Central Bureau of the Section of Scientific Workers, the Commissariat of Workers' and Peasants' Inspection, and the State Planning Commission.[91] The Science Section then presented the scientific institutions

[89] *Ibid.*, p. xi.
[90] *Ibid.*
[91] Arkhiv Akademii Nauk, f. 277, op. 3, d. 31, l. 34; cited by Ermakov, "Bor'ba kommunisticheskoi partii," p. 200.

of the country, including the State Planning Commission, with
the basic guidelines of their work, i.e., what problems each of
the major institutions should work on, and what problems
carried the highest priority. The institutions then drew up their
own plans; in the case of the Academy of Sciences, the thematic sector of the Council for the Study of Productive Forces
(SOPS) and the Planning-Organizational Commission (POK)
supervised this work. The final intermeshing of all the plans
was to occur at large conferences called by the State Planning
Commission and attended by representatives of all the scientific institutes in the country, as well as delegates from interested governmental offices, such as the Commissariats of
Education and Agriculture.

The planning procedure never managed to work according
to this blueprint. The delegates to the meetings of the Science
Section merely transferred their feuds to that level. The scientists capable of the most outstanding research, the academicians, continued to be suspicious of the planning of science,
even though they now usually paid lip service to the principle.
Volgin complained that many delegates invited to the planning
conferences failed to attend.[92] In 1930 the Academy made a
second attempt to draw up a plan of work (the first try had
been in 1929, when many of the academicians failed to submit
more than a few lines).[93] This time both a one-year and a five-
year plan were composed, but although the results were more
satisfactory than the previous year the government judged the
plans unsuitable because of their "unsystematic character and
the lack of ties with socialist construction."[94] Volgin concluded
ruefully, "In 1931 we must draw up the plans earlier and check
and agree on them in a more organized fashion, with the active
participation of Gosplan, VSNKh, and a broader circle of
scientific institutions."[95]

The crisis over the control and planning of scientific research

[92] *Otchet o deiatel' nosti akademii nauk SSSR za 1930 g.*, p. xii.
[93] See above, p. 180.
[94] Ermakov, "Bor'ba kommunisticheskoi partii," p. 207.
[95] *Otchet o deiatel' nosti akademii nauk SSSR za 1930 g.*, p. xii.

in the Academy was at its peak when the all-Union Conference
for the Planning of Scientific-Research Work met in April 1931.
At that meeting Bukharin found himself at cross-purposes with
Molotov over the question of threatening scientists with re-
prisals.[96] Bukharin coldly warned the scientists sitting before
him:

> The workers of the USSR, sacrificing many of today's needs
> for the good of the future, developing fearful energy, demon-
> strating the wonders of heroic labor and exertion, cannot beg
> the pardon of the servitors of capitalism, of the great powers
> of imperialism: they are obligated before history to send
> physically or spiritually to the *guillotine* the saboteurs, the
> subversive wreckers, the agents of imperialist intelligence.
> . . . All technicians, engineers, and scientists must understand
> that history has posed again a basic question about two
> camps, in all its sharpness: for there is no third, and one
> must definitely *choose*, and choose boldly, directly, deci-
> sively, irrevocably.[97]

In a subsequent speech at the same conference Molotov disagreed with Bukharin's aggressive approach; he pulled in the
leash leading to the Party's propagandists and local workers.
Molotov comforted the scientists who, he said, had become
overly frightened by recent events in their institutions, and
asked the press to stop badgering them. He said that although
dialectical materialism corresponds to the interest of science,
forcing it on science can be harmful. He specifically warned
against the "dressing down" of "those specialists who still have
not accepted the correctness of the Marxist–Leninist scientific
method."[98]

The explanation for this difference of opinion between
Bukharin and Molotov is not clear. Bukharin's past position on

[96] The difference between Bukharin and Molotov at this conference may
have been connected with the recent conflict between Stalin and the "Right
Opposition." See below.

[97] *Vsesoiuznaia konferentsiia po planirovaniiu nauchnoissledovatel'skoi raboty, 1-ia*, p. 18.

[98] *Ibid.*, pp. 382-87.

industrialization was more moderate than that of such Stalinists as Molotov. One could guess that Bukharin, who was often associated with scientists, would have been the person urging restraint in policies toward science, rather than Molotov. It may be that Bukharin was trying to prove that he no longer stood for "moderate" policies, that he could be more "Left" than Molotov. Or it could be that Bukharin was explaining to the assembled scientists that, in view of recent political events, he could no longer protect them, as some of them may have thought he could do in the past. In this latter interpretation, Bukharin may actually have been confessing his powerlessness.

In August Bukharin corrected himself and simultaneously signaled a decrease in the pace of the terror. Bukharin's committee in charge of personnel in the Academy published an article maintaining that the Academy had been thoroughly reformed and should no longer be packed with Marxist graduate students merely for the purpose of coercion; the emphasis should now be on obtaining graduate students of high quality.[99]

In this slightly more relaxed atmosphere the Academy returned to the task of composing an acceptable work plan. The first such plan was the Academy's program of research for 1931, which was not completed until the year was half over.[100] The plan met the requirements of the State Planning Commission and the Council of Peoples Commissars, but its defects were well known to the members of the Academy; Academician Borisiak confided in a letter to Academician Komarov that the work plan of the Botanical Garden was not a plan but a list of Latin names of plants written in the Russian alphabet.[101] Nevertheless, the program was more serious in intent and more detailed in the descriptions of future research than any previous plan. In a few months, the General Assembly approved the research plan of the Academy for the following

---

[99] N. Bukharin *et al.*, "Podgotovka nauchnykh kadrov i akademiia nauk," *Pravda*, August 24, 1931, p. 4.

[100] *Proizvodstvennyi plan akademii nauk SSSR na 1931 g.*, Leningrad, 1931.

[101] Arkhiv AN SSSR, f. 277, op. 2, d. 67, l. 2, cited by Ermakov, "Bor'ba kommunisticheskoi partii," pp. 214-15.

year (1932); the new plan also won governmental approval.
Most important of all, the Academy was composing a draft of
a plan to cover the second five-year period, and on November
17, 1932 the General Assembly approved this 142-page document. Thus the Academy had definitely adopted the idea of
planned research, and continued on that basis, although all
difficulties were far from resolved.[102]

The problem of overall coordination of Soviet science

The problem of creating a supreme coordinating science
committee seemed much simpler after the Academy submitted
to the national economic plan. The last obstacle had been
cleared. Strangely enough, again the committee or commissariat failed to appear; the reason for the omission surely lies in
the political situation. As Fed'kin indicated, the Party no
longer seemed interested in the idea of a central scientific
committee—most of the steam had gone out of the entire
reform movement. The dissenting and often stimulating discussions over the creation of a new relationship between
science and society were silenced. The grip of Stalinism had
closed on the entire society. Anyone reading Soviet journals
over the period 1927 to 1932 will notice an essential qualitative
difference: the earlier articles are provocative and original,
compared to the later monotonous and uninspired offerings.

Nevertheless, the tremendous physical growth of science
continued, and the Academy occupied an expanding role.
Between 1917 and 1930 the role of the Academy of Sciences
in the total scene of Soviet science had shrunk, but after the
reorganization the status of the Academy began to grow again.
There were many signs of this expansion; some institutions
that had been previously outside the Academy, such as the

[102] The mere submission of the Academy to the principle of planning did
not mean that the Communist Party was in complete control of the plans.
Michael Samygin began working in the Academy in 1936 and remarked that
genuine Party control of the Academy's research was just barely beginning at
that time. Michael Samygin, "Partiinoi kontrol' i kontrol' MVD v akademii nauk
SSSR," p. 4, in "Riad otryvok vospominanii ob akademii nauk SSSR v 1920
godakh i 1930 godakh," Russian Archive, Columbia University.

Botanical Garden and the Museum of Anthropology and Ethnography, were now brought inside the Academic framework. In the absence of any other senior science committee, the Academy was assuming, by default, functions completely outside its normal ones. Consequently, in July 1930 the Academy assumed "cultural patronage" (*kul'turnoe shefstvo*) over the military and naval establishments, an inaccurate term reflecting a generally amorphous relationship.[103] The Academy was nevertheless moving toward a position at the pinnacle of Soviet science and technology. As the Academy became more involved in applied science it recovered some organs which had previously been taken away from it, such as the State Optical Institute.[104] Another example of the expanding authority of the Academy was the formation of the Committee of Scientific Consultation and Scientific Propaganda, which soon assumed much of the national responsibility for the dissemination of popular scientific information, even though the Academy had no monopoly on this information. Again, the reason for this expansion was the enormous prestige and talent of the Academy, which far exceeded that of any other body in the Soviet Union.

[103] "Khronika," *Nauchnyi Rabotnik* (July 1930), p. 86.
[104] *Vestnik Akademii Nauk* (May 1932), col. 50.

CHAPTER VI

A NEW SCIENCE?

In his unceasing desire for freedom . . . man rends one after another of all the chains which fetter him, but there is one chain which he never flings off, but forges ever stronger and stronger—that is the anchor chain of the development of human thought, and every honest scientific researcher feels and must feel that he is a link in that great chain. / The report of the Academy of Sciences for the revolutionary year 1918[1]

The fate of socialist science

The revolutionaries who came to power in Soviet Russia believed they would create a new culture. The adherents of the theory of proletarian culture believed the new culture would begin to develop quickly, during the initial period of the dictatorship of the proletariat. Others, aware that this period should be relatively short, predicted a novel culture only after the creation of a socialist state. A number of other revolutionary thinkers believed that the new culture would contain important elements of past cultures. All, however, subscribed in some degree to the belief that culture is a derivative superstructure above the economic base and that a modification of the base inevitably results in a transformation of culture. Science was one of the layers of culture—perhaps the highest layer—and would also acquire unique characteristics. These characteristics would include a new theory of the place of science in society,

[1] *Otchet o deiatel'nosti Rossiiskoi akademii nauk za 1918*, Petrograd, 1919, p. 1.

a more fertile economic environment for technological growth, unprecedented governmental support for research, a superior organizational scheme of research institutes, and a methodology for the planning of science. A socialist science would eventually evolve, a science superior to all its capitalist competitors. That transformation would be difficult, but the final product would be worth the cost.

By 1932 one could easily see that Soviet science was experiencing a transformation. What sort of transformation was it? Beyond any doubt, the nation's science and technology program was undergoing a vast physical expansion. During the first five-year plan the total enrollment in engineering and industrial specialties jumped almost 450 percent.[2] The introduction of compulsory education in 1930 was an effort to sustain continued expansion. Hundreds of thousands of students were funneled into higher educational institutions and the best were attracted and cajoled into science. The Academy of Sciences was converted from a society of scientists into an enormous governmental institution, endowed with both research and pedagogical functions, and spread throughout the Soviet Union. Fundamental decisions concerning the organization of scientific research had been reached which remain valid today. The Soviet Union was creating a network of laboratories, organized on the institute system, which departed from the more conventional university laboratories and industrial institutes elsewhere in the world. The Soviet Academy of Sciences was the only one of the 18th century academies of science of Europe that continued to dominate the scientific research of its nation in the 20th century. Research in the Academy, as well as in the universities and industries, was at least formally conducted on the basis of the planning principles which had evolved in the years of the first five-year plan.

And yet, all this development was not in itself what the reformers of Soviet science had aimed to achieve. In Hegelian

[2] Nicholas DeWitt, *Education and Professional Employment in the U.S.S.R.*, Washington, 1961, p. 318.

terms a transformation of quantity had occurred, but the goal had been a transformation of quality. The unique Soviet science did not appear. Future years would demonstrate ever more clearly that Soviet science, impressive as it became, would compete with the science of other nations on the same terms by which the scientists of those nations rated each other. In the Soviet Union, the ideologists eventually admitted that the natural sciences are not in the ideological superstructure.[3]

The fate of the attempt to reform science was paralleled by those of other better known experiments of the 1920s. The liberal laws on marriage and divorce, the experiments in elementary education, the creation of new forms in art, theatre, and literature—all these innovations were also halted as political control tightened upon Soviet society. At the end of the NEP period the Party adopted a policy of rapid industrialization and collectivization requiring terror for its enforcement. This violence stifled the intellectual content of the revolutionary movement. The theoreticians were replaced by *apparatchiki*, led by the most adept of them all, Stalin.

It would be a mistake, however, to blame the failure of the attempt to reform science entirely on Stalin, even though he was guilty of far worse crimes. The original plan itself was faulty, not only because it required violence to enforce, but because some of its premises were incorrect.

The basic premise of the reform movement in science was that science, like art or law or literature, has a public character which is of primary importance. This assumption was incorrect. The retreat from the belief that a socialist science could be created was much more marked than the similar retrenchments in the areas of culture which more conveniently fit into the Marxist superstructure. The natural sciences did not cleave to standard Soviet Marxist categories and did not respond to the attempts of the Soviet communists to draw them into the social sphere.

The unique position of the sciences was apparent throughout

[3] See references at bottom of p. 38.

the entire period under study and was evidenced primarily by the reluctance of the Party to initiate a reform of the Academy. This observation should not be taken to mean that the Party intended all along to subject the Academy to the kind of violent conquest which actually occurred. In the 1920s the Party was divided in its attitudes toward science, and certainly was not merely waiting for the tactically best moment for an attack on the Academy. Some Party spokesmen believed that the academicians would spontaneously come to the side of the Party; others believed it would gradually be replaced by Marxist institutions like the Communist Academy; still others believed that even politically hostile scientists could serve the interests of the Soviet state indefinitely. But despite this spectrum of attitudes toward the Academy, the Party leaders looked forward to the moment when, as a result of one process or another, the Academy or its equivalent was politically committed to the Soviet regime and willing to help promote an expanding science program under new conditions. The speeches of Party activists revealed that any discussion of how this conversion could occur encountered problems totally unlike those presented by other institutions.

Once the reform in the natural sciences had begun, their differences from the social sciences and humanities became even more apparent. Lenin's dictum that "Law is politics" made reform of the legal system seem relatively straightforward.[4] Soviet Marxism contained no such simple description of natural science, not even in terms of the superstructure theories, which usually hedged on the most important points. Natural science is not politics. The many areas in which natural science touches upon, and relates to, politics should not blind one to the differences between them. The effects of science are often political, its philosophy may have political implications, its promotion

---

[4] The reform of the legal system was not simple, however. For a discussion of the unsuccessful early Soviet attempts to substitute a primitive law court based on the judge's "revolutionary conscience" for a complex judicial system, see John N. Hazard, *Settling Disputes in Soviet Society: The Formative Years of Legal Institutions*, New York, 1960.

is usually political, and it is, in turn, frequently affected by politics, but the practice of science is divisible from the practice of politics.

Another considerable error of the Marxists was their view of the history of natural science. They believed that natural science, in the final analysis, develops in response to the needs of material production; ideas alone, they said, cannot govern the development of the sciences. The origin of scientific progress, according to the Marxists, was ultimately the need for economic and material improvement. This theory seemed more exciting in the late 19th and early 20th centuries than it does today. Modern research into the sociology of science points to a number of factors affecting the development of science, of which economic progress is only one; intellectual, political, and religious influences have also qualified the development of science.[5] The specific characteristics of scientific development in ancient China, the French Revolution, Renaissance, medieval period, Nazi Germany, and Soviet Russia cannot all be explained on the basis of the economic foundations of those societies. Furthermore, scientific and technological innovations are often not products of pressing material necessity. Derek Price has commented on the absence of a "social need" for the development of certain scientific gadgets of the 17th century: "Curiously enough, this movement does not seem to have sprung into being in response to any need or desire on the part of the scientists for devices they might use to make experiments and perform measurements. Galileo and Hooke extended their senses by telescope and microscope, but it took decades before these tools found further application."[6]

The old controversy over whether social demand or new scientific knowledge is the primary influence on the development of science is probably an eternal question with no manifest answer, as are many genuine historical and philosophical questions. Neither social necessity nor scientific theorization is primary in all situations; the relationship is intertwined. The

[5] See Barber, *Science and Social Order*, p. 31.
[6] Derek J. de Solla Price, *Science Since Babylon*, New Haven, 1961, p. 27.

hero-theory of invention and discovery, which so long dominated the history of science, was in great need of revision. Such authors as S. C. Gilfillan in his *Sociology of Invention* provided welcome counterbalances to the hero-theory by stressing that social need, perceived through the profit motive, is a cause of invention. The number of books in the 1930s and 1940s, written both by Marxists and non-Marxists, which emphasized the "social roots of science," expanded the neglected aspect of the history of science. By the middle of the century, however, the value of this viewpoint had been exaggerated and a countervailing interpretation became more important.

The Marxist denial of the categories of "pure" and "applied" science was also valuable in the context of the late 19th century attitude toward science. The old manner of dividing the sciences into sharply delineated "pure" and "applied" categories has been discredited; the applications of many research projects even in abstract mathematics and logic, not to speak of physics, chemistry, and biology, prohibit the easy assignment of labels. Similarly, advanced engineering, especially in the fields of automation and cybernetics, explore and help explain basic human concepts and values so acutely that one should not unhesitatingly classify this work as "derivative" or "applied."[7] Nevertheless, a sophisticated use of the terms "pure" and "applied" is helpful even if not universally applicable. Research which has as a primary goal the enlargement or creation of conceptual systems may be classified, for convenience, as "pure." Research which aims at a purpose other than conceptualization may be classified as "applied." Between the two ends of the spectrum there will be many research projects that cannot be classified.[8]

[7] Ortega y Gasset's comments are appropriate here: "Pure contemplation does not exist and cannot exist. When we stand before the universe unmoved by any personal interest we see nothing well. . . . The most favorable position for gathering knowledge . . . lies somewhere in between pure contemplation and pressing interest. Some vital interests that are not too narrow and oppressive are required for organizing our contemplation. . . ." *The Dehumanization of Art and Other Writings on Art and Culture*, Garden City, N.Y., n.d., pp. 77-79.

[8] See Barber, *Science and Social Order*, p. 135; and Conant, *Science and Common Sense*, pp. 57-60, 312-15.

The particular interpretation of the doctrine of the unity of theory and practice which was accepted in the early thirties resulted in a distortion of the pattern of Soviet scientific research. The link between research in the centers of theoretical work and that in the engineering institutions was exaggerated. Academicians trained in physics and mathematics became, in some cases, consulting engineers. To a certain extent this distortion was understandable. It was a correction, carried to an extreme, of Russia's earlier tradition, which was weak in engineering. It was, further, a response to the need to industrialize rapidly. The sacrifice of some basic research in such a period is not surprising. But the exaggeration required, in time, yet another correction in the opposite direction. After World War II the goal of the Soviet Union in science and technology became the surpassing of the West in all fields of scientific work, not just in industrial technology. The new emphasis necessitated new organizational changes. The Academy shed some of its more restricted engineering duties.[9]

The policy toward science and technology adopted in the Soviet Union in the late twenties is not without irony. A number of Marxists of the early twenties believed a narrow utilitarian attitude toward science was a peculiarly capitalist defect. The Western industrialist was the person who supposedly asked of each scientific innovation not what it could do for mankind, but what profit it could bring him. There is considerable truth in this criticism of science and technology in capitalist countries. In the West research in the industrial laboratories has indeed largely been governed by the desire for profit. Even university research in Britain and the United States has often

[9] The reform of Soviet science announced on April 12, 1961 included the removal of many engineering institutes from the Academy. See "O merakh po uluchsheniiu koordinatsii nauchnoissledovatel'skikh rabot v strane i deiatel'nosti akademii nauk SSSR," *Pravda*, April 12, 1961; DeWitt, "Reorganization of Science"; Senior, "Organization of Scientific Research" and Swanson, "Reorganization: 1963," in The Editors of *Survey, The State of Soviet Science*, Cambridge, Mass., 1965; and Loren R. Graham, "Reorganization of the Academy of Sciences," in Peter H. Juviler and Henry W. Morton, eds., *Soviet Policy-Making: Studies of Communism in Transition*, New York, 1967, pp. 133-61.

found its direction determined by governmental or industrial research grants. Yet the diversity of institutions and interests in these countries has helped preserve a multiplicity of scientific efforts, some of which have been purely philanthropic and humanitarian, others seeking merely to satisfy man's curiosity about nature. In the Soviet Union the presence of the guiding Party in all institutions, combined with the total mobilization of the society for industrialization, resulted in a scientific program more pragmatic than in the West. The Party placed primary emphasis on increasing national strength, and neglected, at least relatively, such fields as basic physical, biological, and social research. Thus, the Soviet Union created the same distortion of science the Party critics believed existed in capitalist countries, but which in Western nations was partially corrected by universities, private foundations, and other independent institutions.

The planning of science

Another major failure of the reform movement, even from the viewpoint of the reformers themselves, was the lack of success in establishing a single planning center for scientific research, despite the early demands for such an organ. None of the governmental committees, not even the Academy itself, became that "general staff" of science which played such an important role in the socialist imagination. Volgin confessed that no one committee could possibly handle all scientific problems and admitted that the hope of creating one had been a "utopian dream."[10] However, he indicated that the Academy would come as close to fulfilling this role as any other body. Much later, President Nesmeianov would refer to the Academy as the "director of the Soviet scientific orchestra," a term purposely expressing a somewhat nebulous relationship.[11] And Academician Topchiev voiced the skepticism of a person who had unsuccessfully struggled to plan science for many years:

[10] Volgin, *Akademiia nauk SSSR za chetyre goda.*
[11] *Vestnik Akademii Nauk SSSR* (April 1960), p. 67.

"The scope of scientific research is so broad and embraces so many different scientific endeavors that the concentration of coordination in any one organ would not lead to the expected results."[12]

The First All-Union Conference on the Planning of Scientific Research Work was never followed by a second conference, although the planners had hoped to hold such conferences frequently. Bukharin's proposals, which actually provided for the planning "for" rather than "of" science, remained unchallenged as the most original advanced during the discussion of the planning of science. The period of probing in the methodology of planning science ended in the early 1930s.

Certain concepts of the debate over the planning of science may be usefully compared with those in the debate in the Soviet Union over economic planning.[13] The economic theorists who in the twenties discussed strategies of industrialization realized that every plan must contain two elements—prognosis and directive. Prognosis is based largely on a study of past trends with an extension into the future; directive is centered on future goals. The theories of the economists who emphasized past trends as a foundation for planning, such as V. G. Groman and V. A. Bazarov, have been classified as the "genetic approach"; the views of those who emphasized future goals, such as S. G. Strumilin and the more enthusiastic Bolsheviks, have been called the "teleological approach." In the debate over science, the "arithmetic sum" approach to planning, favored by Academicians Bakh and Borisiak, may be compared with the genetic approach. Both emphasized that overall plans should be summations and extensions of individual work plans, and that orderly growth from positions established in the past is the most valid goal of planning. Those persons who centered their attention on the Soviet Union's hope to become the fore-

[12] A. V. Topchiev, "Iarkoe svidetel'stvo zaboty partii o nauke," *Vestnik Akademii Nauk SSSR* (No. 8, 1961), pp. 19-20.

[13] See Nicholas Spulber, *Soviet Strategy for Economic Growth*, Bloomington, Indiana, 1964, especially pp. 53-77 and 100-108; and Alexander Erlich, *The Soviet Industrialization Debate, 1924-1928*, Cambridge, Mass., 1960.

most country in the world in scientific research, and who wished to draft research plans reflecting this intention, may be compared with the "teleologists" among the economists. The activists of VARNITSO, the association of Marxist scientists, were clearly in this group. Bukharin had a foot in both camps. His emphasis on the necessity of sharpening intuition by the careful staging of experiments in a large laboratory was essentially an extension of the past, and therefore representative of the genetic approach; so also was his statement, "A concrete 'guess' is an unconscious continuation of a conscious process." But Bukharin went on to establish the ultimate goal that the Soviet Union must catch up with the capitalist countries in a maximum of 10 years, and emphasized that scientific research must grow even faster than heavy industry. The teleological approach had obviously influenced Bukharin's views on science.

In still another area of Bukharin's opinions on science one may see a parallel with economic thought. Bukharin believed that the most important principle in the planning of science should be that the supreme organs should stipulate only the main directions of scientific research, leaving the determination of research in other areas to local bodies. In economic theory such an approach would be called "open-ended planning," in which the plan is constructed around a few major commodities with flexibility on all other items. Bukharin emphasized that a scientific research plan should contain a great deal of such flexibility and that eccentric scientists should be excused from rigid controls.

Michael Polanyi, in his *The Logic of Liberty*, argued that it is mathematically demonstrable that central monolithic control cannot be maintained over a planning system which continues to grow in complexity and in numbers of hierarchical levels.[14] He concluded that a system of spontaneous or autonomous units must be introduced to prevent disorder intensifying at an exponential rate. Polanyi's theoretical conclusions have been supported on the practical level by the pattern of oscillation

[14] *Logic of Liberty*, Chicago, 1951.

between consolidation and dispersal of authority in the Soviet economic planning system in recent years. The weakness of centralized planning which Polanyi believes is the overriding factor in extremely large planning systems does not, however, come into play when the planning is restricted to specific goals and limited programs. For any one goal the organizational factors *alone* are probably not major factors of limitation.

The reform of the Academy

The great accomplishment of the Academy of Sciences in the 1920s was the preservation of academic standards and the tradition of scientific creativity. During years when throughout the Soviet Union the cultural heritage of past decades, even centuries, was in danger of being jettisoned, the Academy of Sciences, representative of the flower of Russian scholarship, carefully guarded its traditions, trained its own personnel, and preserved the remarkable scholarship of the last years of the empire. An element of continuity in an age of discontinuity, the Academy performed an immense service for the Soviet regime in its very resistance to Soviet pressures. When it was forced to capitulate, standards in Soviet universities were already beginning to improve. Furthermore, the influence of the tradition of genuine scholarship in the Academy continued far beyond the assertion of control by the Communist Party; it is still important today. The Soviet government rather reluctantly recognized the full value of the Academy, but eventually even gave it a much greater measure of support than the previous regime; thus, the present Academy draws heavily on both tsarist and Soviet sources of strength.

The position of the older academicians towards the Soviet regime was not one of simple opposition. Many of them made peace with the regime during the years that followed. Most of them were, to one degree or another, committed to the Soviet Union. Vernadskii envisioned a great prospering of science under governmental patronage, a social experiment unprecedented in the world. Ipat'ev stated after his emigration that the Revolution had "saved the country from anarchy and at least temporarily preserved its intelligentsia and material wealth."[15] After the emergence of German fascism Academician Pavlov became increasingly complimentary toward the Soviet government. Academician Komarov, who became president of the Academy, demonstrated sympathies both for the old pre-revolutionary intelligentsia and the emerging Soviet educated class. And throughout the entire period the academicians maintained a pride in Russian science which was more essential to their achievements than their opinions of the government. The very immersion of the scientists in their work in order to avoid politics may have resulted in greater intensity of scientific labor.[16]

To describe the winning of control over the Soviet Academy of Sciences as merely "Sovietization" or "communization" is to emphasize only the first steps of a long process. The permanent alteration of the Academy was twofold: (1) Henceforth, the Academy possessed both a scientific and a political character. No longer could one speak of the insularity of science in the Soviet Union. (2) The Academy's activities were permanently turned toward applied science, or more accurately, science as a means of serving the state. Engineering emerged as an important area of the Academy's attentions. The new orientation did not mean, however, that the Academy's functions were henceforth always confined to narrow, engineering topics. The academicians developed many ways of rationalizing their research interests in pragmatic terms. Furthermore, as time passed, strict application became less and less important as a criterion of research, and the prestige of the Soviet state grew in importance. In certain cases, unapplied fundamental research could serve the needs of the Soviet state by increasing

[15] Ipatieff, *Life of a Chemist*, p. 257.

[16] See Raymond Bauer, Alex Inkeles, and Clyde Kluckhohn, *How the Soviet System Works*, New York, 1960, p. 169: ". . . some people do an effective job precisely because they do *not* like the regime. Their work is their refuge *from* the regime because it brings them a reasonable measure of security and a chance to enjoy aspects of their personal lives through 'the inner emigration.'"

the prestige of the Soviet Union among other nations. Thus applied research in the technology of consumers goods frequently received lower priority than theoretical research in areas of international attention.

In developing new organizational forms for scientific research the Soviet leaders time and again looked over their shoulders at the new type of research institute evolving in the West. Scientists there also believed that a revolution was occurring in science, and even before the beginning of the 20th century they created new organizational patterns. Germany, which led the way in the cultivation of pure science at university centers, also led in the formation of the integrated research institutes. The groups of industrial chemists in Germany in the 1860s and 1870s established completely new norms in the direction of scientific research. Later developments, especially in physics and chemistry, determined the prosperous future of the research institute. Norbert Wiener has called Thomas A. Edison's greatest invention "the industrial research laboratory, turning out inventions as a business."[17] Developments in electronics, especially the vacuum tube, opened possibilities for amazingly diverse applications which could be exploited only through the cooperative labor of many highly educated engineers and technicians. These institutes were sponsored by either private industry or the government; the Kaiser Wilhelm Institutes at Dahlem were, as the Russians noted, quite significant as prototypes of research institutes depending, at least partially, upon governmental funds.

These developments left Russia behind in the late 19th and early 20th centuries. Unquestionably, an 18th or 19th century scientific academy was not suitable for research in the 20th century. As a result of the peculiarities of Russian history, that antiquated type of academy dominated scientific research in Russia before 1917 more than it did in any modern Western state. Dependent on Western capital for much of its industrial-

[17] Norbert Wiener, *The Human Use of Human Beings: Cybernetics and Society*, Garden City, N.Y., 1954, p. 115.

ization, and imitative of Western technology, imperial Russia had little opportunity or need to develop its own industrial research laboratories of the type of the Kaiser Wilhelm Institutes or General Electric.[18] Its Academy of Sciences was still absorbed with the spirit of pure science, taken from the German universities, and its industrial research laboratories were underdeveloped almost to the point of nonexistence. Furthermore, its backward governmental bureaucracy made no real effort to develop an extensive set of publicly owned research institutes of the type of the British National Physical Laboratory and Department of Scientific and Industrial Research, or the French *Centre National de la Recherche Scientifique.*

When the Soviet Union began the process of industrial modernization during the first five-year plan, it tried to correct its backwardness in the development of research organizations at one stroke. Enormous laboratories supported by the government were created in a few years. In the process, the Soviet leaders overlooked the probability that there is a maximum size for a research laboratory and a maximum degree of centralization for fruitful scientific labor.

In their eagerness to overtake the West the Soviet leaders incorrectly evaluated the organizational forms of scientific research of the 20th century. The West European and American trend indicated to them that the important research of this century would not be done in the academies or the universities but in the specialized institutes. They attempted to anticipate this trend. The new Academy of Sciences they were creating was not to be an academy of the old style, but a network of institutes. The universities would be primarily centers of teaching, while the institutes of the new Academy would be the centers of advanced research. This division of responsibilities was not altogether wise; universities in the West have not lost their positions as centers of theoretical research, and a number

[18] After World War II, the Kaiser Wilhelm Institutes were renamed the Max Planck Institutes.

of Soviet scientists have indicated in recent years that the Western pattern possesses genuine virtues.

Creativity and freedom

Although the purpose of this study is not to make an attempt to determine the degree to which political control over scientists affects their creativity in research, the history of the Soviet Academy of Sciences following 1927 is a period which should provide important information for scholars investigating this question. On the basis of the evidence presented in this study, and with the benefit of knowledge of more recent events, certain indications of the directions of future research can be given, along with a few tentative conclusions.

The major question, in the simplest terms, is "How can a scientific institution take all the abuse the Academy took and still retain its greatness?" No one will ever know, of course, how much valuable research that was not done *would* have been done had political controls not been imposed. The fact that the quantity of research publications of the Academy during the renovation rose is not necessarily important evidence. Neither is the impressive growth of Soviet science in later years. Such growth might have been in spite of the reform. But even to ask the question about how much important research would have been done if the Academy had been left free is not a fair question—unless one assumes that simultaneously this hypothetical free Academy of the 1930s had received dramatic infusions of material support. This commitment to the idea of science was probably more inherently an aspect of bolshevism than the principle of political control over scientists. Thus, the question of what an Academy of Sciences in Russia free of Communist Party influence could have accomplished involves considerations of both the Party's promotion of science and its suppression of scientists. No simple answer is possible.

The history of science in the Soviet Union provides enough

evidence to cause scholars to examine more closely a few of their more elementary concepts concerning science and political controls. The most common approach is to compare political control with a pervasive poison that, once introduced into a system, gradually causes deleterious effects in areas quite distant from the area where it was originally introduced. No doubt this theory has some validity, but it rests on a rather mysterious explanation involving very unclear causal relationships. It implies that just as creativity is surrounded by mystique so also is its prevention.

Since a flourishing scientific establishment is a fairly new development in history one tends to equate it with an extremely delicate organism, one of the ultimate products of civilization. Ultimate in terms of time it may be, but it becomes increasingly resilient with the development of industrialized society. Modern civilization is so intertwined with science that for a government to destroy it would be not only unthinkable but probably impossible. Bernard Barber asked, "How long does it take to 'kill' science? Indeed, can it really be extinguished in modern industrial society? Probably not, and probably it cannot even be weakened beyond a certain point in such a society. . . ."[19] The offspring of civilization possesses an inner inertia of its own. In time, the question seems to be not whether governments will destroy science but whether science will destroy governments.

Governments can without question limit the productivity of their scientists; it would be an error to maintain, as Academician Ipat'ev did, that scientific creativity is unaffected by governmental control.[20] Among the governments which have consciously aided their scientists, the Soviet Union occupies a conspicuous place. At work in Soviet science were two completely opposite influences: strangling political control and invigorating material assistance. The worth of Bernal's statement

[19] *Science and Social Order*, p. 115.
[20] Ipat'ev disputed this point with the communist leader A. V. Lunacharskii. See N. Zamkov, "Nauka i politika," *Narodnoe Prosveshchenie*, i (1930), 29-31.

that "lack of means fetters science as effectively as police supervision" was being given what amounted to an unintentional laboratory test. Which of the influences would be the stronger? When one attempts to answer the question by comparing science in the Soviet Union with science in other countries the variables are so great that they almost prohibit comparison. In Britain in the 1930s there was no police control of research, but then neither was there much material assistance, relative to the total economy. In the United States there was both a free political situation and a fairly free purse, despite the restrictions of the depression. The scientific test between the US and the USSR, which would become so politically inflated a generation later, was already discernible. But here again many other variables entered in: the United States had a strong tradition in engineering, a weak one in theory; the Soviet Union's traditional strength was in theory, its historical weakness in engineering. Both countries in the next decades exerted tremendous efforts, and both with marked success, to overcome their old weaknesses.

How strangling was political control in science at the worst moments in the Academy in 1927 to 1932? Obviously the purge of a scientist, his removal from his laboratory, would end a personal line of research and demoralize his colleagues. Such effects were clear in the Academy in the social sciences. Research in aspects of history, philosophy, orientology, and related fields was curtailed. The significance of this calamity to Russian scholarship can hardly be exaggerated. But not a single academician of the natural sciences was purged in this period, and, to the extent that we have evidence, few of the workers in the natural science laboratories.

The question, then, becomes more indefinite and difficult. How much were the natural scientists affected by the fate of their less fortunate colleagues? The test was a moral one with very cruel and uncertain dimensions. Not only were the natural scientists expected to go on with their research, but to expand it, buy new equipment, open new institutes, bring in more graduate students. The money available, although not unlimited, was much greater than before. And what would be gained by a wringing of the hands, a protest? An expansion of the purge, the total elimination of the possibility of preserving honest scholarship in the Soviet Union? Different people reacted in different ways to this quandary. A few did protest. Others were destroyed intellectually. Still others rationalized the need to go on with their work. And still others, especially those newly arrived on the scene, did not reflect or look back. And Soviet science continued to grow.

The turn toward applied science, although destructive to certain lines of research, was probably not as damaging to creativity as might be thought. The Academy of Sciences' relationship to Soviet industry in the early thirties was in some ways similar to that of a large industrial research laboratory in the West serving a particular industry, with one difference being the fact that in the Soviet Union the particular industry was the whole industrialization effort. The focusing of attention on industrial problems which occurs in every industrial laboratory is not always contradictory to creativity. If the freedom to undertake projects within the prescribed areas is large enough the researcher is likely to find some problems provocative enough to retain his interests.

Robert K. Merton described the ethos of modern science as containing four institutional imperatives:[21]

1. Universalism. Truth claims "are to be subjected to *pre-established impersonal criteria.*"
2. Communism. "The substantive findings of science are a product of social collaboration and are assigned to the community."
3. Disinterestedness. As a result of institutional controls, science is based on objectivity, not subjectivity.
4. Organized skepticism. Science is based on "the suspension of judgment until 'the facts are at hand.'"

[21] *Social Theory and Social Structure*, Glencoe, Ill., 1949, pp. 309-16.

To what extent had the Soviet Union destroyed the ethos of modern science in 1932? On reflection it seems clear that these imperatives apply mainly to the endogenous aspects of science; they define the criteria by which a scientist checks his findings, the ways in which he disseminates them, and the relations he has towards his fellow scientists. These imperatives were not the main objects of attack in the period 1927-32, but they were affected. The forced attention on applied science endangered the imperative of disinterestedness, and the talk of a "socialist science" contradicted that of universalism. A number of academicians were influenced by the attention given to applied science, but almost none viewed science as "socialist" or "capitalist," whatever the ideologists may have been saying. By and large, Soviet scientists in 1932 were still a part of the international scientific community and applied the same standards to their research as their foreign colleagues. A more serious threat to the endogenous aspects of Soviet science came in later years, when attempts to apply peculiar interpretations of dialectical materialism were made in several of the sciences, including genetics, quantum mechanics, relativity physics, resonance chemistry, physiology, and related fields. But these episodes belong in a later book.

The point of this discussion of creativity and political controls is not, then, that the quality of scientific research in the Soviet Union was unaffected by the events in the Academy. I believe Soviet science suffered genuine and serious damage in this period. Scientists lost control over certain aspects of their research, and the principle of intellectual freedom was so abused that even today full recovery has not been achieved. The scene was also set for further incursions in later years. But I also think that the negative effects of political controls on science are more selective than popular opinion usually admits. Science is not shattered by a few blows. Like an injured plant, it grows around its wounds, seeks other paths to its goals, and continues its development so long as it can find minimum sustenance.

Soviet historians often complain that Western historians of the Soviet Union stress the conflicts of the Party leaders and ignore the great material achievements of the Soviet Union. The history of the Soviet Union in the 1920s and 1930s is represented by bourgeois historians, the Soviet critics say, as a story of a struggle between the "left" and the "right" resulting in the emergence of the Stalin cult. The Western historians, the critics continue, concentrate on these political events and ignore the achievements of the five-year plans, the creation of heavy industry, and the expansion of education and research. A Soviet historian would probably consider this account of the Academy of Sciences in the Soviet Union during the first five-year plan a distortion in the same vein; the purge of the Academy and police control are prominent elements in this book. The point, however, is that coercion and violence were extremely significant aspects of the transformation of the Academy, without an understanding of which one cannot understand the reforms that followed.

As time passes, the essential decisions to expand science at a rapid rate and to organize Soviet science around the Academy of Sciences will seem more and more important, while the suppression of dissident scientists will become only a distant memory. The Soviet Union was promoting science in this period more vigorously than any state in history, with results that were to become internationally significant. An examination of the following supplement will reveal the almost immeasurable contribution which the Academy of Sciences was making, both to its country's strength and to science in general. Nevertheless, the costs of the Soviet science program, measured in terms of lost freedom, were very great. Only by keeping both the achievements and the failures of Soviet science in mind can one correctly evaluate its development.

Major Institutions and Research Work, Academy of Sciences of the USSR, 1932[1]

Chemical Association

The Chemical Association consisted of eight laboratories and institutes: the Laboratory of General Chemistry (LAOKh), the Institute of Physical-Chemical Analysis (IFKhA), the Laboratory of High Pressures and Temperatures (LAVD), the Laboratory of Organic Synthesis (LOS), the Colloidal-Electrochemical Laboratory (LAKE), the Institute for the Study of Platinum and Other Noble Metals (PLATIN), the Laboratory for the Research and Synthesis of Vegetable and Animal Products (LASIN), and the Biogeochemical Laboratory (BIOGEL).

The new utilitarian credo of the Academy meant that all of these centers of theoretical research were forced to announce their contributions to the practical tasks of socialist construction. Thus the Laboratory of General Chemistry, headed by the chairman of the association, Academician N. S. Kurnakov, established contacts with industrial commissariats, with the governmental Committee on Chemicalization, and with individual chemical plants. The Institute of Physical-Chemical Analysis, also under Kurnakov's leadership, accepted commissions from governmental committees and fertilizer industries to investigate the bromo-potassium equilibriums in the area of the Solikamsk potash deposits. The Institute also studied means of exploiting the salt lakes of western Siberia. The Laboratory of High Pressures, founded by Academician Ipat'ev, worked with several industrial trusts in trying to obtain liquid fuel by the synthesis of the metallo-organic compounds of lead and by the cracking of primary tars from the coal of the Cheremkhovo basin and from sapropelite coal in the Barzas area. The Insti-

[1] Based on information in *Otchety o deiatel' nosti akademii nauk SSSR, 1927 32*, Leningrad (9 volumes).

tute for the Study of Platinum and Other Noble Metals worked with governmental organizations in charge of mining non-ferrous metals in order to improve the methods of refining precious metals. By 1932 the Academy announced that as a result of its help the refinery in Sverdlovsk was producing platinum of a quality "not inferior" to the purest from Germany. The state rubber industry requested the Laboratory of Organic Synthesis to work on the production of synthetic rubber from acetylene; the head of the laboratory, Academician A. E. Favorskii, devoted long years to the study of means of producing synthetic rubber. The Colloidal-Electrochemical Laboratory, headed by Academician V. A. Kistiakovskii, conducted a number of researches designed to reduce the effects of the corrosion of iron, magnesium, and several alloys. The Laboratory for the Research and Synthesis of Vegetable and Animal Products still listed, in 1932, Academician Chichibabin as head, even though he had long since emigrated. Chichibabin's laboratory worked on the structure and synthesis of napthoate, the synthesis of dyes, and the manufacture of industrial and medical organic compounds. The Biogeochemical Laboratory, under Academician V. I. Vernadskii, worked on the geochemical history of chemical elements whose locations and characteristics have been influenced by living organisms. The laboratory also studied the influence of geography on the chemical composition of organisms. The laboratory worked closely with the State Oceanographic Institute and the research institutes for the food industry.

Although the reports of the Chemical Association for the years 1930-32 contain these pointed and numerous references to the practical applications of their research, the major preoccupation of several of the most talented academicians continued to be mainly theoretical. This research was justified in the annual reports by statements such as "the execution of this work will permit several theoretical generalizations which will be of great practical significance."[2] Academician Kurnakov led his Laboratory of General Chemistry and Institute of

[2] *Otchet o deiatel'nosti akademii nauk SSSR za 1932*, p. 85.

Physical-Chemical Analysis along lines of research which were logical continuations of his theoretical studies, begun long before the Revolution, of metallic alloys, their properties and their diagrammatical representations. An academician with great prestige, such as Kurnakov, could continue theoretical research more easily than a younger chemist who had not yet achieved a high degree of credibility for his projects.

Geological Association

A direct connection between research and practical applications was easily achieved in the geological sciences. By 1932 the Geological Association, headed by Academician A. A. Borisiak, included the Geochemical Institute (GEOKhI), Mineralogical Institute (MIN), the Petrographic Institute (PETRIN), Geological Institute (GIN), Soil Institute (IP), Salt Laboratory (SOLAB), Sapropelic Institute (SIN), and the Khibiny Mining Station (KhIGS). The Soviet economic organs assigned a number of specific problems to the Geological Association. The Geochemical and Mineralogical Institutes, both headed by Academician Fersman, studied the use of nepheline in the leather and textile industries and examined native deposits of apatite, pegmatite, and other minerals. The Mineralogical Institute also undertook the examination of the mineralogy and geochemistry of the Southern Urals area in connection with the developing industries of that region. The Soil Institute, led by Academician B. A. Keller, devoted itself especially to the soil conditions of the Lower Volga and the excessively salty regions of Siberia and Central Asia. The Petrographic Institute, directed by Academician Levinson-Lessing, continued its early study of rock formation and also searched the Ural and Angara regions, especially the areas of former volcanic activity, for construction materials. The Geological Institute, under V. A. Obruchev, prepared an atlas of the chief mineral deposits of the USSR, studied the coal deposits of the Kuznetsk basin, and presented information on the feasibility of the enormous Ural-Kuzbas *kombinat*. The Salt

Laboratory searched for applications of salt deposits in the regions of the Aral and Caspian Seas. The Sapropelic (Cannel Coal) Institute, directed by Academician N. D. Zelinskii, similarly searched for better uses of the deposits of sapropelite coal. The Khibiny Scientific Mining Station studied the geological and biological characteristics of the Khibiny massif, especially the apatite deposits. The expeditionary work of the geological sciences developed enormously in this period. The geologists worked closely with SOPS and participated in many of its expeditions.

Physical-Mathematical Association

The Physical–Mathematical Association, chaired by Academician I. M. Vinogradov, included the Steklov Physical–Mathematical Institute (FMI), the Seismological Institute (SI), the Commission for the Study of the Sun (KISO), and the Energetics Institute (EIN), which was later transferred to the newly created "Technology Group." The association was also closely connected with the Demographic Institute (DIN), which was directly subordinate to the General Assembly. The Physical–Mathematical Association was organized in February 1932.

The Physical–Mathematical Institute studied the applications of mathematical physics to electronics, atomic structure, the optical properties of colloidal systems, and the nature of photoelectric effects. The Seismological Institute investigated the diffraction and transmission of elastic vibrations, compiled seismo-tectonic maps of the Soviet Union, and constructed models of earthquake-proof buildings. The Energetics Institute, headed by Academician Krzhizhanovskii, studied possible means of applying solar energy, the temperature differentials of polar regions, the use of Caucasian water potential, and the utilization of gas, liquid, and solid fuels. The Commission for the Study of the Sun investigated the physical motion, composition, and radiations of the sun. Academician Vinogradov's Demographic Institute studied methods of directing the growth of population concentrations in the USSR, the birth and mortality rates of the population, and the connection between population growth and the five-year plans of economic growth.

Geographical Association

The Geographical Association was headed by Academician V. L. Komarov, and consisted of: Geomorphological Institute (GEOMIN), Institute of Forestry (INIL), Desert Institute (PUIN), Baikal Limnological Station (BLS), and the Commission for the Study of Permafrost (KIVM). The director of the Geomorphological Institute, A. A. Grigor'ev, reported the results of his institute on the basis of success in fulfilling the Plan. He assigned five different areas of the USSR for geomorphological research to an equal number of teams and challenged them to socialist competition; all of them reported that they finished their work before the expiration of the planning period. The Geomorphological Institute devoted special attention to the physical geography of the Angara River region, the Urals-Kuzbas area, the tundra regions, and the Kola peninsula. The Desert Institute worked closely with economic organs of Uzbekistan and Turkmenistan in the study of methods of utilizing desert resources. Academician V. A. Obruchev's Commission on Permafrost studied the problems in construction in the Angara area and also sent expeditions to define the southern limits of the permafrost region. The commission also investigated the coal deposits of the Pechora River basin and surveyed the Baikal–Amur railroad line. G. Iu. Vereshchagin's Baikal Limnological Station studied the natural peculiarities of Lake Baikal, its fauna and flora, and its seasonal influence on the flow of the Angara River. Academician V. L. Komarov's Institute of Forestry studied the forest resources of the Iakutsk, Leningrad, Karelian and Kazakhstan regions.

Biological Association

The Biological Association, headed by Academician V. L.

Komarov, included the Botanical Institute (BIN), Zoological Institute (ZIN), Paleozoological Institute (PIN), Physiological Institute (FIN), Laboratory of Genetics (LAG), Laboratory of Biochemistry and Animal Physiology (LABIFR), Microbiological Laboratory (ML), Laboratory of Evolutionary Morphology (LEM), Laboratory of Experimental Zoology and Animal Morphology (LEZM), Laboratory of Zoogeography (LZO), Laboratory of Applied Zoology (LAPRIZ), and the Sevastopol' Biological Station.

The Botanical Institute, directed by Academician B. A. Keller, continued its compilation of the massive "Flora of the USSR," a work which had begun many years before. However, in order to underscore the possible benefits from its researches, the Institute now paid special attention to plants producing useful products. The Institute also emphasized the flora of the immense tundra areas. Goszemtrest, the State Land Trust, asked the Botanical Institute to study the potential of the Caucasian mountain pasture lands for additional grazing. Other institutes of the Biological Association accepted similar requests; one group studied the potential of the Lake Baikal and Aral Sea fisheries industry, others examined the possible effects of the Volga and Angara hydroelectric stations on plant and animal life, and still others suggested irrigation projects. The expedition leaders of the Biological Association prided themselves, according to their reports, on their "social-political" work among the natives of the distant regions where they collected samples. Beneath all of the interest in obvious applications of the biological sciences, a considerable amount of theoretical work was still being pursued. The main problems which Academician Komarov said his scientists were studying were those common to the profession everywhere: the problem of evolution and the origin of species, the mutual relations of environment and organisms, and the inventory of flora and fauna. Academician N. I. Vavilov directed his Laboratory of Genetics in the study of hybridization and mutations. Academician S. A. Zernov's Zoological Institute pursued the problems of natural selection, the history of the fauna of the USSR, and the inventory of the animals of the USSR. Academician A. A. Borisiak's Paleozoological Institute studied evolution as revealed by fossil remains. The Institute was particularly interested in the origin of domestic animals. The Microbiological Laboratory, under Academician G. A. Nadson, devoted special attention to the alterations of bacteria and microorganisms induced by chemical and physical action.

The Department of Social Sciences

In 1932 the social sciences had not yet been organized into a separate association; this reorganization occurred in November 1933. The chairman of the bureau of the new association was Academician A. S. Orlov.

In 1932 the following organizations belonged to the Department of Social Sciences: Historical–Archaeographic Institute (IAN), Institute of Language and Thought (IIaM), Museum of Anthropology and Ethnography (MAE), Institute for the Study of the Nationalities of the USSR (IPIN), the Economics Office (EK), Museum of the History of Religion (MIR), Institute of Russian Literature (IRLI), Institute of Slavic Studies (INSLAV), and the Institute of Oriental Studies (IV).

The Historical–Archaeographic Institute, directed by Academician M. N. Pokrovskii until his death on April 13, 1932, worked on the history of the nationalities of the USSR, the history of the proletariat and industrialization, the class-struggle in the feudal period, and the history of technology in feudal Russia. During 1932 the Institute published works on the histories of Tadzhikistan, Uzbekistan, Turkmenistan, and manufacturing in the seventeenth century. Many other works were in preparation.

The Institute of Language and Thought, directed by Academician N. Ia. Marr, investigated the problem of modifications in language and thought, the methodology of linguistics, the origin and development of grammatical categories, and structural linguistics. The Museum of Anthropology and Ethnography studied the modifications and growth of society according to the Marxist interpretation, devoting special attention to the development of society from the period of the earliest tribal societies to the beginnings of the class struggle. According to Academician Marr, the Institute for the Study of the Nationalities of the USSR studied the "process of the non-capitalistic development of the nationalities of the USSR and the problems of constructing a culture which is socialist in content, but national in form." The Economics Office was organized only in April 1932. Its major function was to serve as a bibliographical office on economic literature. The Museum of the History of Religion organized atheistic exhibitions in Kazan Cathedral in Leningrad, devoting special attention to the "anti-Christmas campaign." The Institute of Russian Literature, headed by Academician Lunacharskii, emphasized the editing and publication of unknown materials on the history of literature of both ancient and modern times. The Institute of Slavic Studies, headed by N. S. Derzhavin, emphasized the "history of the class-struggle of the Slavs," as reflected both in political and cultural history. The Institute of Oriental Studies studied the history and literature of the following eastern cultures: Chinese, Arabian, Japanese, Indo-Tibetan, Persian, Turkic, Mongolian, Central Asian, and Caucasian. The scholars of the institute utilized materials written in 55 eastern languages.

The Council for the Study of the Productive Forces of the USSR (SOPS)

SOPS, under the chairmanship of Academician I. M. Gubkin, organized 41 expeditions in 1932, consisting of 676 scientific workers. SOPS also financed 32 laboratory projects for the chemical industries of the USSR, organized conferences on natural resources, and helped draft the work plan for the Academy in the second five-year plan. During 1932 SOPS prepared 43 separate publications for the press.

APPENDIX A

Abbreviations Used in the Text

BSE — Bol'shaia Sovetskaia Entsiklopediia (Great Soviet Encyclopedia)

Glavnauka — (Chief Administration of Scientific Institutions)

GOELRO — Gosudarstvennaia komissiia po elektrifikatsii Rossii (Governmental Commission for the Electrification of Russia)

GOK (under STO) — Gosudarstvennaia obshche-planovaia komissiia (Governmental General-Planning Commission)

KEPS — Komissiia po izucheniiu estestvennykh proizvoditel'nykh sil (Commission for the Study of Natural Productive Forces)

MEN — Otdelenie matematicheskikh i estestvennykh nauk (Department of Mathematics and Natural Sciences)

NONT — Nauchnaia organizatsiia nauchnogo truda (Scientific organization of scientific labor)

NOT — Nauchnaia organizatsiia truda (Scientific organization of labor)

NTO (under VSNKh) — Nauchno-tekhnicheskii otdel (Scientific-Technical Department)

ON — Otdelenie obshchestvennykh nauk (Department of Social Sciences)

RANION — Rossiiskaia assotsiatsiia nauchno-issledovatel'skikh institutov obshchestvennykh nauk (Russian Association of Scientific-Research Institutes of the Social Sciences)

SOPS — Sovet po izucheniiu proizvoditel'nykh sil (Council for the Study of Productive Forces)

Sovnarkom — Sovet narodnykh komissarov (Council of People's Commissars)

STO — Sovet truda i oborony (Council of Labor and Defense)

TsEKUBU — Tsentral'naia komissiia po uluchsheniiu byta uchenykh (Central Commission for the Improvement of the Living Standard of Scientists)

TsGAOR	Tsentral'nyi gosudarstvennyi arkhiv oktiabr'skoi revoliutsii (Central State Archive of the October Revolution)
TsIK	Tsentral'nyi Ispolnitel'nyi Komitet (Central Executive Committee)
VARNITSO	Vsesoiuznaia assotsiatsiia rabotnikov nauki i tekhniki na pomoshch' sotsialisticheskomu stroitel'stvu (All-Union Association of Workers of Science and Technology for the Assistance of Socialist Construction)
VSNKh	Vysshii Sovet Narodnogo Khoziaistva (Supreme Economic Council)
VTsIK	Vsesoiuznyi tsentral'nyi ispolnitel'nyi komitet (All-Union Central Executive Committee)

Academy of Sciences

December 1926

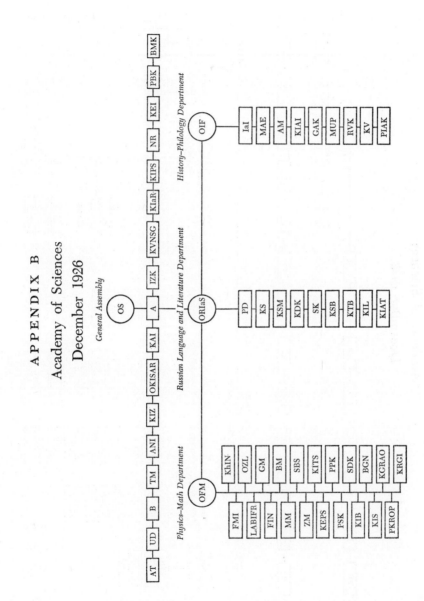

APPENDIX C

Academy of Sciences
December 1932

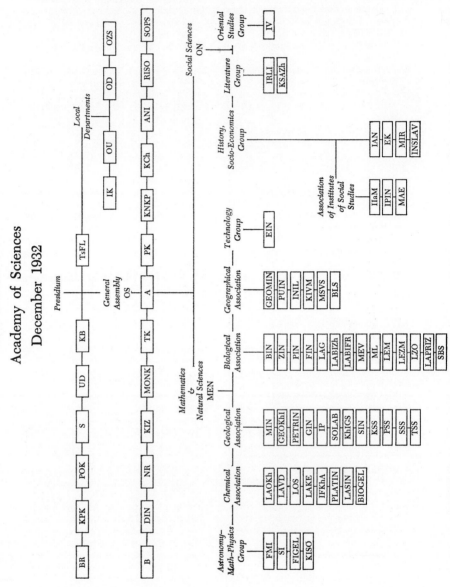

A Arkhiv (Archives)

AM Aziatskii muzei (Asian Museum)

ANI Izdatel'stvo akademii nauk (Press)

AT Akademicheskaia tipografiia (Academic Printing Plant)

B Biblioteka (Library)

BGN Biblioteka geologicheskikh nauk (Library of the Geological Sciences)

BIN Botanicheskii institut (Botanical Institute)

BIOGEL Biogeokhimicheskaia laboratoriia (Biogeochemical Laboratory)

BLS Baikal'skaia limnologicheskaia stantsiia (Baikal Limnological Station)

BM Botanicheskii muzei (Botanical Museum)

BMK Biuro po mezhdunarodnomu knigoobmenu (Bureau of International Book Exchange)

BR Biuro ratsionalizatsii (Rationalization Bureau)

DIN Demograficheskii institut (Demographic Institute)

EIN Energeticheskii institut imeni G. M. Krzhizhanovskogo (G. M. Krzhizhanovskii Energetics Institute)

EK Ekonomicheskii kabinet (Economics Office)

FIGEL Fizicheskaia i geofizicheskaia laboratoriia (Physical and Geophysical Laboratory)

FIN Fiziologicheskii institut (Physiological Institute)

FMI Fiziko-matematicheskii institut imeni V. A. Steklova (V. A. Steklov Physical–Mathematical Institute)

GAK Gosudarstvennaia arkheograficheskaia komissiia (State Archaeographical Commission)

GEOKhI Geokhimicheskii institut (Geochemical Institute)

GEOMIN Geomorfologicheskii institut (Geomorphological Institute)

GIN Geologicheskii institut (Geological Institute)

GM Geologicheskii muzei (Geological Museum)

IaI Iafeticheskii institut (Japhetic Institute)

IAN Istoriko-arkheograficheskii institut (Historical–Archaeographic Institute)

IFKhA Institut fiziko-khimicheskogo analiza (Institute of Physical–Chemical Analysis)

IIaM Institut iazyka i myshleniia (Institute of Language and Thought)

IK Otdelenie na Kavkaze Institut kavkazovedeniia (Institute of Caucasian Studies)

INIL Institut po izucheniiu lesa (Forestry Institute)

INSLAV Institut slavianovedeniia (Institute of Slavic Studies)

IP Pochvennyi institut imeni V. V. Dokuchaeva (V. V. Dokuchaev Soil Institute)

IPIN Institut po izucheniiu narodov SSSR (Institute for the Study of the Nationalities of the USSR)

IRLI Institut russkoi literatury (Institute of Russian Literature)

IV Institut vostokovedeniia (Institute of Oriental Studies)

IZK Izdatel'skaia komissiia (Publication Commission)

KAI Knigokhranilishche akademicheskikh izdanii (Library of Academic Publications)

KB Komissiia po bazam (Commission on Bases)

KCh Komissiia po izucheniiu chetvertichnogo perioda (Commission for the Study of the Quarternary Period)

KDK Komissiia dlia sostavleniia dialektologicheskoi karty russkogo iazyka (Commission for the Compilation of a Dialectological Chart of the Russian Language)

KEI Komissiia po nauchnym ekspeditsiiam (Commission on Scientific Expeditions)

KEPS Komissiia po izucheniiu estestvennykh proizvoditel'nykh sil SSSR (Commission for the Study of Natural Productive Forces of the USSR)

KGRAO Komitet po delam glavnoi Rossiiskoi astronomicheskoi observatorii (Administrative Committee for the Chief Russian Astronomical Observatory)

KhIGS Khibinskaia gornaia stantsiia (Khibiny Mining Station)

KhIN Khimicheskii institut (Chemical Institute)

KIAI Kavkazskii istoriko-arkheologicheskii institut (Caucasian Historical–Archaeological Institute)

KIaR Komissiia po izucheniiu Iakutskoi avtonomnoi respubliki (Commission for the Study of the Iakutsk Autonomous Republic)

KIAT Komissiia po izdaniiu arkhiva br. Turgenevykh (Commission for the Publication of the Turgenev Brothers Archive)

KIB Komissiia po izucheniiu ozera Baikala (Commission for the Study of Lake Baikal)

KIL Komissiia po izdaniiu sochinenii Lomonosova (Commission for the Publication of the Works of Lomonosov

KIS Russkoe otdelenie mezhdunarodnogo komissii po izucheniiu solntsa (Russian Section of the International Commission on Solar Research)

KISO Komissiia po issledovaniiu solntsa (Commission on Solar Research)

KIPS Komissiia po izucheniiu plemennogo sostava (Commission for the Study of Tribal Composition)

KIPS Komissiia po izucheniiu plecheskikh stran (Commission for the Study of Tropical Countries)

KIVM Komissiia po izucheniiu vechnoi merzloty (Commission for the Study of Permafrost)

KIZ Komissiia po istorii znanii (Commission on the History of Knowledge)

KNKP Komitet nauchnoi konsul'tatsii i propagandy nauchnykh dostizhenii (Committee for Scientific Consultation and the Propaganda of Scientific Achievements)

KPK Komitet po podgotovke kadrov (Committee on the Preparation of Cadres)

KRGI Komitet po delam Rossiiskogo gidrologicheskogo instituta (Administrative Committee of the Russian Hydrological Institute)

KS Postoiannaia slovarnaia komissiia (Permanent Dictionary Commission)

KSAZh Kabinet po sobiraniiu materialov satiricheskogo zhanra (Office for the Collection of Materials of the Satirical Genre)

KSB Komissiia po nauchnomu izdaniiu slavianskoi biblii (Commission for the Scholarly Publication of the Slavic Bible)

KSM Komissiia po sobiraniiu slovarnykh materialov po drevne-russkomu iazyku (Commission on the Collection of Lexicographical Materials for the Ancient Russian Language)

KSS Karabugazskaia solianaia stantsiia (Kara-Bogaz Salt Station)

KTB Komissiia po sostavleniiu "tolkovoi bibliografii" drevne-russkoi literatury (Commission for Compiling an Explanatory Bibliography of Old Russian Literature)

KV Kollegiia vostokovedov (College of Orientalists)

KVNSG Komissiia po voprosam nauchnykh snoshenii s zagranitsei (Commission on Questions of Foreign Scientific Relations)

LABIFR Laboratoriia biokhimii i fiziologii rastenii (Laboratory of Biochemistry and Plant Physiology)

LABIZh Laboratorii biokhimii i fiziologii zhivotnykh (Laboratory of Biochemistry and Animal Physiology)

LAG Laboratoriia genetiki (Genetics Laboratory)

LAKE Laboratoriia kolloido-elektrokhimicheskaia (Colloidal-Electrochemical Laboratory)

LAOKh Laboratoriia obshchei khimii (Laboratory of General Chemistry)

LAPRIZ Laboratoriia prikladnoi zoologii (Laboratory of Applied Zoology)

LASIN Laboratoriia po issledovaniiu i sintezu rastitel'nykh i zhivotnykh produktov (Laboratory for the Research and Synthesis of Vegetable and Animal Products)

LAVD Laboratoriia vysokikh davlenii i temperatur (Laboratory of High Pressures and Temperatures)

LEM Laboratoriia evoliutsionnoi morfologii (Laboratory of Evolutionary Morphology)

LEZM Laboratoriia eksperimental'noi zoologii i morfologii zhivotnykh (Laboratory of Experimental Zoology and the Morphology of Animals)

LOS Laboratoriia organicheskogo sinteza (Laboratory of Organic Synthesis)

LZO Laboratoriia zoogeografii (Laboratory of Zoogeography)

MAE Musei antropologii i etnografii (Museum of Anthropology and Ethnography)

MEN Otdelenie matematicheskikh i estestvennykh nauk (Department of Mathematics and Natural Sciences)

MEV Muzei evoliutsii (Museum of Evolution)

MIN Mineralogicheskii institut (Mineralogical Institute)

MIR Muzei istorii religii (Museum of the History of Religion)

ML Mikrobiologicheskaia laboratoriia (Microbiological Laboratory)

MM Mineralogicheskii muzei (Mineralogical Museum)

MONK Mongol'skaia komissiia (Mongolian Commission)

MSVS Merzlotnaia stantsiia v Vostochnom-Sibirskom krae (East Siberian Frost Station)

MUP Muzei paleografii (Paleographical Museum)

NR Komissiia nauka i nauchnye rabotniki (Commission on Science and Scientists)

OD Otdelenie v Dal'nevostochnom krae (Far Eastern Department)

OFM Otdelenie fiziko-matematicheskikh nauk (Department of Physical and Mathematical Sciences)

OIF Otdelenie istoricheskikh nauk i filologii (Department of Historical Sciences and Philology)

OKISAR Osobaia komissiia po issledovaniiu soiuznykh i avtonomnykh respublik (Special Commission for the Study of the Union and Autonomous Republics)

ON Otdelenie obshchestvennykh nauk (Department of Social Sciences)

ORIaS Otdelenie Russkogo iazyka i slovesnosti (Department of Russian Language and Literature)

OS Obshchee sobranie (General Assembly)

OU Otdelenie na Urale (Urals Department)

OZL Osobaia zoologicheskaia laboratoriia (Special Zoological Laboratory)

OZS Otdelenie v Zapadnoi Sibiri (Western Siberian Department)

PBK Postoianaia bibliotechnaia komis-siia (Permanent Library Commission)

PD Pushkinskii Dom (Pushkin House)

PETRIN Petrograficheskii institut (Petrographic Institute)

PIAK Postoiannaia istoriko-arkheograficheskaia komissiia (Permanent Historical–Archaeographical Commission)

PIN Paleozoologicheskoi institut (Paleozoological Institute)

PK Poliarnaia komissiia (Polar Commission)

PKROP Postoiannaia komissiia po raskopkam ostatkov pozvonochnykh (Permanent Commission on the Excavations of the Remains of Vertebrates)

PLATIN Institut po izucheniiu platiny i drugikh blagorodnykh metallov (Institute for the Study of Platinum and Other Noble Metals)

POK Planovo-organizatsionnaia komissiia (Planning and Organization Commission)

PPK Postoianaia poliarnaia komissiia (Permanent Polar Commission)

PSK Postoianaia seismicheskaia komissiia (Permanent Seismological Commission)

PSS Pavlodarskaia solianaia stantsiia (Pavlodar Salt Station)

PUIN Peschano-pustynnyi institut (Sand Desert Institute)

RISO Redaktsionno-izdatel'skii sovet (Editorial–Publication Council)

RVK Russko-vizantiiskaia komissiia (Russian-Byzantine Commission)

S Sekretariat akademii nauk (Academy of Sciences Secretariat)

SGS Sevastopol'skaia biologicheskaia stantsiia (Sevastopol Biological Station)

SDK Severo-dvinskaia komissiia (Northern Dvinsk Commission)

SI Seismologicheskii institut (Seismological Institute)

SIN Sapropelicheskii institut (Sapropelic Institute)

SK Slavianskaia nauchnaia komissiia (Commission of Slavic Scholarship)

SOLAB Solianaia laboratoriia (Salt Laboratory)

SOPS Sovet po izucheniiu proizvo-

ditel'nykh sil (Council for the
Study of Productive Forces)
SSS Sakskaia solianaia stantsiia (Saki
Salt Station)
TK Tikhookeanskii komitet (Pacific
Ocean Station)
TM Tolstovskii muzei (Tolstoi Museum)
TsFL Tsentral'naia foto-laboratoriia
(Central Photo Laboratory)

TSS Turalinskaia solianaia stantsiia
(Turalinsk Salt Station)
UD Upravlenie delami akademii nauk
(Administrative Office of Academy
of Sciences)
ZIN Zoologicheskii institut (Zoological
Institute)
ZM Zoologicheskii muzei (Zoological
Museum)

Membership of the Academy in December 1932
(Date elected to Academy is in parentheses)

NAME	FIELD
Adoratskii, V. V. (1932)	History of Marxism
Aleksandrov, I. G. (1932)	Power Engineering
Alekseev, V. M. (1929)	Chinese Studies
Arkhangel'skii, A. D. (1929)	Geology
Baikov, A. A. (1929)	Metallurgy
Bakh, A. N. (1929)	Biochemistry
Bardin, I. P. (1932)	Metallurgy
Belopol'skii, A. A. (1900)	Astronomy
Bernshstein, S. N. (1929)	Mathematics
Bogomolets, A. A. (1932)	Physiology
Borisiak, A. A. (1929)	Paleontology
Britske, E. V. (1932)	Chemical Engineering
Bukharin, N. I. (1929)	Economics, Sociology
Chaplygin, S. A. (1929)	Theoretical Mechanics, Aerodynamics
Chernyshev, A. A. (1932)	Electrical Engineering
Chichibabin, A. E. (1929)	Organic Chemistry
Deborin, A. M. (1929)	Philosophy
Demianov, N. Ia. (1929)	Organic Chemistry
Derzhavin, N. S. (1931)	History of the Slavs
Favorskii, A. E. (1929)	Organic Chemistry
Fersman, A. E. (1919)	Mineralogy, Geochemistry
Frumkin, A. M. (1932)	Physical Chemistry
Graftio, G. O. (1932)	Power Engineering
Grebenshchikov, I. V. (1932)	Inorganic Chemistry
Grushevskii, M. S. (1929)	History of the Ukraine
Gubkin, I. M. (1929)	Geology
Gulevich, V. S. (1929)	Biochemistry
Ioffe, A. F. (1920)	Physics
Ipat'ev (Ipatieff), V. M. (1916)	Chemistry

NAME	FIELD
Istrin, V. M. (1907)	Russian Literature
Karpinskii, A. P. (1886)	Geology
Keller, B. A. (1931)	Botany
Kistiakovskii, V. A. (1929)	Physical Chemistry, Electrochemistry
Kokovtsov, P. K. (1903)	Linguistics
Komarov, V. L. (1920)	Botany
Krachkovskii, I. Iu. (1921)	Arabic Philology
Krylov, A. N. (1916)	Mathematics, Marine Engineering
Krylov, N. M. (1929)	Mathematics
Krzhizhanovskii, G. M. (1929)	Power Engineering
Kurnakov, N. S. (1913)	Chemistry
Lazarev, P. P. (1917)	Physics, Biophysics
Lebedev, S. V. (1932)	Chemistry
Levinson-Lessing, F. Iu. (1925)	Geology, Petrography
Liapunov, B. M. (1923)	Slavic Linguistics
Lukin, N. M. (1929)	European History
Lunacharskii, A. V. (1930)	Education, Public Affairs
Luzin, N. N. (1929)	Mathematics
Mandel'shtam, L. I. (1929)	Physics
Marr, N. Ia. (1909)	Philology, Archaeology
Maslov, P. P. (1929)	Economics
Menzbir, M. A. (1929)	Zoology
Meshchaninov, I. I. (1932)	Linguistics, Archaeology
Mitkevich, V. F. (1929)	Electrical Engineering
Nadson, G. A. (1929)	Physiology, Biology
Nasonov, N. V. (1906)	Zoology, Morphology
Nikol'skii, N. K. (1916)	Ancient Russian Literature
Obruchev, V. A. (1929)	Geology, Geography
Ol'denburg, S. F. (1900)	Oriental Studies, Ethnography
Orlov, A. S. (1931)	Russian Literature
Osinskii, V. V. (1932)	Socio-economic Sciences
Pavlov, I. P. (1907)	Physiology
Pavlov, M. A. (1932)	Metallurgy

NAME	FIELD
Pavlovskii, N. N. (1932)	Hydraulic Engineering
Peretts, V. N. (1914)	History of Literature
Petrushevskii, D. M. (1929)	History
Pisarzhevskii, L. V. (1930)	Chemistry
Pokrovskii, M. M. (1929)	Linguistics, Classical Philology
Prianishnikov, D. N. (1929)	Agricultural Chemistry
Rikhter, A. A. (1932)	Botany
Rozanov, M. N. (1921)	European Literature
Rozhdestvenskii, D. S. (1929)	Physics
Samoilovich, A. N. (1929)	Orientology
Savel'ev, M. A. (1932)	Communist Party History, Journalism
Semenov, N. N. (1932)	Chemistry
Severtsov, A. N. (1920)	Biology, Animal Morphology
Shcherbatskoi, F. I. (1918)	Oriental Studies
Shenfer, K. I. (1932)	Electrical Engineering
Solntsev, S. I. (1929)	Economics
Speranskii, M. N. (1921)	History of Russian Literature
Strumilin, S. G. (1931)	Economics
Tiumenev, A. I. (1932)	Ancient History
Tulaikov, N. M. (1932)	Agronomy
Vavilov, N. I. (1929)	Plant Genetics
Vavilov, S. I. (1932)	Physics
Vedeneev, B. E. (1932)	Power Engineering
Vernadskii, V. I. (1906)	Geology, Biogeochemistry
Vil'iams (Williams), V. R. (1931)	Agrobiology
Vinogradov, I. M. (1929)	Mathematics
Vinter, A. V. (1932)	Power Engineering
Volgin, V. P. (1930)	History
Zelinskii, N. D. (1929)	Chemistry
Zernov, S. A. (1931)	Zoology, Hydrobiology
Zhebelev, S. A. (1927)	Ancient History, Archaeology

SELECTED BIBLIOGRAPHY

I. Books

Abdullaev, Kh. M. *Sorok let sovetskoi nauki v Uzbekistane.* Tashkent, 1958.
Academic Freedom Under the Soviet Regime. New York, 1954.
L'Académie des sciences de l'Union des Républiques Soviétiques 1917-1927. Leningrad, 1928.
Akademiia nauk soiuza sovetskikh sotsialisticheskikh respublik: ee zadachi, razdelenie i sostav. Leningrad, 1925.
Akademiia nauk SSSR respublikam Srednei Azii, 1924-34. Moscow-Leningrad, 1934.
Akademiia nauk XVII parts"ezdu. Leningrad, 1934.
Alpatov, M. A., A. L. Sidorov, and M. N. Tikhomirov, eds. *Ocherki istorii istoricheskoi nauki v SSSR.* Moscow, 1955.
Ambartsumian, V. A. *Nauka v Armenii za 40 let.* Erevan, 1960.
Anuchin, D. N. *O liudiakh russkoi nauki i kultury.* Moscow, 1950.
Asmus, Valentin F., ed. *Marks, Engel's, Lenin, Stalin o tekhnike.* Moscow, 1934.
Asratyan, E. A. *I. P. Pavlov: His Life and Works.* Moscow, 1953.
Babkin, Boris P. *Pavlov: A Biography.* Chicago, 1949.
Bach [Bakh], Aleksei Nikolaievich. *Planning Science.* Moscow, 1939.
Baikov, A. A. *Twenty-five years of the Academy of Sciences of the USSR.* Matthew E. Zaret, trans. New York, 1944.
———, N. I. Vavilov, and V. I. Volgin, eds. *Nauchnyi Leningrad k XVII s"ezdu VKP (b).* Leningrad, 1934.
Baker, John R. *Science and the Planned State.* London, 1945.
Bakh, Aleksei N. *Chto takoe khimizatsiia narodnogo khoziaistva?* Leningrad, 1931.
———. *Zametki o roli nauki v sotsialisticheskom khoziaistve.* Moscow–Leningrad, 1939.
Barber, Bernard. *Science and the Social Order.* New York, 1962.
Bartol'd, V. V. ed. *Sredniaia Aziia v uchrezhdeniiakh akademii nauk, 1917-27.* Leningrad, 1927.
Bauer, Raymond, Alex Inkeles, and Clyde Kluckhohn. *How the Soviet System Works.* New York, 1960.
Belov, Mikhail Vasil'evich. *Rukovodiashchaia rol' kommunisticheskoi partii v razvitii nauki.* Moscow, 1957.
Bernal, J. D. *The Social Function of Science.* London, 1939.
Boldyrev, N. I. ed. *Direktivy VKP(b) i postanovleniia sovetskogo pravitel'stva o narodnom obrazovanii: sbornik dokumentov za 1917-1947 godu.* 2 vols. Moscow, 1947.
Boranetskii, P. *Filosofiia tekhniki: tekhnika i novoe mirosozertsanie.* Paris, 1947.
Bruevich, Nikolai Grigor'evich. *Two hundred and twenty years of research in the Academy of Sciences of the USSR.* Moscow, 1945.
Bukharin, N. I. *Culture in Two Worlds.* New York, 1934.
———. *Darvinizm i Marksizm.* Leningrad, 1932.
———. *Etiudy.* Moscow, 1932.
———. *Imperialism and World Economy.* New York, 1929.
———. *O kharaktere nashei revoliutsii i o vozmozhnosti pobedonosnogo sotsialisticheskogo stroitel'stva v SSSR.* Leningrad, 1926.
———. *Socialist reconstruction and the struggle for technique.* Moscow, 1932.
———. *Tekhnika i ekonomika sovremennogo kapitalizma.* Leningrad, 1932.
———. A. M. Deborin, S. I. Vavilov, et al. *Marxism and Modern Thought.* London, 1935.
Bukharin, N. I. and E. Preobrazhenskii. *Azbuka kommunizma: populiarnoe ob"iasnenie programmy rossiiskoi K. P. (b).* Saratov, 1927.

Conant, James B. *Science and Common Sense.* New Haven, 1951.
Counts, G. S. *The Soviet Challenge to America.* New York, 1931.
Crowther, J. G. *Soviet Science.* London–New York, 1936.
——. *Science in Soviet Russia.* London, 1930.
Darlington, T. *Education in Russia.* London, 1909.
Deborin, A. *Dialektika i estestvoznanie.* Moscow–Leningrad, 1930.
Dekrety sovetskoi vlasti, 3 vols. Moscow, 1957-64.
Derzhavin, Nikolai Sevastianovich. *L'Académie des sciences de l'U.R.S.S.* Moscow, 1944.
DeWitt, Nicholas. *Education and Professional Employment in the U.S.S.R.* Washington, 1961.
Dobb, Maurice. *Soviet Economic Development Since 1917.* New York, 1966.
Doklady, predstavlennye k torzhestvennoi iubileinoi sessii AN SSSR, posviashchennyi XV-letiiu oktiabrskoi revoliutsii. Leningrad, 1932.
Dom uchenykh, 1922-1947. Moscow–Leningrad, 1948.
El'meev, Vasilii Iakovlevich. *Nauka i proizvoditel'nye sily obshchestva.* Moscow, 1959.
Erlich, Alexander. *The Soviet Industrialization Debate, 1924-1928.* Cambridge, Mass., 1960.
Ermolaev, Herman. *Soviet Literary Theories, 1917-1934.* Berkeley, 1963.
Ershin, Aleksandr. *Molodaia akademiia.* Leningrad, 1935.
Fainsod, Merle. *How Russia is Ruled.* Cambridge, Mass., 1963.
Fataliev, Khalil M. *Estestvennye nauki i material'noproizvodstvennaia baza obshchestva.* Moscow, 1960.
Fed'kin, G. I. *Pravovye voprosy organizatsii nauchnoi raboty v SSSR.* Moscow, 1958.
Fersman, A. E. *Akademiia nauk soiuza sovetskikh sotsialisticheskikh respublik v 1927 godu.* Report given to Academy of Sciences, February 2, 1928. Leningrad, 1928.
——. *Twenty-Five Years of Soviet Natural Science.* Moscow, 1944.
——, ed. *Akademiia nauk soiuza sovetskikh sotsialisticheskikh respublik za desiat' let 1917-27.* Leningrad, 1927.
Figurovskii, N. A. *Dmitrii Ivanovich Mendeleev, 1834-1907.* Moscow, 1961.
——, ed. *Istoriia estestvoznaniia v Rossii.* 2 vols. Moscow, 1957.
Finkel', I. *Sovremennyi kapitalizm i nauchnoe issledovanie.* Moscow, 1936.
Gabriel'ian, G. G. *Nauka i ee rol' v obshchestve.* Erevan, 1956.
Galkin, I. S., ed. *Rol' russkoi nauki v razvitii mirovoi nauki i kulturi.* 3 vols. in the *Uchenye zapiski Moskovskogo Gosudarstvennogo Universiteta,* Nos. 91-92, 103-104, 106-107 (1946).
Gasset, Ortega y. *The Dehumanization of Art and Other Writings on Art and Culture.* Garden City, N.Y., n.d.
Glavnoe upravlenie nauchnymi uchrezhdeniiami: pervaia otchetnaia vystavka glavnauki narkomprosa. Moscow, 1925.
Gnedenko, B. V. *Ocherki po istorii matematiki v Rossii.* Moscow, 1946.
Gnucheva, V. F. *Geograficheskii departament akademii nauk XVIII veka.* Moscow, 1940.
Golder, F. A. *Bering's voyages: an account of the efforts of the Russians to determine the relation of Asia and America.* 2 vols. New York, 1922-25.
Grekov, V. I. *Ocherki iz istorii russkikh geograficheskikh issledovanii v 1725-1765 gg.* Moscow, 1960.
Gurko, Z. V. and O. Stulova. *Razvitie sovetskoi nauki za 40 let: ukazatel' iubileinoi literatury 1957-58 gg.* Moscow, 1960.
Hans, Nicholas. *History of Russian Educational Policy.* London, 1931.
Hazard, John N. *Settling Disputes in Soviet Society: The Formative Years of Legal Institutions.* New York, 1960.
Holland, M. *Organizatsiia promyshlennogo issledovaniia.* Moscow, 1927.

Huxley, Julian. *Scientific Research and Social Needs*. London, 1934.
Iablokov, Vladimir Sergeevich. *220 let akademii nauk SSSR: spravochnaia kniga*. Moscow–Leningrad, 1945.
Ioffe, A. F. *et al. Nauka i tekhnika SSSR 1917-1927*. 3 vols. Moscow, 1927-28.
Ionidi, P. P. *Mirovozzrenie D. I. Mendeleeva*. Moscow, 1959.
Ipat'ev, V. N. *Zhizn' odnogo khimika: vospominaniia*. 2 vols. New York, 1945.
Ipatieff [Ipat'ev], V. N. *The Life of a Chemist*. Stanford, 1946.
Islamov, I. M. *Nauka v Uzbekistane za 15 let, 1924-39*. Tashkent, 1939.
Istoricheskii ocherk i obzor fondov rukopisnogo otdela biblioteka akademii nauk. 2 vols. Moscow, 1956-1958.
Ivanov, D. D. and Starosel'skaia-Nikitina, O. A. *Istoriia estestvoznaniia: literatura opublikovannaia v SSSR*. 2 vols. Moscow–Leningrad, 1949-55.
Ivanova, M. *et al. Akademiia nauk SSSR: izuchenie proizvoditel'nykh sil: bibliografiia trudov KIPS i SOPS, 1915-1955*. Moscow, 1957.
Izdaniia akademii nauk SSSR, 1917-1947. Moscow, 1947.
Iz istorii otechestvennoi tekhniki. Issledovaniia i materialy. Leningrad, 1950.
Johnson, William Herman Eckart. *Russia's Educational Heritage*. New Brunswick, N.J., 1950.
Joravsky, David. *Soviet Marxism and Natural Science, 1917-1932*. New York, 1961.
Kaftanov, S. V. *Vydaiushchaiasia rol' laureatov stalinskoi premii v razvitii nauki i tekhniki v SSSR*. Moscow, 1949.
Kakabadze, V. M., ed. *Nauka v Gruzii za 25 let, 1921-46*. Tblisi, 1947.
Kalendar' spravochnik akademii nauk SSSR. 7 vols. Moscow, 1931-38.
Katalog imeiushchikhsia v prodazhe izdanii akademii nauk, 1769-1935. Moscow–Leningrad, 1936.
Katalog izdanii akademii nauk SSSR 1930 g. Leningrad, 1931.
K dvukhsotletiiu vsesoiuznoi akademii nauk. Leningrad, 1925.
Keller, Boris A. *The Soviet Scientist*. Moscow, 1939.
Kim, M. *Kommunisticheskaia partiia-organizator kul'turnoi revoliutsii v SSSR*. Moscow, 1955.
Kirgiziia: trudy pervoi konferentsii po izucheniiu proizvoditel'nykh sil Kirgizskoi ASSR. Leningrad, 1934.
Kniazev, G. A., ed. *Arkhiv akademii nauk SSSR: obozrenie arkhivnykh materialov*. 3 vols. Leningrad, 1933-50.
Kniazev, G. A. and A. V. Kol'tsov. *Kratkii ocherk istorii akademii nauk SSSR*. Moscow–Leningrad, 1964.
Kolubovskii, I. *et al. Nauka na sluzhbe sotsialisticheskogo stroitel'stva: rabota nauchno-issledovatel'skikh institutov Leningrada*. Moscow–Leningrad, 1931.
Komarov, V. L. *An outline of the history of the academy*. London, 1946.
———, ed. *Iubileinaia sessiia akademii nauk SSSR, posviashchennaia 25-letiiu velikoi oktiabr'skoi sotsialisticheskoi revoliutsii*. Moscow–Leningrad, 1943.
———, V. M. Molotov and I. V. Stalin. *Za peredovuiu nauku*. Moscow–Leningrad, 1939.
Korneev, M. Ia. *Nauka i nadstroika*. Leningrad, 1958.
Korol, Alexander G. *Soviet Research and Development*. Cambridge, Mass., 1965.
Krachkovskii, I. Iu., ed. *Nauchnye uchrezhdeniia akademii nauk SSSR: kratkoe obozrenie ko dniu desiatiletiia 1917-1927*. Leningrad, 1927.
Kratkii bibliograficheskii ukazatel' izdanii SOPS, 1931-36. Moscow–Leningrad, 1936.
Krzhizhanovskii, G. M. *Programma rabot akademii nauk SSSR na 1936 g*. Moscow.
Kuibyshev, V. V., ed. *Ratsionalizatsiia promyshlennosti SSSR*. Moscow, 1928.
Kunik, A. *Sbornik materialov dlia istorii akademii nauk v XVIII v*. St. Petersburg, 1865.
Kuprevich, V. F. *Akademiia nauk Belorusskoi SSR*. Minsk, 1957.

Kuznetsov, B. *Lomonosov, Lobachevskii, Mendeleev; ocherki zhizni i mirovozzreniia.* Moscow, 1945.
————. *O novom etape v razvitii nauki.* Moscow, 1939.
————. *Ocherki istorii russkoi nauki.* Moscow, 1940.
Kuznetsov, I. V., ed. *Liudi russkoi nauki: ocherki o vydaiushchikhsia deiateliakh estestvoznaniia i tekhniki.* Moscow, 1962.
Lamanskii, V. I. *Lomonosov i Peterburgskaia akademiia nauk.* Moscow, 1865.
Lappo-Danilevskii, A. S. *Petr Velikii, osnovatel' imperatorskoi akademii nauk v St. Peterburge.* St. Petersburg, 1914.
Lauridsen, P. *Vitus Bering: The Discoverer of the Bering Strait.* Chicago, 1889.
Lazarev, Petr Petrovich. *Ocherki istorii russkoi nauki.* Moscow, 1950.
————. *Istoricheskii ocherk razvitiia tochnykh nauk v Rossii v prodolzhenie 200 let.* Leningrad, 1926.
Lenin, V. I. *Sochineniia.* Izd. 5, Moscow, 1958-65; Izd. 4, Moscow, 1941-62; Izd. 3, Moscow, 1928-37.
Lindener, B. A. *Raboty rossiiskoi akademii nauk v oblasti issledovaniia prirodnykh bogatstv rossii; obzor deiatel'nosti KEPS za 1915-1921 gg.* Petrograd, 1922.
Little, Arthur D. *The Handwriting on the Wall.* Boston, 1928.
Liudi russkoi nauki: ocherki o vydaiushchikhsia deiateliakh estestvoznaniia i tekhniki. 2 vols. Moscow–Leningrad, 1948.
Lovell, Bernard. *Science and Civilization.* London, 1939.
Lunacharskii, A. V. *Stati o sovetskoi literature,* Moscow, 1958.
Luppol, Ivan Kapitonovich. *Nauka i rekonstruktivnyi period: stenogramma doklada na s''ezde po izucheniiu povedeniia cheloveka, ianvar' 1930 g.* Moscow–Leningrad, 1931.
Maizel', I. A. *Kommunizm i prevrashchenie nauki v neposredstvennuiu proizvoditel'nuiu silu.* Moscow, 1963.
Malinovskii, A. A. *Elementy proletarskoi kul'tury v razvitii rabochego klassa.* Moscow, 1920.
————. *Tektologiia, vseobshchaia organizatsionnaia nauka.* Moscow, 1922.
Mamedaliev, Iu. G., ed. *Dostizheniia nauk v Azerbaidzhane. 1920-60.* Baku, 1960.
Marchenko, V. P. *Planirovanie nauchnoi raboty v SSSR.* Munich, 1953.
Marx, Karl and Friedrich Engels. *Werke.* 32 vols. Berlin, 1961-65.
————. *Sochineniia,* 2nd edn., 39 vols. Moscow, 1955-66.
Materialy k kharakteristike prikladnoi nauchnoi raboty akademii nauk SSSR: otdely i instituty komissii po izucheniiu estestvennykh proizvoditel'nykh sil soiuza. Leningrad, 1929.
Mavrodin, Vladimir V. *Rol' russkoi i sovetskoi nauki v istorii mirovoi kul'tury: stenogramma publichnoi lektsii, prochitannoi v Leningrade v 1948 g.* Leningrad, 1948.
Mees, C. E. Kenneth. *The Organization of Industrial Scientific Research.* New York, 1920.
Memoires de l'Académie des sciences de l'URSS. Classe des sciences physiques et mathématiques. Petrograd, 1914-23, Leningrad, 1925-30. *Classe des sciences historico-philologiques.* Petrograd, 1915-22.
Menshutkin, Boris N. *Russia's Lomonosov.* Princeton, 1952.
Merton, R. K. *Social Theory and Social Structure.* Glencoe, Ill., 1949.
Meshkov, Abram Romanovich. *Sovetskaia nauka za 30 let: lektsiia prochitannaia na oblastnom soveshchanii rukovoditelei raionskikh lektorskikh grupp 29-go oktiabria 1947 g.* Voronezh, 1948.
Mond, A. (Sir A. M. M. Melchett). *Industry and Politics.* London, 1927.
Morozov, Aleksandr. *Mikhail Vasil'evich Lomonosov, 1711-1765.* Leningrad, 1952.

Nauchnaia organizatsiia truda dvadtsatykh godov: sbornik dokumentov i materialov. Kazan, 1965.

Nauchnye doklady, soobshcheniia i predlozheniia predstavlennye k maiskoi sessii akademii nauk SSSR 1930 g. Leningrad, 1930.

Nauka v Azerbaidzhanskoi SSR za 15 let: trudy Azerbaidzhanskogo filiala akademii nauk SSSR. 55 vols. to date, Baku, 1936- .

Needham, Joseph, ed. *Science in Soviet Russia.* London, 1942.

Nekrasova, I. M. *Leninskii plan elektrifikatsii strany i ego sushchestvlenie v 1921-1931 gg.* Moscow, 1960.

Nelson, Richard R. *Invention, Research and Development: A Survey of the Literature.* U.S. Air Force RAND Research Memorandum. Santa Monica, Calif., 1958.

Nicolaevsky, Boris I. *Power and the Soviet Elite.* Ed. Janet D. Zagoria. New York, 1965.

Nouveau reglement et nouvel état de l'Académie Impériale des sciences de St. Petersburg. 1803.

Novikov, Mikhail Mikhailovich. *Velikany rossiiskogo estestvoznaniia.* Frankfurt, 1960.

Ocherki po istorii akademii nauk. 7 vols.:

    Bardin, I. *Tekhnicheskie nauki.* Moscow, 1945.

    Ioffe, A. F. *Fiziko-matematicheskie nauki.* Moscow, 1945.

    Meshchaninov, I. *Lingvisticheskie i literaturovedcheskie nauki.* Moscow, 1945.

    Obruchev, V. A. *Geologo-geograficheskie nauki.* Moscow, 1945.

    Orbeli, L. *Biologicheskie nauki.* Moscow, 1945.

    Vol'fkovich, S. *Khimicheskie nauki.* Moscow, 1945.

    Volgin, V. P. *Istoricheskie nauki.* Moscow, 1945.

Ol'denburg, S. F. *Nauka v Rossii: spravochnyi ezhegodnik.* Petrograd, 1920.

————. *Rossiiskaia akademiia nauk v 1920 godu.* Petrograd, 1921.

————. *Rossiiskaia akademiia nauk v 1921 godu.* Petrograd, 1922.

————. *Rossiiskaia akademiia nauk v 1922 godu.* Petrograd, 1923.

————. *Akademiia nauk SSSR v 1926 g.* Report given to Academy of Sciences, February 2, 1927. Leningrad, 1927.

————. *Akademiia nauk soiuza sovetskikh sotsialisticheskikh respublik za dvesti let.* Speech given by S. F. Ol'denburg at the ceremonial meeting of the Academy of Sciences, September 6, 1925. Leningrad, 1925.

————, ed. *Nauka v Rossii: spravochnik.* Moscow, 1923.

————, ed. *Nauka i nauchnye rabotniki SSSR.* 4 vols. Moscow, 1926-34.

————, ed. *Spisok deistvitel'nykh chlenov akademii nauk soiuza sovetskikh sotsialisticheskikh respublik, 1725-1925.* Leningrad, 1925.

Ol'denburg, S. S. *Tsarstvovanie imperatora Nikolaia II.* Belgrade, 1939–49.

Ornstein, Martha. *The Role of the Scientific Societies in the Seventeenth Century.* New York, 1913.

Ostrovitianov, K. V. *et al.,* eds. *Istoriia akademii nauk SSSR.* Vol. ɪ, Moscow, 1958; Vol. ɪɪ, Moscow, 1964.

Otchet o deiatel'nosti akademii nauk soiuza sovetskikh sotsialisticheskikh respublik. 1916-1919; 1923-1934:

  . . . *za 1916 g.* S. F. Ol'denburg, ed. Petrograd, 1917.

  . . . *za 1917 g.* ————, ed. Petrograd, 1918.

  . . . *za 1918 g.* ————, ed. Petrograd, 1919.

  . . . *za 1919 g.* ————, ed. Petrograd, 1920.

  . . . *za 1923 g.* ————, ed. Leningrad, 1924.

  . . . *za 1924 g.* ————, ed. Leningrad, 1925.

  . . . *za 1925 g.* ————, ed. Leningrad, 1926.

  . . . *za 1926 g.* 2 vols. ————, ed. Leningrad, 1927.

  . . . *za 1927 g.* 2 vols. A. E. Fersman, ed. Leningrad, 1928.

  . . . *za 1928 g.* 2 vols. S. F. Ol'denburg, ed. Leningrad, 1929.

. . . *za 1929 g.* 2 vols. V. L. Komarov, ed. Leningrad, 1930.
. . . *za 1930 g.* V. P. Volgin, ed. Leningrad, 1931.
. . . *za 1931 g.* ———, ed. Leningrad, 1932.
. . . *za 1932 g.* ———, ed. Leningrad, 1933.
. . . *za 1933 g.* ———, ed. Leningrad, 1934.
. . . *za 1934 g.* ———, ed. Leningrad, 1935.
Otchet o rabote akademii nauk SSSR za 1939. Moscow, 1940.
Pekarskii, Petr. *Istoriia imperatorskoi akademii nauk.* Vol. ɪ, St. Petersburg, 1870; Vol. ɪɪ, St. Petersburg, 1873.
Pervaia vsesoiuznaia konferentsiia po planirovaniiu nauchno-issledovatel'skoi raboty, 6-11 aprelia 1931. Statisticheskii otchet. Moscow–Leningrad, 1931.
Petrov, F. N., ed. *Desiat' let sovetskoi nauki 1917-27.* Moscow–Leningrad, 1927.
Piat' let raboty tsentral'noi komissii po uluchsheniiu byta uchenykh pri sovete narodnykh komissarov RSFSR (TsEKUBU), 1921-26. Moscow, 1927.
Piksanov, N. K. *Gor'kii i nauka.* Moscow, 1948.
Pinkevitch, A. P. *The New Education in the Soviet Republic.* G. S. Counts, ed. New York, 1929.
———. *Science and Education in the U.S.S.R.* New York, 1935.
Pisarzhevsky, O. N. *Dmitry Ivanovich Mendeleyev* (in English; Soviet transliteration), Moscow, 1954.
Plan nauchno-issledovatel'skikh rabot akademii nauk soiuza SSSR na 1939 g. Moscow–Leningrad, 1939.
Plan rabot akademii nauk SSSR na vtoroe piatiletie, 1933-37. Leningrad, 1932.
Poincaré, Henri. *La Valeur de la Science.* Paris, n.d.
———. *Tsennost' nauki.* Moscow, 1906.
Pokrovskii, M. N. and A. Timiriazev. *Nauka v sovetskoi rossii.* Moscow, 1922.
Polanyi, Michael. *The Logic of Liberty.* Chicago, 1951.
Pollock, Friedrich. *Die planwirtschaftlichen Versuche in der Sowjetunion.* Leipzig, 1929.
Polonska-Vasylenko, N. *Ukrainska Akademiya Nauk* [Institute for the Study of the USSR] 2 vols. Munich, 1955, 1958.
Predtechenskii, Anatolii Vasil'evich and Veniamin Iakovlevich Golant. *Kolybel' russkoi nauki: istoricheskii ocherk o nauchnykh uchrezhdeniiakh strelki vasil'evskogo ostrova v Leningrade.* Leningrad, 1959.
Prezidentu akademii nauk SSSR akademiku Vladimiru Leont'evichu Komarovu k semidesiatiletiiu so dnia rozhdeniia i sorokapiatiletiiu nauchnoi deiatel'nosti. Leningrad, 1939.
Price, Derek J. de Solla. *Science Since Babylon.* New Haven, 1961.
Proekt ustava i shtata imperatorskoi akademii nauk. St. Petersburg, 1864.
Programmy nauchno-issledovatel'skikh rabot uchrezhdenii akademii nauk soiuza SSR na 1937 god. Moscow–Leningrad, 1937.
Proizvodstvennyi plan akademii nauk soiuza sovetskikh sotsialisticheskikh respublik na 1931 g. Leningrad, 1931.
Protokoly zasedanii konferentsii imperatorskoi akademii nauk. Vol. ɪv, St. Petersburg, 1911.
Pushkinskii dom, AN SSSR, 1725-1925. Leningrad, 1925.
Radovskii, M. I. *M. V. Lomonosov i peterburgskaia akademiia nauk.* Leningrad, 1961.
Raigorodskii, N. A. *Imperializm i uchenye.* Moscow–Leningrad, 1934.
Riazanovskii, Valentin Aleksandrovich. *Razvitie russkoi nauchnoi mysli v XVIII-XX st. st.; nauki o prirode.* New York, 1949.
Rol' russkoi nauki v razvitii mirovoi nauki i kul'tury: nauchnaia konferentsiia, 5-12 iiunia 1944. Moscow, 1944.
Rothstein, Andrew, ed. *Wreckers on Trial: a record of the trial of the industrial party held in Moscow, November-December 1930.* New York, 1931.

Rubinstein, Modest Iosifovich. *Burzhuaznaia nauka i tekhnika na sluzhbe ameri-kanskogo imperializma.* Moscow, 1951.

————. *Soviet Science and Technique in Service of Building Communism in the U.S.S.R.* Moscow, 1954.

Rutkevich, M. N. *Praktika—osnova poznaniia i kriterii istiny.* Moscow, 1952.

Satpaev, K. I., ed. *Nauka v Kazakhstane za sorok let sovetskoi vlasti.* Alma-Ata, 1957.

Sbornik postanovlenii i rasporiazhenii otnosiashchikhsia do imperatorskoi akademii nauk. St. Petersburg, 1869.

Sbornik statei po arkheologii i vizantinovedeniiu, izdavaemym seminariem imeni N. P. Kondakova. 5 vols. Prague, 1928.

Schapiro, Leonard. *The Communist Party of the Soviet Union.* New York, 1960.

Science at the Crossroads. Papers presented to the International Congress of the History of Science and Technology held in London, June 29 to July 3, 1931, by the delegates of the USSR. London, 1931.

Science in Soviet Russia. Papers presented at the Congress of American–Soviet friendship, New York City, November 7, 1943. Lancaster, Pa., 1944.

S. F. Ol'denburg: K piatidesiatiletiiu nauchnoobshchestvennoi deiatel'nosti, 1882-1932. Speeches at the Academy of Sciences on February 1, 1933, honoring Academician S. F. Ol'denburg. Leningrad, 1934.

Shmidt, O. Iu., and Smushkevich, B. Ia. *Nauchnye kadry i nauchno-issledova-tel'skie uchrezhdeniia SSSR.* Moscow, 1930.

Shteppa, Konstantin F. *Russian Historians and the Soviet State.* New Bruns-wick, N.J., 1962.

Sistematicheskii ukazatel' izdanii akademii nauk soiuza sovetskikh sotsialisti-cheskikh respublik vyshedshikh v svet s 1 ianvaria 1917 g. po 1 sentiabria 1925 g. Leningrad, 1925.

Skriabin, K. I., ed. *Nauka v Kirgizii za 20 let, 1926-46.* Frunze, 1946.

Smirnov, Il'ia S. *Lenin i sovetskaia kul'tura.* Moscow, 1960.

Sobranie uzakonenii i rasporiazhenii rabochego i krest'ianskogo pravitel'stva RSFSR, Moscow, 1917-32.

Sobranie zakonov i rasporiazhenii raboche-krest'ianskogo pravitel'stva SSSR. Moscow, 1924-1932.

Sokolov, Boris. *Nauka v Sovetskoi Rossii.* Berlin, 1921.

Spravochnik dlia uchastnikov prazdnovaniia dvukhsotletnego iubileia akademii nauk, 1725-1925. Leningrad, 1925.

Spulber, Nicholas. *Soviet Strategy for Economic Growth.* Bloomington, Ind., 1964.

Steelman, J. R. *Science and Public Policy.* 5 vols. Washington, D.C., 1947.

Stepanov, I. *Elektrifikatsiia RSFSR v sviazi s perekhodnoi fazoi mirovogo khoziaistva.* Moscow–Petrograd, 1923.

Sukhomlinov, M. I. *Istoriia rossiiskoi akademii.* 8 vols. 1874-87.

————, ed. *Materialy dlia istorii imperatorskoi akademii nauk.* 10 vols. St. Petersburg, 1885-1900.

Editors of *Survey, The State of Soviet Science.* Boston, 1965.

Sverzhin, L. *Nauka na sluzhbe tiazheloi promyshlennosti SSSR.* Khar'kov, 1934.

Tezisy k dokladam, predstavlennykh na martovskuiu sessiiu akademii nauk SSSR 1935 goda. Leningrad, 1935.

Timiriazev, A. *Nauka v sovetskoi Rossii za piat' let.* Moscow, 1922.

Timiriazev, Kliment A. *Nauka i demokratiia.* Leningrad, 1926.

Topchiev, Aleksandr Vasil'evich. *Stroitel'stvo kommunizma i nauka.* Moscow, 1957.

Troshchin, D. M. *Mesto i rol' estestvoznaniia v razvitii obshchestva.* Moscow, 1961.

Trotsky, L. *Literature and Revolution.* New York, 1925.

Trudy noiabr'skoi sessii akademii nauk SSSR, 1931 g. Leningrad, 1932.
Trudy noiabr'skoi sessii akademii nauk SSSR, 1932 g. Leningrad, 1933.
Trudy noiabr'skoi sessii akademii nauk SSSR, 1933 g. Leningrad, 1934.
Trudy soveta po izucheniiu proizvoditel'nykh sil. Leningrad, 1934.
Tsetlin, Lev Solomonovich. *Iz istorii nauchnoi mysli v Rossii: nauka i uchenye v Moskovskom universitete vo vtoroi polovine XIX veka.* Moscow, 1958.
Ul'ianovskaia, V. A. *Formirovanie nauchnoi intelligentsii v SSSR, 1917-1937 g.g.,* Moscow, 1966.
Universitety i nauchnye uchrezhdeniia. Moscow–Leningrad, 1935.
Ural'skii filial akademii nauk SSSR v g. Sverdlovske. Leningrad, 1933.
Usloviia priema v aspiranty-doktoranty akademii nauk SSSR na 1935 g. Moscow–Leningrad, 1935.
Ustav akademii nauk soiuza sovetskikh sotsialisticheskikh respublik. Leningrad, 1927.
Ustav akademii nauk soiuza sovetskikh sotsialisticheskikh respublik, utverzhden 23 maia 1930 goda. Leningrad, 1930.
Ustav akademii nauk soiuza sovetskikh sotsialisticheskikh respublik, utverzhden 23 noiabria 1935 goda. Moscow, 1935.
Vasil'chikov, A. A. *Semeistvo Razumovskikh.* St. Petersburg, 1880.
Vasil'evskii, V. G. *Trudy.* Petrograd, 1915, Leningrad, 1930.
Vavilov, Sergei Ivanovich. *Nauka Stalinskoi epokhi.* Moscow, 1950.
————. *Tridtsat' let sovetskoi nauki.* Moscow, 1947.
————, ed. *Trudy komissii po istorii akademii nauk SSSR.* 2 vols. Moscow–Leningrad, 1947.
————. *Voprosy istorii otechestvennoi nauki: obshchee sobranie akademii nauk SSSR, posviashchenoe istorii otechestvennoi nauki 5-11 ianvaria 1949 g.; doklady.* Moscow–Leningrad, 1949.
Vernadskii, G. V. *O znachenii nauchnoi deiatel'nosti N. P. Kondakova.* Prague, 1924.
Volgin, V. P. *Akademiia nauk SSSR za chetyre goda, 1930-33.* Leningrad, 1934.
————, et al. *Planirovanie nauki i zadachi komakademii i akademii nauk.* Reports by V. Volgin, M. Gubkin, and E. Kol'man. Moscow-Leningrad, 1931.
Vucinich, Alexander. *Science in Russian Culture: A History to 1860.* Stanford, 1963.
————. *The Soviet Academy of Sciences.* Stanford, 1956.
Wetter, Gustav A. *Dialectical Materialism: A Historical and Systematic Survey of Philosophy in the Soviet Union.* New York, 1958.
Wiener, Norbert. *The Human Use of Human Beings: Cybernetics and Society.* Garden City, N.Y., 1954.
Woolf, Harry. *The Transits of Venus: A Study of Eighteenth-Century Science.* Princeton, 1959.
Zadachi akademii nauk SSSR v oblasti geologicheskikh distsiplin. Leningrad, 1929.
Zankevich, E. Kh. *K istorii sovetizatsii rossiiskoi akademii nauk.* Munich, 1957. (Institute for the Study of the USSR, Series 2, No. 59.)
Zapisnaia knizhka akademii nauk SSSR. 7 vols. Leningrad, 1923-29.
Za povorot na fronte estestvoznaniia: diskussiia na zasedaniiakh prezidiuma komakademii 1930 g.–1931 g. Moscow, 1932.
Za sotsialisticheskuiu rekonstruktsiiu akademii nauk SSSR. Leningrad, 1930.
Zavrotskii, A. I. *Krasnye vandaly: obzor sostoianiia nauki v sovetskoi Rossii.* Shanghai, 1934.
Zvorykin, A. A., ed. *Biograficheskii slovar' deiatelei estestvoznaniia i tekhniki.* 2 vols. Moscow, 1958-59.
————, et al. *Istoriia tekhniki.* Moscow, 1962.

VII vsesoiuznomu s"ezdu sovetov akademiia nauk SSSR. Moscow–Leningrad, 1935.

II. Articles

"Akademiia nauk pered litsom XVII s'' ezda kommunisticheskoi partii," *Vestnik Akademii Nauk SSSR* (No. 3, 1934), pp. 1-18.

Arshinov, V. V. "O nauchnoi organizatsii nauchnogo izdatel'stva," *Nauchnyi Rabotnik* (Nos. 7-8, 1926), pp. 31-37.

Bakh, A. N. "K voprosu o planirovanii raboty nauchno-issledovatel'skikh uchrezhdenii soiuza," *VARNITSO* (No. 3, 1929).

———. "Vsesoiuznaia akademiia nauk i sotsialisticheskoe stroitel'stvo," *Front Nauki i Tekhniki* (Nos. 11-12, 1932), pp. 20-24.

Banasiukevich, V. D. "V. I. Lenin i nauchnaia organizatsiia truda," *Istoriia SSSR* (No. 2, 1965), pp. 108-13.

Bauer, Raymond A. "The Bolshevik Attitude Toward Science," in Carl J. Friedrich, ed., *Totalitarianism*, Cambridge, Mass., 1954.

Belomortsev, Sergei. "Bol'shevizatsiia akademii nauk," *Posev*, XLVI (November 18, 1951), 11-12.

———. "Zhertvy 'dela' akademii nauk SSSR," *Volia*. Munich (No. 10, 1952), pp. 24-28.

Berg, A. I. "Lenin i nauchnaia organizatsiia truda," *Pravda*. (October 24, 1962).

Besterman, Theodore. "A Bibliography of the Bulletin (Izvestiia) of the Academy of Sciences of the USSR," *Journal of Documentation*, I (June 1945), 45-56.

Bezbakh, S. A. "Nauchno-issledovatel'skaia ekspeditsionnaia rabota, ee uchet i soglasovanie v predelakh RSFSR," *Krasnaia Letopis'* (No. 2, 1928), pp. 73-92.

———. "Uchet i soglasovanie nauchno-issledovatel'skoi raboty v RSFSR," *Nauchnyi Rabotnik* (March 1928), pp. 8-13.

Borisiak, A. "K rabote podkomissii po uchrezhdeniiami otdeleniia fiziko-matematicheskikh nauk," *Za sotsialisticheskuiu rekonstruktsiiu akademii nauk SSSR* (No. 1, 1930).

Bukharin, N. I. "Science and Politics in the Soviet Union," *New Statesman and Nation* (July 11, 1931), pp. 37-38.

———. "Theory and Practice from the Standpoint of Dialectical Materialism," *Science at the Cross Roads*. London, 1931, pp. 11-33.

——— et al. "Podgotovka nauchnykh kadrov i akademiia nauk," *Pravda*, No. 233 (August 24, 1931), p. 4.

Bulgakov, F. I. "Nemetskaia partiia v russkoi akademii," *Istoricheskii Vestnik*, Vol. 4 (1881), 421-31.

Caldwell, Oliver J. and Loren R. Graham. "Moscow in May 1963" (Office of Education Bulletin), Washington, D.C., 1964.

"Chistka apparata akademii nauk," *Izvestiia*, September 4, 1929, p. 3.

"Chistka apparata akademii nauk: pochemu nuzhna byla chistka," *Izvestiia*, August 30, 1929, p. 4.

Chudinov, D. K. "Sostoianie i perspektivy nauchno-issledovatel'skikh rabot v Kazakhstane," *Narodnoe Khoziaistvo Kazakhstana* (Nos. 11-12, 1928), pp. 277-90.

Dedijer, Stevan. "The Science of Science: A Programme and a Plea," *Minerva* (Summer 1966), pp. 489-504.

Derzhavin, N. S. "Uchenye i sovetskaia obshchestvennost," *Nauchnyi Rabotnik* (December 1927), pp. 3-7.

DeWitt, Nicholas. "Reorganization of Science and Research in the U.S.S.R." *Science*, CXXXIII (June 23, 1961), 1,987.

———. "Scholarship in the Natural Sciences," in C. E. Black, ed., *The Transformation of Russian Society*, Cambridge, Mass., 1960.

Dobrynin, V. V. "Problema organizatsii tvorcheskogo truda," *Nauchnyi Rabotnik* (Nos. 5-6, 1928), pp. 54-64.

Dubinin, N. P. "I. V. Michurin i sovremennaia genetika," *Voprosy Filosofii* (No. 6, 1966), pp. 59-70.

Dynnik, Mikhail. "Problema nauchnoi organizatsii nauchnogo truda," *Nauchnyi Rabotnik* (No. 1, 1925), pp. 180-92.

Egorshin, V. P. "Estestvoznanie i klassovaia bor'ba," *Pod znamenem marksizma* (No. 6, 1926), pp. 108-36.

Epstein, Fritz. "Die marxistische Geschichtswissenschaft in der Sovetunion seit 1927," *Jahrbücher für Kultur und Geschichte der Slaven*, vi (No. 1, 1930), 78-203.

Fedorovskii, N. M. "Rol' issledovatel'skikh institutov v razvitii promyshlennosti SSSR," *Nauchnyi Rabotnik* (February 1926), pp. 28-32.

Figatner, Iu. "Proverka apparata akademii nauk," *VARNITSO* (February 1930), p. 73.

Finkel', N. "Kapitalizm i issledovatel'skaia rabota," *Molodoi Bol'shevik* (Nos. 14-15, 1931), pp. 22-30.

Gastev, A. "O tendentsiiakh proletarskoi kul'tury," *Proletarskaia kul'tura* (Nos. 9-10, 1919), pp. 35-45.

Gastev, Iu. A. "O metodologicheskikh voprosakh ratsionalizatsii obucheniia," in A. I. Berg *et al.*, eds., *Kibernetika, myshlenie, zhizn'*, Moscow, 1964, pp. 459-72.

Glonti, Kh. and A. Amiranashvili. "Nauka i nauchnye uchrezhdeniia v SSR Gruzii," *Front Nauki i Tekhniki* (Nos. 10-11, 1934), pp. 107-12.

Graham, Loren R. "Bukharin and the Planning of Science," *The Russian Review* (April 1964), pp. 135-48.

————. "Reorganization of the Academy of Sciences," in Peter H. Juviler and Henry W. Morton, eds., *Soviet Policy-Making: Studies of Communism in Transition.* New York, 1967, pp. 133-61.

————. "Science Policy and Planning in the USSR," *Survey* (July 1967), pp. 61-79.

Gubkin, I. M. "Osnovnye zadachi i organizatsionnye formy soveta po izucheniiu proizvoditel'nykh sil SSSR," *Vestnik Akademii Nauk SSSR* (No. 3, 1931), pp. 7-16.

Guins, George C. "The Academy of Sciences of the USSR," *The Russian Review*, xii (1952), 269-71.

Iarilov, A. "Staraia i novaia akademiia nauk," *Front Nauki i Tekhniki* (July-August 1931), pp. 50-59.

"Intellectual Freedom in Russia," *The New Republic* (March 30, 1932), pp. 183-84.

Ioffe, A. F. "Vpechatleniia ot poezdki po amerikanskim laboratoriiam," *Nauchnyi Rabotnik* (April 1926), pp. 59-65.

Ipat'ev, V. N. "Nauka v sovremennoi Rossii," *Novyi Zhurnal* (No. 5, 1943), pp. 293-302.

"Ipatieff Back in News," *Chemical and Engineering News* (September 6, 1965), p. 168.

Ivanitskii, S. M. "Planirovanie nauchno-issledovatel'skoi raboty vo vseu-krainskoi akademii nauk," *Vestnik Akademii Nauk SSSR* (No. 3, 1939), pp. 15-26.

Ivanov, P. "Sledstvennoe delo o sovetnike akademii nauk Shumakhere," *Chteniia v imperatorskom obshchestve istorii i drevnostei rossiiskikh*, xxxiv (No. 3, Chap. V, 1860), pp. 64-122.

"Iz otcheta lokal'nogo biuro SNR akademii nauk," *Za sotsialisticheskuiu rekonstruktsiiu akademii nauk SSSR* (No. 1, 1930), p. 3.

"Iz postanovlenii obshchego sobraniia i prezidiuma," *Vestnik Akademii Nauk SSSR* (No. 10, 1931), cols. 61-66.

"Iz postanovlenii obshchego sobraniia i prezidiuma," *Vestnik Akademii Nauk SSSR* (No. 2, 1932), cols. 59-62.

"Iz postanovlenii obshchego sobraniia i prezidiuma," *Vestnik Akademii Nauk SSSR* (No. 3, 1932), cols. 49-54.

Joravsky, David. "Soviet Marxism and Biology Before Lysenko," *Journal of the History of Ideas*, xx (January 1959), 85-104.
_____. "Soviet Views on the History of Science," *Isis*, xLvi (March 1955), pp. 3-13.
Kalinin, M. I. "K nauchnym rabotnikam i studentam," *Nauchnyi Rabotnik* (January 1928), pp. 3-8.
Kekcheev, K. Kh. "Biudzhet vremeni studentov," *Nauchnyi Rabotnik* (No. 10, 1926), pp. 38-53.
_____. "Organizatsiia truda uchenogo," *Nauchnyi Rabotnik* (September 1926), pp. 21-30.
Keller, B. A. "Na vyezdnoi sessii," *Front Nauki i Tekhniki* (July-August 1931), pp. 59-61.
_____. "Revoliutsiia i uchenye starshego pokoleniia," *Al'manakh*, xvi (No. 2, 1933), 404-14.
Khvol'son, O. D. "Nauka chistaia i prikladnaia," *Nauchnyi Rabotnik*, i (January 1926), 32-49.
Kline, George L. "Darwinism and the Russian Orthodox Church," in Ernest J. Simmons, ed., *Continuity and Change in Russian and Soviet Thought*. Cambridge, Mass., 1955, pp. 307-28.
Kniazev, G. A. "Akademiia nauk SSSR za 30 let (kratkii khronologicheskii obzor)," *Vestnik Akademii Nauk SSSR* (No. 11, 1947), pp. 117-33.
_____. "Iz proshlogo akademii nauk: D. I. Mendeleev i imperatorskaia akademiia," *Vestnik Akademii Nauk* (No. 3, 1931), p. 34.
_____. "Iz proshlogo akademii nauk: poritsanie akademikam za uchastie v 'zapiske 342 uchenykh'," *Vestnik Akademii Nauk* (No. 4, 1931), cols. 13-22.
_____. "Maksim Gor'kii i tsarskoe pravitel'stvo," *Vestnik Akademii Nauk* (No. 2, 1932), cols. 33-34.
Kol'man, E. "Vreditel'stvo v nauke," *Bol'shevik* (January 31, 1931), pp. 73-81.
Komari, M. *et al*. "Mesto i rol'nauki v razvitii obshchestva," *Bol'shevik*, iv (February, 1952), 9-23.
Krassovsky, Dimitry, and Vosper, Robert. "The Structure of the Russian Academy of Sciences from its beginning to 1945; a guide for bibliographers," *Kentucky University, Margaret I. King Library, Occasional Contributions*, No. 39, Lexington, 1952.
Krzhizhanovskii, G. M. "Lenin i nauka," *Priroda* (No. 4, 1955), p. 5.
_____. "Na pomoshch' sotsialisticheskomu stroitel'stvu," *Vestnik Akademii Nauk SSSR* (special number, 1931), pp. 3-10.
_____. "Zadachi sotsialisticheskogo stroitel'stva i nauchnye rabotniki," *Nauchnyi Rabotnik* (May-June 1928), pp. 3-13.
Kulieva, A. K. "Rol' akademii nauk SSSR v razrabotke plana vtoroi piatiletki," *Uchenye Zapiski Turkmenskogo Universiteta*, viii (1956), pp. 181-88.
Kuznetsov, B. G. "Iz proshlogo russkoi nauki," *Novyi Mir*, viii (1938), pp. 175-96.
Lapirov-Skoblo, M. Ia. "Problema nauchnykh kadrov," *Pravda* (November 21, 1929), p. 5.
_____. "Revoliutsiia kul'turnaia i revoliutsiia tekhnicheskaia," *Nauchnyi Rabotnik* (May-June 1928), pp. 36-41.
Lappo-Danilevsky, A. S. "The Development of science and learning in Russia," in J. D. Duff, ed., *Russian Realities and Problems*. Cambridge, England, 1917.
Lazarev, Petr Petrovich. *Istoricheskii ocherk razvitiia tochnykh nauk v Rossii v prodolzhenie 200 let*. Speech given to the Academy of Sciences in 1925 at Moscow. Leningrad, 1926.
Leontief, W. W., Sr. "Scientific and Technological Research in Russia," *American Slavic and East European Review*, iv (1945), 70-79.

Lepin, T. K., Ia. Ia. Lus, and Iu. A. Filipchenko. "Deisvitel' nye chleny akademii nauk za poslednie 80 let (1846-1924)," *Izvestiia biuro po evgenike* (No. 3, 1925), pp. 7-49.

Levinson, N. G. "Tekhnika umstvennoi raboty," *Nauchnoe Slovo* (No. 3, 1928), pp. 141-63.

Lipski, A. "The Foundation of the Russian Academy of Sciences," *Isis*, XLIV (1953), 349-54.

Loboda, N. I. "Nauchnye rabotniki i sovetskaia obshchestvennost'," *Nauchnyi Rabotnik* (February 1927), pp. 3-12.

Lozinski, G. "L'Académie des sciences de Saint-Petersbourg," *Le monde slave*, II (1925), 308-20.

Lunacharskii, A. V. "K 200-letiiu vsesoiuznoi akademii nauk," *Novyi Mir* (No. 10, 1925), p. 110.

———. "Akademiia nauk i sovetskaia vlast' (K dvukhsotletiiu akademii)," *Rabochaia Gazeta*, CLXXXIV (August 14, 1925), 3.

Luppol, I. K. "K vyboram v akademiiu nauk SSSR," *Nauchnyi Rabotnik* (November 1928), pp. 3-9.

———. "Ob otnoshenii sovetskikh uchenykh k uchenym emigratsii," *Nauchnyi Rabotnik* (December 1928), pp. 13-22.

———. "Rekonstruktivnyi period i nauchnyi front," *Nauchnyi Rabotnik* (November 1929), pp. 3-8.

———. "Vopros prosveshcheniia i nauki na XV s''ezde VKP(b)," *Nauchnyi Rabotnik* (February 1928), pp. 3-7.

———. "IV plenum tsentral'nogo soveta (sektsii nauchnykh rabotnikov soiuza rabotnikov prosveshcheniia SSSR) o rabote akademii nauk SSSR," *Nauchnyi Rabotnik* (July 1928), pp. 14-21.

Lurquin, Constant. "Un jubilé académique au pays des Soviets," *Université de Bruxelles Revue*, XXXI (1926), 210-31.

Magerovskii, D. A. "Rossiiskaia assotsiatsiia nauchno-issledovatel'skikh institutov obshchestvennykh nauk (RANION)," *Nauchnyi Rabotnik* (November 1927) pp. 51-61.

"Materialist." "Ob akademii nauk RSFSR," *Pod znamenem marksizma* (No. 1, 1923), pp. 190-91.

Mikhailov, A. A. "The Organization of Scientific Work in the U.S.S.R." *American Review of the Soviet Union*, VIII (1947), 26-35.

Mindlin, Z. "O planirovanii nauchnoi raboty," *Kommunisticheskaia Revoliutsiia* (No. 3, 1928), pp. 59-64.

Modestov, V. I. "Russkaia nauka v posledniia dvadtsat' piat' let'," *Russkaia Mysl'*, V (1890), 73-91.

Modzalevskii, B. "Akademiia nauk, imperatorskaia sanktpeterburgskaia," in F. A. Brockhaus and I. A. Efron, eds., *Entsiklopedicheskii Slovar'*, Vol. I, St. Petersburg, 1911.

Moravcsik, Michael J. "Improvement of Science in Developing Countries," *Minerva* (Spring 1966), pp. 381-90.

Mosely, P. E. "Freedom of Artistic Expression and Scientific Inquiry in Russia," *Annals of the American Academy of Political and Social Science*, CC (November 1938), 254.

"Novaia struktura vsesoiuznoi akademii nauk," *Nauchnoe Slovo* (Nos. 2-3, 1931), pp. 115-18.

"Novyi ustav akademii nauk," *Za sotsialisticheskuiu rekonstruktsiiu akademii nauk SSSR* (No. 1, 1930).

"O krupnykh nedostatkov v rabote komissii po istorii akademii nauk SSSR i o merakh po ikh ustraneniiu," *Vestnik Akademii Nauk SSSR* (No. 1, 1953), p. 81.

"O merakh po uluchsheniiu koordinatsii nauchno-issledovatel'skikh rabot v strane i deiatel'nosti akademii nauk SSSR," *Pravda*, April 12, 1961, p. 1.

"O meropriatiiakh po ukrepleniiu nauchnoi raboty," *Nauchnyi Rabotnik* (September 1929), pp. 124-25.
"O nauchnykh kadrakh VKP(b)," *Pravda*, August 18, 1929, p. 6.
"Ob uluchshenii podgotovki novykh spetsialistov," *Pravda*, July 13, 1928, p. 3.
"Obzor deiatel'nosti VARNITSO," *VARNITSO* (No. 2, 1929).
Ol'denburg, S. F. "Akademiia nauk SSSR," *Bol' shaia Sovetskaia Entsiklopediia*, Vol. I, Moscow, 1929, cols. 783-92.
———. "Kul'turnye zadachi nauchnykh rabotnikov," *Nauchnyi Rabotnik* (April 1926), pp. 13-15.
———. "Maksim Gor'kii i nauka," *Nauchnoe Slovo* (No. 3, 1928), pp. 3-6.
———. "O razvitii nauchnoi deiatel'nosti v SSSR za desiat' let," *Nauchnyi Rabotnik* (November 1927), pp. 26-31.
———. "Polozhenie nashei nauki sredi nauki mirovoi," in Abram F. Ioffe, ed., *Nauka i tekhnika SSSR, 1917-27*, I, Moscow, 1927.
———. "Vpechatleniia o nauchnoi zhizni v Germanii, Frantsii i Anglii," *Nauchnyi Rabotnik* (February 1927), pp. 88-101.
———. "Zadachi sektsii nauchnykh rabotnikov v dele kul'turnoi revoliutsii," *Nauchnyi Rabotnik* (May-June 1928), pp. 26-35.
Orlov, A. S. "Akademiia nauk u poroga 1932 goda," *Vestnik Akademii Nauk* (No. 10, 1931), cols. 22-32.
Osadchii, P. S. "Pervyi s''ezd prezidiumov gosudarstvennykh planovykh komissii," *Nauchnyi Rabotnik* (April 1926), pp. 3-12.
Oster, G. "Scientific Research in the U.S.S.R.," *The Annals of the American Academy of Political and Social Science*, CCLXIII (May 1949), 134-40.
Ostrovitianov, K. V. "O perspektivakh i metodakh raboty sektsii nauchnykh rabotnikov," *Nauchnyi Rabotnik* (July-August 1929), pp. 3-10.
Pal'chinskii, V. O. "Organizatsiia nauchnogo izdatel'stva i blizhaishie prakticheskie zadachi," *Nauchnyi Rabotnik* (September 1927), pp. 9-14.
Pankevich (no initial given). "Belorusskaia akademiia nauk za piat' let," *Front Nauki i Tekhniki* (No. 3, 1934), pp. 107-12.
Pashukanis, E. B. "Kommunisticheskaia akademiia pri TsIK SSSR," *Nauchnyi Rabotnik* (September 1927), pp. 15-20.
Petrov, F. N. "K voprosu o planovoi organizatsii nauchno-issledovatel'skoi raboty SSSR," *Nauchnyi Rabotnik* (December 1927), pp. 8-15.
———. "Vsesoiuznaia konferentsiia Glavnauk," *Nauchnyi Rabotnik* (February 1926), pp. 12-16.
Petrov, M. P. "Sovetskaia nauka v Turkmenii za 20 let," *Izvestiia Turkmenskogo Filiala Akademii Nauk SSSR* (Nos. 2-3, 1944), pp. 5-21.
Petrunkevich, Alexander. "Russia's Contribution to Science," *Transactions of the Connecticut Academy of Arts and Sciences*, XXIII (1920), 611-41.
"Piatnadtsataia godovshchina oktiabria i nauka," *Vestnik Kommunisticheskoi Akademii* (Nos. 11-12, 1932), pp. 3-19.
Pierre, André. "L'Académie des Sciences de l'U.R.S.S.," *Monde Slave* (July 1933), pp. 90-104.
"Podgotovka nauchnykh kadrov i akademiia nauk," *Vestnik Kommunisticheskoi Akademii*, XXXV-XXXVI (1929), 281-85.
Podkopaev, N. A. "O planirovanii nauchnoi raboty," *Vestnik Akademii Nauk* (No. 3, 1931), pp. 1-6.
Pokrovskii, M. N. "K deviatoi godovshchine," *Nauchnyi Rabotnik* (November 1926), pp. 3-22.
Popovskii, Aleksandr. "Zametki o russkoi nauke," *Novyi Mir* (No. 3, 1948), pp. 154-90.
"Postanovlenie prezidiuma tsentral'nogo ispolnitel'nogo komiteta soiuza SSR po dokladam vsesoiuznoi, vseukrainskoi, i belorusskoi akademii nauk (o rabote akademii)," *Vestnik Akademii Nauk SSSR* (Nos. 8-9, 1933), pp. 1-4.
"Postanovlenie tsentral'nogo ispolnitel'nogo komiteta soiuza SSR o peredache

akademii nauk SSSR v vedenie SNK SSSR," *Vestnik Akademii Nauk SSSR* (No. 1, 1934), pp. 1-2.

Pozern, B. P. "Ocherednye voprosy sotsialisticheskogo stroitel'stva i nauchnye rabotniki," *Nauchnyi Rabotnik* (March 1929), pp. 3-10.

Predtechenskii, A. V. and A. V. Kol'tsov. "Istoriia AN SSSR v trudakh sovetskikh uchenykh," *Voprosy Istorii Estestvoznaniia i Tekhniki* (No. 6, 1958), pp. 151-94.

Preobrazhenskii, N. F. "K voprosu ob obshchestvennoi kul'turno-prosvetitel'noi rabote sektsii nauchnykh rabotnikov," *Nauchnyi Rabotnik* (January 1928), pp. 1-59.

"Programma kommunisticheskoi partii sovetskogo soiuza," *Pravda*, July 30, 1961, pp. 1-9.

Raevskii, A. S. "K voprosu ob organizatsionnykh formakh nauchnoi raboty," *Nauchnyi Rabotnik* (November 1928), pp. 10-12.

"Rezoliutsii III vsesoiuznogo s''ezda nauchnykh rabotnikov," *Nauchnyi Rabotnik* (April 1929), pp. 40-57.

"Rezoliutsii IV plenum tsentral'nogo soveta sektsii nauchnykh rabotnikov," *Nauchnyi Rabotnik* (July 1928), p. 103.

"Rezoliutsiia po dokladu ob uchastii VARNITSO v obsuzhdenii piatiletnego plana narodnogo khoziaistva SSSR," *VARNITSO* (No. 3, 1929).

"Rezul'taty vyborov v chleny akademii nauk," *Vestnik Akademii Nauk SSSR* (No. 4, 1932), cols. 55-56.

Rogers, James A. "Charles Darwin and Russian Scientists," *The Russian Review*, XIX (No. 4), 371-83.

———. "Darwinism, Scientism, and Nihilism," *The Russian Review*, XIX (No. 1), 10-23.

Romanova, S. "Nekotorye vyvody iz chistki v akademii nauk," *Izvestiia*, September 10, 1929, p. 2.

Samoilovich, A. N. "K reorganizatsii otdeleniia gumanitarnykh nauk," *Za sotsialisticheskuiu rekonstruktsiiu akademii nauk SSSR* (No. 1, 1930).

———. "Rekonstruktsiia vsesoiuznoi akademii nauk," *Front Nauki i Tekhniki* (April-May, 1931), pp. 68-74.

———. "Sotsialisticheskoe sorevnovanie trekh akademii (vseukrainskoi, belorusskoi i SSSR)," *Vestnik Akademii Nauk* (No. 2, 1931), pp. 1-10.

Schwartz, Harry, "A Defector Wins Praise in Soviet," *New York Times* (August 22, 1965).

Semenov, N. N. "Nauka: segodnia i zavtra," *Izvestiia* (August 9, 1959).

Senior, D. A. "The Organization of Scientific Research," *SURVEY* (July 1964), pp. 19-35.

Sergeev, P. "Ratsionalizatsiia truda nauchnykh rabotnikov," *Nauchnyi Rabotnik* (September 1929), pp. 8-17.

Sergeevich, L. V. "Zadacha sobiraniia nauki," *Nauchnyi Rabotnik* (September 1926), pp. 31-34.

———. "Formy i zadachi nauchnoi informatsii," *Nauchnyi Rabotnik* (May-June 1927), pp. 20-26.

Shidlovskii, P. G. "Sotsialisticheskaia rekonstruktsiia akademii nauk," *Vestnik Akademii Nauk* (No. 7, 1933), p. 20.

Solosin, I. I. "K voprosu ob issledovatel'skoi rabote v vysshikh uchebnykh zavedeniiakh," *Nauchnyi Rabotnik* (February 1927), pp. 39-41.

"Spornye voprosy evgeniki," *Vestnik Kommunisticheskoi Akademii* (No. 20, 1927), pp. 212-54.

Starchakov, A. "Akademiia velikoi strany," *Novyi Mir*, XII (1932), 169-75.

"Stenograficheskii otchet 1 vsesoiuznoi konferentsii VARNITSO," *VARNITSO* (No. 2, 1928), p. 36.

Stepanov, I. "Engel's i mekhanisticheskoe ponimanie prirody," *Pod znamenem marksizma* (Nos. 8-9, 1925), pp. 44-72.

Strumilin, S. G. "Nauka i proizvoditel'nost' truda." Speech at the extraordinary session of the Academy of Sciences, Moscow, June 21-27, 1931. Moscow–Leningrad, 1931.

———. "Nauka i razvitie proizvoditel'nykh sil," *Voprosy Filosofii* (No. 3, 1954), pp. 46-61.

———. "Nauka v svete ucheniia I. V. Stalina o bazise i nadstroike," *Izvestiia Akademii Nauk: Otdelenie Ekonomiki i Prava* (No. 4, 1951), pp. 287-88.

Suvorov, N. P. "O metodakh izucheniia effektivnosti nauchnykh rabot," *Nauchnyi Rabotnik* (December 1928), pp. 23-33.

Sverdlov, V. M. "Nauchnye rabotniki i VARNITSO," *Nauchnyi Rabotnik* (December 1929), pp. 77-83.

———. "Za sotsialisticheskuiu nauku i tekhniku," *Front Nauki i Tekhniki* (June 1931), pp. 4-9.

Swanson, James M. "Reorganization," *SURVEY* (July 1964), pp. 36-40.

Ter-Organesov, V. T. "Industrializatsiia SSSR i voprosy organizatsii nauki," *Nauchnyi Rabotnik* (September 1926), pp. 3-20.

Teslenko, F. A. "Neobkhodimo korennaia reorganizatsiia nauchno-issledovatel'skogo dela," *Nauchnyi Rabotnik* (November-December 1930), pp. 26-49.

Topchiev, A. V. "Iarkoe svidetel'stvo zaboty partii o nauke," *Vestnik Akademii Nauk* (No. 8, 1961), pp. 17-21.

Trotskii, L. "Kachestvo produktsii i sotsialisticheskoe khoziaistvo," *Pravda*, July 17, 1925, p. 4.

Vangengeim, A. and Troianovskii, K. "Organizatsiia nauk v SSSR," *Nauchnyi Rabotnik* (November 1929), pp. 27-32.

Veinberg, B. P. "Metodika nauchnoi raboty i podgotovka k nei," *Nauchnyi Rabotnik* (December 1926), pp. 5-20.

Vernadskii, V. I. "Ocherednaia zadacha v izuchenii estestvennykh proizvoditel'nykh sil," *Nauchnyi Rabotnik* (July-August 1926), pp. 3-21.

Vol'fson, S. "Nauka i bor'ba klassov," *VARNITSO* (February 1930), pp. 23-36.

Volgin, V. P. "Akademiia nauk v sotsialisticheskom stroitel'stve soiuza SSR," *Sovetskoe Stroitel'stvo* (No. 1, 1933), pp. 43-53.

———. "Reorganizatsiia akademii nauk," *Vestnik Akademii Nauk* (No. 1, 1931), pp. 3-12.

———. "Sovetskaia vlast' i nauchnye rabotniki za 10 let," *Nauchnyi Rabotnik* (November 1927), pp. 17-25.

———. "Uvelichenie chisla kafedr po naukam tekhnicheskim," *Vestnik Akademii Nauk SSSR* (special issue, 1931), cols. 79-80.

Voronov, S. "Iz proshlogo i nastoiashchego akademii nauk," *Novyi Mir*, v (1930), 135-49.

Vostokov, P. "La philosophie russe durant la période post-revolutionnaire," *Le monde slave*, XI-XII (1932).

"Vse sily nauchnykh rabotnikov na teoreticheskuiu razrabotku problem sots-stroitel'stva i klassovoi bor'by proletariata. Postanovlenie TsK VKP(b) ot 15 marta 1931 po dokladu prezidiuma kom. akademii," *Vestnik Kommunisticheskoi Akademii* (Nos. 2-3, 1931), pp. 3-5.

Vyshinskii, A. Ia. "Delo 'Prompartii,'" *Nauchnyi Rabotnik* (November-December 1930), pp. 7-25.

"V zasedaniiakh grupp, otdelenii, obshchego sobraniia i prezidiuma akademii nauk SSSR," *Vestnik Akademii Nauk SSSR* (No. 6, 1931), cols. 51-56.

"V zasedaniiakh prezidiuma akademii nauk SSSR," *Vestnik Akademii Nauk SSSR* (No. 7, 1931), cols. 51-52.

"Zadachi VARNITSO na perevyborakh professury," *VARNITSO* (No. 4, 1929).

Zamkov, N. "Nauka i politika," *Narodnoe Prosveshchenie* I (1930), 29-31.

Zavadovskii, B. M. "Nauka v Sovetskoi Rossii," *Krasnaia Nov'*, IV (December 1921), 132.

Zelenko, V. A. "Iz opyta raboty leningradskoi sektsii nauchnykh rabotnikov," *Nauchnyi Rabotnik*, ɪ (January 1926), 113-19.

——. "Osnovnye linii raboty leningradskogo biuro sektsii nauchnykh rabotnikov," *Nauchnyi Rabotnik* (January 1929), pp. 63-65.

——. "Rekonstruktsiia vsesoiuznoi akademii nauk," *Nauchnyi Rabotnik* (November-December 1930), pp. 50-66.

Ziskind, A. "Organizatsiia nauchno-issledovatel'skoi raboty v promyshlennosti, *Front Nauki i Tekhniki* (June 1931), pp. 49-56.

"XVI parts''ezd i nauchno-issledovatel'skaia rabota," *Vestnik Kommunisticheskoi Akademii* (No. 39, 1930), pp. 3-7.

"XVII partkonferentsiia. Nauka i tekhnika," *Sotsialisticheskaia Rekonstruktsiia i Nauka* (No. 2, 1932), pp. 3-7.

"XVII parts''ezd i zadachi nauchnoi raboty," *Vestnik Kommunisticheskoi Akademii* (No. 1, 1934), pp. 5-13.

III. Unpublished Sources

Davydov, A. V. "Ideologicheskaia rabota kommunisticheskoi partii v period mezhdu XV i XVI s''ezdami VKP(b)" (unpublished dissertation, Institute for the Improvement of Qualifications of Teachers of Marxism–Leninism, Moscow State University), Moscow, 1954.

Ermakov, Vladimir Tikhonovich. "Bor'ba kommunisticheskoi partii za perestroiku raboty nauchnykh uchrezhdenii v gody pervoi piatiletki" (unpublished dissertation for the degree of *kandidat*, Department of the History of the Communist Party of the Soviet Union, Moscow State University), Moscow, 1956.

Folomeev, Grigorii Ivanovich. "Klassovaia bor'ba v SSSR v period sotsialisticheskoi industrializatsii strany (1926-1929 gg.)" (unpublished dissertation, Institute for the Improvement of Qualifications of Teachers of Marxism–Leninism, Moscow State University), Moscow, 1957.

Grushkovskaia, Vera Vasil'evna. "Rol' nauki v razvitii proizvoditel'nykh sil sovetskogo obshchestva" (unpublished dissertation, Institute for the Improvement of Qualifications of Teachers of Marxism–Leninism, Moscow State University), Moscow, 1953.

Interview, George Vernadsky, East Haven, Conn., July 21, 1964.

Ipat'ev, V. N. Personal Papers, on file in the Ipat'ev High Pressure Laboratory, Northwestern University.

Kitaeff, Michael. "Akademiia nauk SSSR," Russian Archive, Columbia University (typed).

Kuznetsov, F. "Bor'ba kommunisticheskoi partii sovetskogo soiuza za razvitie nauki v pervye gody sovetskoi vlasti, 1918-20 gg." (unpublished dissertation for the degree of *kandidat*, Moscow State University), Moscow, 1954.

Letter to the author from N. A. Figurovskii, Director of the Institute of the History of Natural Sciences and Technology, Academy of Sciences, Moscow, June 1961.

Rachkov, Petr Alekseevich. "Rol' i mesto nauki v razvitii sotsialisticheskogo obshchestva" (unpublished dissertation, Department of Dialectical and Historical Materialism, Moscow State University), Moscow, 1953.

Rakhmatullin, K. Kh. "Znachenie kritiki i samokritiki v razvitii sovetskoi nauki" (unpublished dissertation for the degree of *kandidat*, Kazakhstan State University), Alma-Ata, 1955.

Rhinelander, Laurens H., Jr., "The Kondakov Seminar and Institute," Russian Archive, Columbia University (Typed).

Samygin, Michael. "Riad otryvok vospominanii ob akademii nauk SSSR v 1920 godakh i 1930 godakh," Russian Archive, Columbia University (typed).

——. "Terror v akademii nauk," Research Program on the History of the Communist Party of the Soviet Union, Russian Archive, Columbia University (typed).

INDEX

Academy of Sciences: archives, 126-27, 173; bases (*bazy*), 161-64; branches (*filialy*), 161-64; charters, 9, 16, 19, 82, 83, 85-88, 138-41, 152-53; founding, 14-15; General Assembly, 90, 110-11, 133, 137, 139; library, 126-27, 169-70; presidium, 86, 107, 113, 182

Accademia del Cimento, 5, 17

Adoratskii, V.V., 115, 148, 227

Ainalov, D.V., 105, 106

Aleksandrov, I.G., 115, 227

Alekseev, V.M., 103, 133, 227

Alexander I, 18

Alexander II, 20

All-Russian Central Council of Trade Unions, 47

All-Russian Congress of Soviets, 68, 71

All-Union Association of Workers of Science and Technology for the Assistance of Socialist Construction (VARNITSO), 88, 92, 93, 96, 107, 112, 121, 127, 148, 149, 177, 178, 179, 181, 184, 199

All-Union Central Council of Trade Unions (VTsSPS), 136

All-Union Conference on the Planning of Scientific-Research Work, 45, 55, 61, 186, 198

Almgren, Beverly S., 21

Andreev, A.B., 55

Andrusov, N.N., 23

Archaeographical Commission, 126, 158, 173. *See also* Historical-Archaeographical Institute

archive affair, 126-27, 171

Arkhangel'ski, A.D., 103, 114, 131, 134, 144, 227

Arshinov, V.V., 50, 51

Asiatic Museum, 123, 159, 169

Baikal Limnological Station (BLS), 214

Baikov, A.A., 115, 227

Bailes, Kendall E., 48

Baker, J.R., 67

Bakh, A.N., 95, 98, 103, 131, 134, 144, 181, 182-83, 198, 227

Bakunin, P.P., 18

Banasiukevich, V.D., 48

Barber, Bernard, 67, 194, 195, 205

Bardin, I.P., 115, 227

Bartol'd, V.V., 105, 108, 116, 131, 133, 144

Bauer, Raymond, 201

Bazarov, V.A., 198

Beliaev, N.M., 105

Belomortsev Sergei, 28, 29, 92, 96, 125, 129, 175

Belopolskii, A.A., 227

Belorussian Academy of Sciences, 170-72

Ber (Bär), K.M., 11

Berg, Aksel I., 48, 49

Bernal, J.D., 67, 205-206

Bernouilli, Daniel, 11

Bernshtein, S.N., 103, 227

Bialynitskii-Birulia, A.A., 123, 142

Biogeochemical Laboratory (BIO-GEL), 161, 210, 211

Biological Association, 214-16

Biological Institute (BIN), 215

Bludov, D.N., 20

Blumentrost, L.L., 14

Bogdanov, A.A., 35, 48

Bogomolets, A.A., 115, 227

Borisiak, A.A., 103, 167, 179, 183, 187, 198, 212, 216, 227

Borodin, I.P., 22

Borsuk, A.K., 55

Botanical Garden and Museum, 161, 169, 187, 188

Botanical Institute, 161

Britske, E.V., 115, 227

Bukharin, N.I., 56, 154, 227; Communist Academy and, 74, 180; culture and, 32, 35; elections to Academy and, 92, 95, 96, 103, 104, 111, 114; Pavlov and, 109; planning of science and, 45, 56-60, 64-65, 198, 199; reorganization of Academy and, 134-35, 137, 148, 157, 158; terror and, 186-87; theory and practice and, 40

Buniakovskii, V.I., 11

Bureau of Eugenics, 46, 161

STUDIES OF THE RUSSIAN INSTITUTE

PUBLISHED BY COLUMBIA UNIVERSITY PRESS

THAD PAUL ALTON, *Polish Postwar Economy*

JOHN A. ARMSTRONG, *Ukrainian Nationalism*

ABRAM BERGSON, *Soviet National Income and Product in 1937*

EDWARD J. BROWN, *The Proletarian Episode in Russian Literature, 1928-1932*

HARVEY L. DYCK, *Weimar Germany and Soviet Russia, 1926-1933: A Study in Diplomatic Instability*

RALPH TALCOTT FISHER, JR., *Pattern for Soviet Youth: A Study of the Congresses of the Komsomol, 1918-1954*

MAURICE FRIEDBERG, *Russian Classics in Soviet Jackets*

ELLIOT R. GOODMAN, *The Soviet Design for a World State*

DAVID GRANICK, *Management of the Industrial Firm in the USSR: A Study in Soviet Economic Planning*

THOMAS TAYLOR HAMMOND, *Lenin on Trade Unions and Revolution, 1893-1917*

JOHN N. HAZARD, *Settling Disputes in Soviet Society: The Formative Years of Legal Institutions*

DAVID JORAVSKY, *Soviet Marxism and Natural Science, 1917-1932*

DAVID MARSHALL LANG, *The Last Years of the Georgian Monarchy, 1658-1832*

GEORGE S. N. LUCKYJ, *Literary Politics in the Soviet Ukraine, 1917-1934*

HERBERT MARCUSE, *Soviet Marxism: A Critical Analysis*

KERMIT E. MC KENZIE, *Comintern and World Revolution, 1928-1943: The Shaping of Doctrine*

CHARLES B. MC LANE, *Soviet Policy and the Chinese Communists, 1931-1946*

JAMES WILLIAM MORLEY, *The Japanese Thrust into Siberia, 1918*

ALEXANDER G. PARK, *Bolshevism in Turkestan, 1917-1927*

MICHAEL BORO PETROVICH, *The Emergence of Russian Panslavism, 1856-1870*

OLIVER H. RADKEY, *The Agrarian Foes of Bolshevism: Promise and Default of the Russian Socialist Revolutionaries, February to October, 1917*

OLIVER H. RADKEY, *The Sickle Under the Hammer: The Russian Socialist Revolutionaries in the Early Months of Soviet Rule*

ALFRED J. RIEBER, *Stalin and the French Communist Party, 1941-1947*

ALFRED ERICH SENN, *The Emergence of Modern Lithuania*

ERNEST J. SIMMONS, editor, *Through the Glass of Soviet Literature: Views of Russian Society*

THEODORE K. VON LAUE, *Sergei Witte and the Industrialization of Russia*

ALLEN S. WHITING, *Soviet Policies in China, 1917-1924*

PUBLISHED BY TEACHERS COLLEGE PRESS

HAROLD J. NOAH, *Financing Soviet Schools*

PUBLISHED BY PRINCETON UNIVERSITY PRESS

PAUL AVRICH, *The Russian Anarchists*

JOHN M. THOMPSON, *Russia, Bolshevism, and the Versailles Peace*

LOREN R. GRAHAM, *The Soviet Academy of Sciences and the Communist Party, 1927-1932.*